Quiz "A"
    Chapters
Quiz "B"   2
Quiz "C"   14 November 1958
Quiz "D"   15 December 1958 (1300 hrs)
    Chapters 7, 8, 9

145-10

INTRODUCTION
TO
ELECTRICAL
ENGINEERING

PRENTICE-HALL ELECTRICAL ENGINEERING SERIES

W. L. EVERITT, *Editor*

INTRODUCTION TO ELECTRICAL ENGINEERING

ALBERT E. SWARTS

BY

ROBERT PAGE WARD

PROFESSOR, ELECTRICAL ENGINEERING DEPARTMENT
AGRICULTURAL AND MECHANICAL COLLEGE OF TEXAS

Second Edition

PRENTICE-HALL, INC.

Englewood Cliffs, N. J.

Preface to the First Edition

This book is the outcome of a set of mimeographed notes used in the first course in electrical engineering at the Agricultural and Mechanical College of Texas since 1939. This course is given to first-semester sophomore students in electrical engineering who, at the same time, are taking their first courses in calculus and college physics. The mathematics used in the text is, therefore, limited in the earlier chapters to algebra and trigonometry, with the concepts of rate of change and derivative introduced later, in the chapter on electromagnetic induction. Derivations using calculus have for the most part been placed in footnotes in order that the main text might be followed by students not taking calculus. The text is covered in recitation sections meeting three hours each week for one semester. There are, in addition, four practice hours each week, equally divided between computation and laboratory exercises. The problems have been found adequate for homework and computing periods.

The author was first led to prepare these notes by the adoption in 1935 of the MKS system of units. The elementary textbooks available at that time used hybrid unit systems that included units of both CGS and the practical systems. This confused the beginner, a confusion that often persisted beyond the completion of the first course. Adoption of the MKS system offered an opportunity to correct this situation. Furthermore, with the exception of the units of force, permeability, magnetic field intensity, and magnetic flux density, the units are substantially the familiar practical units used in industry. The CGS systems are developed, and the units compared with the MKS units in the Appendix.

The notes also developed adequate methods for marking the directions selected as positive for the various currents, voltage drops, electromotive forces, magnetomotive forces, and fluxes encountered in problems of engineering. Also, in these notes, mathematical analysis was closely related to these positive directions. The student learned from the outset that the arrow represents the direction in which a current will be considered positive rather than the direction in which current actually flows. This viewpoint, which is consistently used throughout this book for currents as well as for other quantities, is the only sound basis for an understanding of alternating-current representation.

R. P. W.

Preface to the Second Edition

In this new edition, the discussion of certain topics has been amplified so that a beginning student may gain a better understanding of them from reading the text. It is hoped thus to conserve class time and permit more discussion of the hard-to-grasp concepts. An attempt has been made to clarify further the matter of voltage notation and to improve the manner of stating the definitions of electric and magnetic field intensity and flux density.

About 250 additional questions and problems have been included. The Study Questions at the end of each chapter are designed to stimulate independent thought about the principles discussed, and their applications. Obvious questions such as "What is the MKS unit of force?" and "In what way does the resistance of a metal conductor vary with temperature?" have generally been avoided. Most of the factual information needed is contained in the text, but it is not intended that the answers to the questions can be read verbatim from the text. Some of the questions are, in fact, problems, and appreciable time will be required for their solution.

The critical comments and suggestions sent in by those using or considering the book are gratefully acknowledged. It is hoped that these are reflected in greater clarity and freedom from error in the new edition.

R. P. W.

College Station, Texas

Contents

INTRODUCTION
TO
ELECTRICAL
ENGINEERING

CHAPTER I
INTRODUCTORY

A note to the student. Much of what follows in this book belongs in one or another of the following categories:

1. Experimental facts—things the truth of which has been determined by observation and experiment.

2. Definitions—things that are true because everybody concerned agrees on their truth.

3. Derived relationships—things that are shown to be true by beginning with experimental facts and definitions, and reasoning logically to a conclusion.

4. Discussion—things that occur to the writer as pertinent to the subject under consideration and that should make for a better understanding on the part of the student.

The student is urged to keep this classification constantly in mind as he reads and to try to place every statement in its proper category. To aid him in this, definitions are either plainly marked *definition* or else the new word or term is in boldface type where it is defined and used for the first time in this book.

The student is warned against falling into the habit of regarding every mathematical expression as a "formula" into which he can substitute numbers and obtain answers. Every such expression is either a definition (defining equation) or a derived relationship and should be recognized as such. In working problems, a conscientious effort should be made to see what has to be done rather than trying to "find a formula." A pretty safe rule to follow is never to use a defining equation unless you can quote the definition, and never to use a derived relationship unless you can derive it yourself. If you know enough about the equation to do that, then as far as you are concerned, it is not a "formula."

1. The place of electricity and magnetism in engineering. Engineering is the art of utilizing for the good of mankind the sources of energy and materials that are found in nature. It does not include any of the processes of utilizing energy or materials that involve living organisms, but if these processes be excepted, there remains but little with which engineering is not concerned. Electrical engineering is particularly concerned with the apparatus and processes by means of which energy is taken from falling water or from burning fuel or from some other source, and, through the medium of electricity, is made to reappear as light or heat or sound or motion at such places and under such circumstances as to serve human needs. Electrical engineering differs from most of the other branches of engineering in that energy, not materials, plays the most important role. The electrical engineer is concerned with materials, but only as they are useful in building apparatus for converting energy from one form to another and transmitting it from one place to another.

Electricity and magnetism is a branch of physics, which is a science. A science, such as physics, differs from an art, such as engineering, in that the emphasis in science is upon the accumulation of exact, systematic knowledge, but the emphasis in engineering is upon the use of this knowledge in order to accomplish certain ends. Thus, the art of engineering rests upon the science of physics, and the student of electrical engineering must begin by acquiring a thorough knowledge of electricity and magnetism and of the other branches of physics.

2. The beginnings. The earliest recorded electrical phenomenon is the attraction of bits of chaff by a piece of amber that has been rubbed. That discovery was made by the ancient Greeks, and was recorded by Thales in 600 B.C. The word electricity comes from the Greek word *ēlektron*, which means *amber*.

Over two thousand years later, Sir William Gilbert, who was court physician to Queen Elizabeth, found that other substances than amber could be *electrified*, as he called it, and he prepared lists of those which could be electrified and those which could not. During the next hundred and fifty years, the methods of electrifying objects by friction were improved and the results studied by several investigators, among whom were Von Guericke, Stephen Gray, Charles François de Cisternay Du Fay, and Benjamin Franklin.

Von Guericke arranged to rotate a sphere of sulphur by using a machine, and so produced charges much larger than had his predecessors. He also found that after an attracted particle had touched the sphere, it was repelled. Gray found that substances could be classified as conductors or nonconductors according to whether they would or would not permit the escape of the charge from an electrified body. Du Fay discovered that bodies that had been electrified by friction would, in some instances, exert forces of attraction upon one another, and in other instances forces of repulsion.

To explain these observed facts, Du Fay put forward the theory that there were two mysterious fluids which were subtle enough to permeate all substances. One of these he called *vitreous*, and the other *resinous*, electricity. A body that was electrified contained an excess of one kind or the other of these fluids. If two bodies each contained an excess of the same kind of electricity, they repelled, but if one contained an excess of vitreous electricity and the other an excess of resinous electricity, they attracted each other.

Benjamin Franklin, besides being a statesman, was an electrical experimenter of note. His experiment which proved that lightning was identical with the electricity produced by friction is known to every schoolboy. Franklin proposed a one-fluid theory of electricity, according to which a neutral body always contained a certain normal amount of the fluid. An excess of the fluid then corresponded to one kind of charge and a deficiency of the fluid, to the other kind. The experiments of Gilbert and Guericke, Du Fay and Franklin can be reperformed in our laboratory today, or even with whatever materials are at hand in almost any place. They constitute the basis of **electrostatics,** that phase of the subject which deals with electricity at rest.

Natural magnets (lodestone) must have been known since ancient times, and the magnetic needle was in use by European navigators by the twelfth century. The first work that might be called a study of magnetism was done by Gilbert, who in 1600 published a treatise on the subject called *De Magnete*. Gilbert was a scientific investigator of the first rank, and working both with electricity and with magnets, he made important discoveries concerning each. He evidently did not suspect, however, that the two phenomena were in any way related.

Throughout the eighteenth century, electrical experimenters were severely limited in what they could do, for the reason that frictional machines were the only sources of charge available. These machines were constantly being improved upon, and the invention of the Leyden jar about 1745 made it possible to store considerable charges of electricity. Gray and Franklin had both demonstrated the possibility of conducting electricity for considerable distances, using wet linen thread as the conductor. But the currents that flowed in these conductors were only momentary, ceasing as soon as the accumulated charge had been neutralized.

The first electric battery was devised by Alessandro Volta, an Italian physicist, who was led to his discovery through results obtained by his friend, Luigi Galvani, in stimulating the muscles of a frog's leg by touching the nerves with metal wires. Galvani evidently thought the stimulus was caused by "animal electricity." Volta was at first inclined to agree with him, but further study and experimenting convinced Volta that the effect was due to electricity caused by the metals. In 1799, he invented his battery, which consisted of alternate disks of copper and zinc arranged in pairs, each pair being separated from the next by paper soaked in acid. This discovery made it possible to send steady currents of electricity through wires and to observe and study two phenomena that are of tremendous practical importance in present-day electrical engineering—namely, the heating of the wires and forces that act between wires carrying currents.

It was not immediately realized that electricity produced by Volta's battery was identical in nature with that produced by friction. We had thus at the close of the eighteenth century three phenomena that were not known to be related: current electricity, frictional electricity, and magnetism. Volta by showing that the two kinds of electricity produced the same effects soon proved them to be identical. The relation between electricity and magnetism was first demonstrated by the Danish physicist, Hans Christian Oersted, in 1820. Oersted discovered that a magnetic needle, when placed beneath a wire carrying current, was acted on by forces which caused it to be oriented in the direction perpendicular to the wire. Conversely, a wire carrying current would be acted on by forces when placed in the vicinity of a magnet. From Oersted's discovery, the advancement of electrical knowledge proceeded with ever-increasing speed. A Frenchman by the name of André-Marie Ampère repeated Oersted's experiments, and in an incredibly short while had discovered the laws which are the basis of **electrodynamics,** which deals with currents and the forces they produce. A few years later Michael Faraday, an Englishman, showed that a current could be caused in a loop of wire by passing a magnet through it. This discovery was also made by Joseph Henry, an American, working independently. Thus by 1832, the relationship between electricity and magnetism had been established and by 1837 a number of workable motors and generators had been constructed.

The first practical applications of electricity, however, were in the field of communications. Samuel Morse's telegraph was put into commercial use in 1844, and for a long time was the most important electrical industry. Several of our present-day electrical units were chosen to suit the convenience of the telegraphers. The development of the electric-light and power industry can be said to have begun about 1880, with the invention by Thomas Edison and his associates of the incandescent lamp and practical means of supplying energy to large numbers of lamps simultaneously.

The modern theory of electricity came as the result of new discoveries about the nature of matter during the closing years of the last century by J. J. Thomson, H. A. Lorentz, E. Rutherford, and others. With this brief historical outline by way of preface, let us now consider the modern theory.

3. The electrical nature of matter. The molecules and atoms of which all material substances are composed are not elemental, but are themselves made up of simpler entities. We know this because we have, to a certain extent, been able to break up atoms and study the resulting products. For instance, if a piece of tungsten wire be heated, as in the filament of an incandescent lamp or vacuum tube, there are driven out of it particles which are not atoms of tungsten, but are much smaller and lighter, and which have the peculiar property of repelling one another with considerable force. Exactly similar particles are obtained by causing ultraviolet light to fall on cold metal surfaces. They are spontaneously ejected from certain radioactive elements. Since these particles are obtained from many different substances under such widely varying conditions, it is believed that they are one of the elemental constituents of all matter. They are called **electrons.** The size and mass of an electron are so small as to be inconceivable, the mass being 1/1837 the mass of a hydrogen atom, which is 1.67×10^{-24} g, and the diameter being 1/50,000 the diameter of a hydrogen atom, which is about 10^{-8} cm. Electrons may be given velocities approaching the velocity of light, and at these tremendous velocities, may be shot through thin sheets of metal. Their most striking property, however, is the force of repulsion which they exert on one another. These forces are called **electric forces** and the property of the electron which gives rise to these forces is called **electricity** or **electric charge.** What this is, or how the force is exerted we cannot explain, for the reason that there are no simpler terms in which to explain electricity. We do know, however, that the charge does not vary from one electron to another. Every electron has exactly the same charge as every other electron. Although we have spoken of the electron as a particle, it does not always behave as we would expect a particle to behave, and the advanced student may have to modify his idea of what it is. But for the present, we may regard the electron as a hard, round particle with the added property of repelling every similar particle with a definite, invariable force.

Several other kinds of particles have been driven or spontaneously ejected from matter. Of these, the first to be discovered was the **proton** which, like the electron, is endowed with the property of repelling particles similar to itself, but which, instead of repelling electrons, attracts them with the same force with which it would repel another proton. We say, therefore, that the proton carries a charge equal in magnitude to that on an electron but opposite in sign. We arbitrarily designate the charge of the proton as a + charge, and the charge of the electron as a − charge. The mass of the proton is almost identical with the mass of the hydrogen atom. In 1932 came the discovery of the **neutron,** a particle with the mass of a proton but no charge. These three entities: electrons, protons and

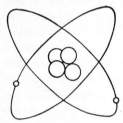

Fig. 1.1. Structure of the helium atom.

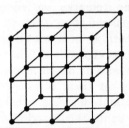

Fig. 1.2. Space lattice of copper—atoms are located at corners of cubes and also (not shown) at centers of cube faces.

neutrons are, according to our present knowledge, the basic building blocks of which atoms are made. Other entities such as the positron and the alpha particle are encountered in atomic research, but these are to be regarded as transitory and not stable components of the atom.

All of the protons and neutrons are bound together into a compact nucleus, which may be thought of as a central sun, about which the electrons revolve in orbits. Fig. 1.1 shows a helium atom, the nucleus of which consists of two protons and two neutrons,[1] with two electrons moving in orbits. The nuclei of atoms, for the purposes of this text, may be regarded as stable and unchanging, though it is now well known that the nuclei of atoms of radioactive elements undergo spontaneous changes in their structure, and that the nuclei of atoms of other elements may be changed by bombardment by subatomic particles moving at certain velocities. In most solids, the nuclei are arranged in space according to some definite geometrical pattern. The structure thus formed is known as the **space lattice,** because this name implies finite quantities of matter, symmetrically placed, and separated from one another by intervals that are considerable as compared to their own dimensions. The apparently solid

---

[1] Every atom of a given element has the same number of protons in its nucleus, but the number of neutrons may vary. About one helium nucleus in a million has only one neutron.

substance, is, after all, mostly space. **Fig. 1.2** shows the space lattice of copper.

Most of the electrons associated with the atom are detached only with some difficulty. In the metals, however, at least some of the electrons appear to leave the atom spontaneously, and to wander about within the space lattice. Such electrons are known as **free electrons,** or **conduction electrons,** and it is in terms of them that electric current, or the conduction of electricity, in metals is explained.

4. Some remarks on energy. Practically every physical and chemical phenomenon, such as the lifting of a weight, the burning of fuel, the turning of a wheel, the utterance of a sound, involves the exchange between bodies of that which we call **energy.** Such exchanges are continually going on in nature whether we will them or not, and our control of them is never complete, yet by promoting certain exchanges and delaying others, we bring about results which we believe to be for the "good of mankind."

Energy is often defined as the capability for doing work. Thus, when a weight is lifted to a certain height above the earth, it becomes able to drive a nail or smash another object simply by falling. It is said to possess **potential energy** by virtue of its position. To lift the weight in the first place, of course, work had to be done, and the potential energy may be regarded as stored work. Now, let us consider the weight as having fallen. It is nearing the earth, and its energy of position is gone. Energy has not been destroyed, however, because the weight is still capable of doing work when it strikes the earth. What has happened is that the weight has gained speed as it fell, and its energy of position has been changed into energy of velocity, or **kinetic energy.** These are the two forms of energy with which we deal in mechanics.

A body may also possess energy by virtue of its temperature—that is, **thermal energy,** or heat energy. Kinetic energy can be readily transformed to thermal energy by friction, as when a meteor burns away because of air friction upon entering the earth's atmosphere, or a cutting tool becomes hot. The transfer in the other direction (from thermal to kinetic energy) is accomplished by heat engines of various kinds. Thermal energy is most often obtained by the burning of fuel, but here again we are dealing with a transformation. The fuel itself is the repository of energy in the **chemical** form, and the process of burning is simply the conversion to the heat form.

It might seem from what has been said that the outstanding fact about energy is that it can readily be changed from one form to another, and this is true. Most of the energy with which we deal in engineering can be traced from the sun, and reaches the earth in the form of radiation, or **radiant energy.** For instance, some of this energy, on reaching the earth appears as heat, and evaporates water from the oceans and lakes. This water vapor rises until it is condensed in the cooler upper atmosphere, and falls as rain or snow, some of it eventually finding its way into the reservoirs of hydro-electric plants. The potential energy of the stored water is in due time converted into mechanical energy by hydraulic turbines, and the mechanical energy in turn is converted into **electrical energy** by electric generators.

The source of the radiant energy from the sun is not definitely known. It is certain now that energy can be created at the expense of matter. This process goes on spontaneously in the radioactive chemical elements at all times. Although the process cannot be arrested, it can be accelerated, as in the atomic bomb, to create immense amounts of energy instantly. Perhaps the sun is creating energy by losing mass, and a tiny fraction of the total energy thus created reaches the earth as radiation. At some future time, prob-ably, energy created from matter will become useful in engineering. At present, however, there is no practical way to make such energy available, and our dealings with energy will consist entirely of trans-formations from one form to another. We may, in all of our work for the present, rely upon the **law of conservation of energy,** which states that the total amount of energy in any system is fixed.

One of the principal uses of electricity is to furnish a means of transmitting energy from one place to another. Electricity itself is not energy any more than the weight used in the foregoing illustra-tion is energy. The free electrons may possess energy by virtue of their position or velocity, just as the weight possessed energy by virtue of its position or its velocity, but to say that electricity itself is a form of energy is confusing rather than enlightening.

We have reasonably efficient devices for changing kinetic to electrical energy (generator, velocity microphone) and electrical to kinetic energy (motor, loud speaker, electromagnet), and these are the changes most often made. Devices for changing chemical energy to electrical (batteries) and electrical energy to chemical (storage batteries) are less economical and less used. Devices for changing heat energy to electrical (thermocouples) exist, but their low efficiency limits their use to extremely small amounts of energy. Devices for changing electrical to heat energy (irons, toasters) are probably the most familiar of all. Several of the devices mentioned (generators, storage

batteries, thermocouples) are reversible, and at least one of them
(the storage battery) is useful precisely for this reason.

As already mentioned, it is possible for energy to reside in, or
be propagated through, empty space from one body to another.
Devices exist for making the transformation from the heat to the
radiant form (radiant heaters, incandescent lamps) and from the
electrical to the radiant form (antennas.) Radiant energy manifests itself as heat or light, which are recognizable, if in sufficient
amount, by the physical senses, and also (depending on the nature
of the radiator) as radio waves or other waves or rays, detectable
only by special devices which convert it to the heat form or electrical
form again. The importance of radiant energy in electrical engineering, particularly in radio and in illumination, is hard to exaggerate.

5. Measuring and units. Physics differs from the other sciences
not in its subject matter alone, but in its methods. We might venture
so far as to say that physics is the science of measurement, or, whereas
in other fields of science we are content to observe and describe
phenomena, in physics we go further and *measure* the effects we
observe. Measuring involves, first, the choice of a **unit,** or standard,
of the same sort as the quantity to be measured, and second, the
comparison of the unit with the quantity to be measured—to find
how many times the former is contained in the latter. The choice
of a unit depends upon the use that is to be made of the measurement.
If an experimenter in an electrical laboratory wishes to cut a piece of
wire of the correct length to connect two terminals together, he may
choose as his unit of measurement any piece of wood or metal rod
that happens to be handy. But if he wishes to place an order for the
piece of wire or to record its length in his notes for the use of others,
then it becomes necessary to choose a unit that is familiar to all
those who may be called upon to interpret the order or the notes.
Such a unit might be the foot or the meter or any of a number of other
units that are recognized as units of length. Our experimenter
could not choose the pound or the quart as his unit, because these
are not standards of length, and we are all so perfectly familiar with
length that there is no danger of our confusing it with any other
quantity. But when we begin to deal with the less familiar units
of electricity and magnetism, we shall have to be careful that we
choose a unit always of the same sort as the quantity which we attempt
to measure.

Having found out how many times our chosen unit is contained
in the quantity measured, we must not, in our haste to set down this
number and get on with something else, forget to write along with

it the name of the unit which was used. To state that a length is seven is meaningless. We must write 7 feet or 7 meters or whatever it is. The student should see clearly that the magnitude of the number depends upon the unit used. If we measure a given quantity in small units, we may obtain a very large number, whereas if we measure the same quantity in large units, we would obtain a much smaller number. Good judgment dictates that we choose units of such size that our measurements will yield numbers that are convenient to manipulate, whenever this is possible. Some of the quantities with which we shall have to deal are so minute or so large that no units so far devised will measure them in convenient numbers.

The student is already familiar, through his everyday experience and his previous studies, with such quantities as length, mass, time, velocity, acceleration, force, energy, and power, and doubtless knows that each of these may be measured in various units of the appropriate sort. He may not be familiar with the fact that there are several comprehensive *systems of units*, any particular system comprising units for each of the quantities mentioned above (and others as well). These systems differ in the quantities that are selected as fundamental and in the units used to measure the fundamental quantities. We would be very fortunate, as students, if only one good system had ever been devised, or if the men of science could agree to scrap all the systems but one. Some progress is being made toward agreement, and in this book use will be made of what now appears to be the most favored system.

6. The MKS system of units. The International Electrotechnical Commission, in June 1935, adopted the system of units known as the Giorgi, or MKS system, based on the meter, the kilogram, and the second as fundamental units. The meter was first conceived as a unit of length in France toward the end of the eighteenth century, and was arbitrarily taken as being one ten millionth of the distance from the earth's equator to either pole, measured at sea level. This length, as carefully determined as was possible, was marked off on a platinum-iridium bar which is preserved by the International Bureau of Weights and Measures at Sèvres in France. The kilogram, chosen as the unit of mass at the same time the meter was chosen as the unit of length, was arbitrarily taken as the mass of one one thousandth of a cubic meter of pure water at a temperature of 4° C. It too, is preserved at Sèvres in the form of a platinum-iridium cylinder, and the standard meters and kilograms of other laboratories are compared to these rather than to the things which they were made to represent. They are the standards for the whole scientific world.

The second is 1/86,400 part of a mean solar day, which is the average time between successive transits of the sun over the meridian. Clocks have been built which approximate this time very closely, and intervals of time may be measured by comparison with these clocks.

From these three fundamental units are derived all the others used in measuring the quantities of mechanics. The velocity of a body is measured by taking the quotient of length traversed, in meters, over the time required to traverse it, in seconds—that is, in meters per second. If we let V stand for velocity, L for length, and T for time, we may write

$$V = \frac{L}{T},\qquad(1.1)$$

which is known as the **defining equation** for velocity. From velocity, we may proceed to define acceleration, then force, then work, and so forth, each definition being based logically on the one before it. Some of the more important MKS units used in mechanics are given in Table I, together with their definitions, defining equations, and symbols.

TABLE I
MKS MECHANICAL UNITS

Quantity Measured	Unit	Symbol	Definition	Defining Equation
Length......	Meter (m)	L	Fundamental	
Mass........	Kilogram (kg)	M	Fundamental	
Time........	Second (sec)	T	Fundamental	
Velocity.....	Meter per second (m per sec)	V	One meter per sec is the velocity when distance is traversed at the rate of 1 m in 1 sec.	$V = \dfrac{L}{T}$ (1.1)
Acceleration.	Meter per second per second (m per sec per sec)	A	One meter per sec per sec is the acceleration when velocity is being changed at the rate of 1 m per sec in 1 sec.	$A = \dfrac{V}{T}$ (1.2)
Force.......	Newton	F	One newton is that force which gives an acceleration of 1 m per sec per sec to a mass of 1 kg.	$F = MA$ (1.3)
Work or energy.	Joule	W	One joule is the work done when a force of 1 newton moves a body through a distance of 1 m in the direction of the force.	$W = FL$ (1.4)
Power.......	Watt (w)	P	One watt is the power used when work is done at the rate of 1 joule per sec.	$P = \dfrac{W}{T}$ (1.5)

7. Conversion from one system of units to another. The MKS system of units, as was pointed out in Section 5, is one of a number of systems which have come into use for measuring physical quantities. In the literature of science and engineering, we find all these systems in use, and for satisfactory understanding and use of knowledge contained in this literature, we must be able to take a quantity expressed in given units and express it in any of the other units used for measuring that quantity. Length, for example, may be expressed in angstrom units, in microns, in millimeters, in centimeters, in

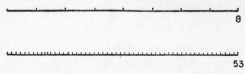

Fig. 1.3.   Measurement of length.

inches, in feet, in yards, in kilometers, in miles, in light-years, as well as in meters. There are two ways of stating the relation that exists between units of the same quantity. We may write

$$\text{Number of inches} = \text{number of meters} \times 39.37, \qquad (1.6)$$

which is an equation, and tells us how to operate on a given length expressed in meters in order to obtain the corresponding length expressed in inches.

EXAMPLE: A piece of wire is 50 m long. Express this length in inches.

SOLUTION: Substituting 50 for "number of meters" in Equation 1.6, we have

$$\text{Number of inches} = 50 \times 39.37 = 1968.5.$$

The number of inches is greater than the number of meters in expressing this same length. Therefore, the inch must be a smaller unit of length than the meter. The use of units of different size for measuring a length is illustrated in Fig. 1.3. Or we may write

$$1 \text{ meter} \equiv 39.37 \text{ inches}, \qquad (1.7)$$

which is an identity and tells us how many inches is the same as 1 m. We cannot substitute a number of meters or a number of inches into this expression as we could in Expression 1.6, which was an equation. Either of these expressions gives us the essential information: it tells us which is the larger unit and what the relative size of the units is, but in making conversions, we must be certain whether the expression we are reading or writing is an identity, like (1.7), or an equation, like (1.6). That we have taken the meter as our basic unit of length does not mean that we are committed to using the meter to the exclusion of all other units, even in a book like this. We shall use centimeters or microns or kilometers, whichever yields numbers most convenient to manipulate. The same applies to units of other quantities as well. A few conversion factors are listed in Table II for the convenience of the student in solving the problems at the end of this chapter. The student, if he has not already done so, should commit to memory a few of the most essential conversion factors to enable him to solve problems when no books are available. He should know also the usual prefixes used in connection with units, shown in Table III.

TABLE II
CONVERSION FACTORS

number of pounds =	number of kilograms ×	2.205	(1.8)
number of miles per hour =	number of meters per second ×	2.237	(1.9)
number of newtons =	number of pounds force ×	4.448	(1.10)
number of dynes =	number of newtons ×	10^5	(1.11)
number of joules =	number of foot-pounds ×	1.356	(1.12)
number of ergs =	number of joules ×	10^7	(1.13)
number of joules =	number of gram-calories ×	4.186	(1.14)
number of joules =	number of Btu ×	1054.8	(1.15)
number of joules =	number of kilowatt hours ×	$3.6 × 10^6$	(1.16)
number of watts =	number of horsepower ×	745.7	(1.17)

TABLE III
PREFIXES

Prefix	Meaning	
micro	a millionth	(10^{-6})
milli	a thousandth	(10^{-3})
centi	a hundredth	(10^{-2})
deci	a tenth	(10^{-1})
deka	ten	(10)
hekta	a hundred	(10^2)
kilo	a thousand	(10^3)
mega	a million	(10^6)

Problems

(1-I) A high-speed passenger elevator in an office building rises 190 ft in 11.4 sec. What is the average velocity in feet per minute? In meters per second?

(2-I) How long a time would be required for a Diesel-electric train traveling at a speed of 29.1 m per sec to cover a distance of 240 miles?

(3-I) The acceleration of passenger elevators is limited to about 7 fps² in order to avoid discomfort to the passengers. At this rate, how long a time would be required to reach a speed of 1100 fpm, starting from rest?

(4-I) An electron starts from rest and reaches a velocity of 5000 miles per sec in 10^{-8} sec. What is the velocity in MKS units? What is the acceleration in MKS units?

(**5-I**) A Diesel-electric train, starting from rest, reaches a speed of 70 mph in 63.6 sec. What is the acceleration in miles per hour per second? In meters per second per second?

(**6-I**) Derive an expression for calculating the distance covered by a body that is undergoing uniform acceleration in terms of acceleration and time. Use this expression to determine the distance covered by the train of Problem 5-I by the time it reaches a speed of 70 mph.

(**7-I**) What force must have acted upon the electron in Problem 4-I to accelerate it? How far will it be from the starting position when it reaches the stated velocity?

(**8-I**) A force of 1.47×10^5 newtons is applied to the drawbar of a train weighing 452 tons. The train is on a straight level track and friction will be neglected. What is the acceleration in meters per second per second?

(**9-I**) Calculate the work done in lifting an elevator weighing 2500 lb through a distance of 310 ft against the force of gravity. Express the answer in foot-pounds, in joules, and in kilowatt-hours. How much potential energy does the elevator possess at a height of 310 ft above the ground?

(**10-I**) Derive an expression for calculating the kinetic energy of a body in terms of its mass and velocity. Use this expression to calculate the kinetic energy of the electron of Problem 4-I.

(**11-I**) If the elevator of Problem 9-I is lifted 310 ft in 30 sec, find the power required in watts and also in horsepower. Repeat the calculations using a time of 30 min.

(**12-I**) The reservoir of a certain hydroelectric power plant contains 800,000 acre-feet of water at an average elevation above the turbines of 270 ft. Calculate the potential energy in the reservoir in kilowatt-years.

(**13-I**) How long would the potential energy in the reservoir of Problem 12-I operate a 20,000-kw (output) generator? Assume the efficiency of the generator and turbine combined is 80 per cent.

(**14-I**) An electron is acted upon by a force of 9×10^{-21} newton. If the electron starts from rest, find the acceleration, time, final velocity, and kinetic energy when it is 1 cm from the starting point.

Study Questions

1. What was the contribution of each of these men to the store of knowledge of electricity: Gilbert, Von Guericke, Gray, DuFay, Franklin, Volta, Galvani, Oersted, Ampère, Faraday, Morse?

2. What distinguishes electrostatics from electrodynamics?

3. Explain the electrification of a body by friction, using the modern theory of the electrical nature of matter. How does this theory differ from that advanced by DuFay?

4. How long a time elapsed from the first recorded discovery in electrostatics until the beginning of electrodynamics? How do you account for this?

5. Why is it more difficult to answer the question "what is electricity," than the question "what is iron"? Which is the more elemental?

6. What evidence is there that such a particle as the electron actually exists? What are some of its properties?

7. The statement is sometimes made that "matter is mostly empty space." What justification is there for such a statement?

8. List by pairs all of the various forms of energy mentioned in the text, pairing each form with all of the others.   By each pair list a device by which conversion from one form to the other may be accomplished.

9. Criticize the statement "electricity is a form of energy."

10. What are the two essential things to be done in measuring anything? What are the two essential things to be given when the result of a measurement is stated?

11. A tank is emptied by bailing out the water with a quart measure, and 2312 measures are counted.   Had a gallon measure been used, how many would have been counted?   Which is the larger unit of measure?

12. Prepare a table of CGS mechanical units similar to Table I.

13. Prepare a table of English mechanical units similar to Table I.

14. For each of the equations in Table II, state which is the larger unit and write the corresponding identity.

15. For each of the following identities, state which is the larger unit and write the corresponding equation.

   (a) 1 acre $\equiv 4.356 \times 10^4$ sq ft.

   (b) 1 sq cm $\equiv 1.973 \times 10^5$ cir mils.

   (c) 1 radian $\equiv 57.3$ degrees.

   (d) 1 abampere $\equiv 10$ amperes.

   (e) 1 statvolt $\equiv 300$ volts.

CHAPTER II

FUNDAMENTAL ELECTRICAL CONCEPTS AND UNITS

1. Electrons in motion—Current. As was stated in the preceding chapter, there are believed to exist in all metals a number of electrons which are not definitely associated with any particular atomic nucleus and which are free to wander about through the space lattice of the metal. No experimental procedure has ever been devised for determining how many of these free, or conduction, electrons exist in a given conductor, but there is some reason to believe that there may be as many as one free electron per atom. Since it is possible to determine how many atoms there are in a given piece of metal, we can make use of the above assumption of one free electron per atom, and determine the number of free electrons present in any certain piece of metal. For example, in a piece of No. 10 copper wire (0.102 in. diam) 100 ft long, there would be 1.36×10^{25} free electrons.

As was also stated in Chapter I, the interstices in the space lattice are enormously wide when compared with the dimensions of an electron. Within the conductor, then, we may picture the free electrons behaving very much like the molecules of a gas inclosed in a tube. They are continually in motion in every direction. The individual electrons dart about in a random manner, the violence of their motions depending upon the absolute temperature of the conductor. If we now cause these electrons to be acted upon by suitable forces, they can be caused to move consistently in some definite direction. This motion is aptly termed a **drift,** for although the individual electrons experience all sorts of interference with their motion, and are buffeted about in every conceivable direction, there is on the average, provided proper forces act, a certain electron velocity in the required direction. This velocity itself is not directly measurable, but basing our calculations on the foregoing assumption of one free electron per atom, it appears that ordinarily it does not exceed a few hundredths of a centimeter per second.[1] This

[1] The velocity of 186,272 miles per sec sometimes given for electricity is the velocity at which waves or impulses are propagated in free space. Waves and

drift of free electrons through the space lattice is an **electric current.**

The nature of the electric current, as might be expected, depends upon the nature of the forces which act upon the electrons. The simplest case of all would be that in which the conductor is made part of a **circuit,** or closed loop, which also contains a battery, as in Fig. 2.1. The forces which act upon the free electrons tend to cause them to drift always in one direction around the circuit, and given enough time, individual electrons may complete the trip around and get back whence they started.

While metal wires are the most commonly used conductors of electricity, they are by no means the only conductors. Many other solid substances are fair conductors of electricity. The earth itself forms part of countless electric circuits, while carbon and graphite have important uses as conductors for special purposes.

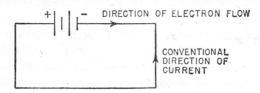

Fig. 2.1.   Simple electric circuit.

Liquids and gases may also be conductors of electricity. The moving particles here are not electrons, but charged molecules or atoms, known as **ions.** The charge on such particles may be either positive or negative, according to whether there is a deficiency or an excess of electrons. Ions of both signs are usually present, and conduction of electricity in a liquid or a gas involves movement of positive ions in one direction and of negative ions in the opposite direction.

Finally it is possible to have a stream of electrons move across empty space, as from the cathode to the plate in a vacuum tube. This also is current. In general, any flow or motion of charged particles, either positive or negative, is a current.

2. Direction of current. In the early days of the study of electricity, it was the rule to think of the current as being the flow of positive electricity around the circuit. This was long before the discovery of the electron, and the rule may have had its origin in the experiments of Faraday with conduction in liquids. As the science developed and electricity began to find practical uses, this rule was accepted without question. By the time the electron was discovered

---

impulses do not move along wires at this speed, and the velocity of the electrons in the wires is something else altogether.

and the nature of the electric current in metal wires became known, the conventional assumption that current was the flow of positive electricity had become so firmly rooted in electrical literature and so many other conventions and rules depended upon it that it could not readily be changed, even if that were desirable. As we have seen, positive electricity as well as negative is actually in motion in liquid and gaseous conductors, though the negative ions account for most of the current in gaseous conductors.

We therefore have to remember that the direction of current is the direction of the movement of positive electricity in those conductors in which movement of positive electricity occurs. In metal wires the direction of current is the direction opposite to that in which the electrons move, as indicated in Fig. 2.1.

This need not be confusing, because the current direction and the direction of electron movement are always opposite. There is no case in which they are the same.

3. Measurement of current—The ampere. Two phenomena that occur when currents flow in conductors are readily demonstrated in the laboratory: (1) The conductors get hot and (2) if two current-carrying conductors lie parallel, they exert forces on each other, of attraction if the currents are in the same direction, of repulsion if the currents are in opposite directions. These phenomena are of tremendous practical importance; the first is the basis of the incandescent lamp and electrical heating appliances of every sort. The second is the underlying principle of the electric motor. The forces exerted between current-carrying conductors are called **electromagnetic forces,** and are not to be confused with the electrostatic forces that act between electrons or charged bodies regardless of whether these bodies are in motion or not (Fig. 2.2).

Experiments originally performed by Ampere about 1824 show that the electromagnetic force that acts between very long current-carrying conductors which lie parallel depends upon: (1) the magnitude of the current in the first wire (directly), (2) the magnitude of the current in the second wire (directly), (3) the length of the parallel parts (directly), (4) the distance between the wires (inversely), and (5) some property of the medium in which the wires are located (directly). These experiments give us a clue as to how current can be measured. If we can measure the distance between the wires, their parallel length and the force of attraction or repulsion that acts between them when they are located in a certain medium and are each carrying the same current, then the current is determined. It remains only for us to define the unit, which is called the **ampere :** *One ampere (amp)* *is that current which will cause a force of attraction of 2×10^{-7} newton per meter between two infinitely long parallel conductors placed 1 m apart in free space.*

def ampere

It can be seen from this definition that for conductors in free space, the forces are rather feeble unless the currents are large.   For parallel conductors a meter apart a current of 4750 amp would be required to give an attractive force of 1 pound per meter length.   Currents of this magnitude (and larger) are encountered in power systems when short circuits occur, in certain applications, especially the electro-chemical industries, and in lightning strokes.

As everyday examples of current magnitudes, about 15 to 30 amp flows when an automobile generator is charging the storage battery,

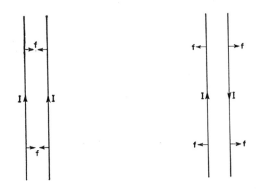

Fig. 2.2.   Forces due to currents in parallel conductors.

while operation of the starter may require from 100 to 300 amp.   The current through the filament of an ordinary 100-w lamp is about 0.8 amp.

The heating effect of a given current depends upon the nature of the conductor through which the current flows.   The current (0.8 amp) which raises the lamp filament to a temperature of about 2700° absolute would scarcely cause enough heating in a No. 14 copper wire to be perceptible to the touch.   A copper wire of this size with Type R (rubber) insulation and located in the open air can carry a current of 20 amp with a temperature rise of about 10° C.

It may be noted in passing that the human body is a conductor of electricity and that currents of more than about 0.1 amp are likely to prove fatal.   The smallest current that can be felt is about 1 milliampere, and for currents larger than about 10 milliamperes, muscular contraction occurs and pain begins to be felt.

4. Permeability. It is important to note that in writing this definition we have had to take account of the medium in which the conductors lie—"in free space." If the conductors had been surrounded by iron, for example, and had been carrying the same current, the force would have been many times greater (Fig. 2.3). In air, the force would have been very slightly greater. This property of space and iron and air that influences the force acting between current-carrying conductors is a fundamental property which cannot be measured in terms of mass, length, and time, as could all the mechanical quantities we considered. It is called **permeability.** This property is not involved when we work with mechanical quantities only, but

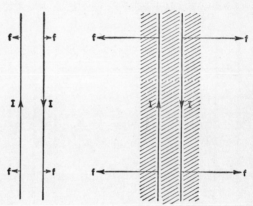

Fig. 2.3. Electromagnetic forces in space and in iron.

has to be introduced as soon as we begin to define electrical quantities and relate them to the units of mechanics. Since permeability is a fundamental quantity, its unit, like the meter, the kilogram, and the second, can be arbitrarily chosen. In the rationalized MKS system, the value $4\pi \times 10^{-7}$ is arbitrarily assigned to the permeability of free space. The student will wonder why such an unwieldy number as $4\pi \times 10^{-7}$ should have been chosen, and the reasons will be explained later because to attempt an explanation at this time would be more confusing than enlightening.

Since the value assigned to the permeability of free space is $4\pi \times 10^{-7}$, it is obvious that a substance having a permeability of 1 would permit much greater forces between current-carrying conductors placed in it than would free space. We can now define unit permeability thus: *Unit permeability is* $\frac{1}{4\pi} \times 10^{7}$ *times the permeability of free space.*

No substance has a permeability as great as 1.   The permeabilities of most substances differ so little from the permeability of space that the value $4\pi \times 10^{-7}$ can be used with but little error.   Iron and steel may have permeabilities as high as 10^4 times the permeability of space—that is, as high as $4\pi \times 10^{-3}$.

The MKS unit of permeability has no name.   The symbol is the Greek letter mu (μ), and for free space the symbol is followed by a subscript zero (μ_0).

5. Defining equation of current.   We can state the experimental facts set forth in Section 3 in mathematical form as follows:

$$F \text{ is proportional to } I_1, \tag{2.1}$$

$$F \text{ is proportional to } I_2, \tag{2.2}$$

$$F \text{ is proportional to } L, \tag{2.3}$$

$$F \text{ is proportional to } \frac{1}{S}, \tag{2.4}$$

$$F \text{ is proportional to } \mu, \tag{2.5}$$

where the meanings of the symbols are clear from the text.   Combining these proportionalities we have,

$$F \text{ is proportional to } \frac{\mu L I_1 I_2}{S}. \tag{2.6}$$

We can always make a proportionality into an equation by inserting a constant:

$$F = \frac{K \mu L I_1 I_2}{S}. \tag{2.7}$$

The value of K is fixed by the definition of the ampere and by the definition of the unit of permeability.   It is $1/2\pi$.   Thus, Equation (2.7) becomes

$$F = \frac{\mu L I_1 I_2}{2\pi S}, \tag{2.8}$$

where F is the force in newtons.

μ is the permeability of the medium in MKS units.

L is the parallel length of the conductors in meters.

I_1 is the current in the first conductor in amperes.

I_2 is the current in the second conductor in amperes.

S is the separation of the conductors in meters.

Equation (2.8) is the defining equation for the ampere.   The student may convince himself of the truth of this by substituting in (2.8) the values of μ, L, I_1, I_2, and S mentioned in the definition.   It is important to note that Equation (2.8) holds exactly only when the conductors are infinitely long—that is, when the end connections and other parts of the circuit are so remote that they have no effect. It is approximately correct, however, in any case where L is large compared to S, or in any case where the effect of other parts of the circuit can be neglected.

EXAMPLE: Two conductors run parallel for a distance of 40 m. They are 10 cm apart on centers and carry equal currents. What is the direction and magnitude of the current in each conductor if they are mutually repelled by a force of 1 lb when situated in air?

SOLUTION: Since

$$F = \frac{\mu L I_1 I_2}{2\pi S}, \tag{2.8}$$

for the case where $I_1 = I_2 = I$, we have

$$I = \sqrt{\frac{2\pi SF}{\mu_0 L}}$$
$$= \sqrt{\frac{2\pi(0.1)(4.44)}{(4\pi \times 10^{-7})(40)}} = 236 \text{ amp.}$$

Since the conductors are repelled, the currents must be in opposite directions.

Problems

(1-II) What force will act between the parallel wires of a power line, when the wires are 2 ft apart and carrying currents of 50 amp each, in opposite directions? Express the result in pounds per foot.

(2-II) The wires of a twin-conductor cable are each 0.25 in. diam and covered with 0.125 in. of insulation. With what force would the wires repel each other if they carried their normal current of 75 amp? Take the permeability of the insulation to be equal to the permeability of free space. Express the result in pounds per foot.

(3-II) With what force would the wires of Problem 2-II repel each other at the instant a short circuit caused the current to increase to 10 times normal?

(4-II) Two current-carrying conductors are placed 10 cm apart in free space and repel each other with a force of 0.1 newton. All the space around and between the conductors is now stacked full of sheet steel and the force is found to have increased to 265 newtons. What is the permeability of the steel?

(5-II) Two parallel conductors lie in free space, one directly above the other. Each conductor weighs 0.1 lb per ft. The upper conductor floats freely between vertical guides, the separation depending upon the current flowing. For what current would the system be in equilibrium for a separation of 1 cm?

(6-II) Two conductors each 5 m long and each weighing 1 kg are suspended by means of threads 50 cm long so that they hang parallel in the same horizontal plane and 1 cm apart. Equal currents are now sent through the conductors and the separation increases to 2 cm.   What are the magnitudes and directions of the currents?

6. Absolute measurement of current.   The definition of the ampere has to be restated in order to make it a workable one.   We cannot have infinitely long conductors, and experiments in free space are difficult.   Fortunately, the permeability of air differs but little from the permeability of free space, and the forces that act between very accurately built coils which carry current can be reduced to terms of the force between long parallel wires carrying the same current.   Such an arrangement, known as a *current balance*, is shown in Fig. 2.4, and is part of the equipment of some standardizing laboratories such as the United States Bureau of Standards at Washington.   By means of it, currents are actually measured in terms of the forces which they cause to act between the coils.   Such a measurement is called **absolute,**

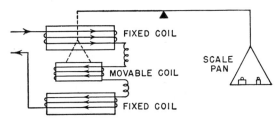

Fig. 2.4.   Absolute current balance.

because current is measured in terms of the fundamental mechanical quantities and permeability.

7. Alternating current.   If the battery in Fig. 2.1 be replaced by a suitable device (an alternating current generator or an oscillator) the electrons will be urged first in one direction around the circuit and then in the other direction, and as a consequence, instead of drifting steadily in one certain direction, the electrons will simply oscillate about their mean positions.   This pattern of electron motion gives rise to the same effects as does the steady drift in one direction—that is, the conductor gets hot and forces of attraction or repulsion act between parallel conductors.   Conductors in which this pattern of electron motion occurs are said to carry **alternating current,** as distinguished from **direct current,** when the electron drift is unidirectional.

We may think of the electrons as being acted upon by forces that cause them to start to move in one direction, and which accelerate them until their average velocity reaches a maximum.   The current at that instant is maximum.   The forces then decrease, and the electrons slow down until their average velocity is again zero.   At this instant, the current is zero. Forces then act to set them in motion in the opposite direction, and they reach maximum velocity in this direction. The forces diminish, and the average electron velocity again falls to zero. This series of events, which is repeated again and again, is called a **cycle.** The time that elapses during a cycle is called a **period,** and the number of cycles which take place per second is called the **frequency.**

An alternating current may vary with time in various ways, depending upon the forces that act upon the free electrons. Some of the possible modes of variation, or **wave forms,** are shown in Fig. 2.5. The graph in Fig. 2.5*a* represents the current as starting at zero, increasing instantaneously to a certain positive value I_m, remaining constant at this value for a time $T/2$, then changing instantaneously to a negative value $-I_m$, remaining constant at this value for a time $T/2$, and changing instantaneously to zero to complete a cycle. This is called a rectangular, or square, wave and is typical of the currents in some radio circuits. The graph in Fig. 2.5*b* represents the current beginning at zero and increasing at a uniform rate to $+I_m$ at time $T/4$, then decreasing uniformly to zero at time $T/2$, then increasing uniformly to $-I_m$ at $3T/4$, then decreasing again to zero at time T. This is a triangular wave. The

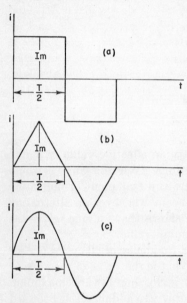

Fig. 2.5. Alternating-current wave forms: (a) rectangular (b) triangular (c) sinusoidal.

graph in Fig. 2.5*c* represents the most common of all wave forms, the sine wave. Commencing at zero, the current increases to $+I_m$, decreases to zero, increases to $-I_m$, and decreases to zero again according to the law,

$$i = I_m \sin 2\pi ft, \tag{2.10}$$

where i is the instantaneous value of the current.

I_m is the maximum value attained by the current at any time.

f is the frequency in cycles per second.

t is the time in seconds since the current was zero increasing in the positive direction.

It will be seen that the product ft is always a number of cycles

$$ft = \frac{\text{cycles}}{\text{seconds}} \times \text{seconds} = \text{cycles}, \qquad (2.11)$$

and $2\pi ft$ is an angle that is zero when t is zero and increases uniformly as t increases. Thus, we see that i varies as the sine of some angle that increases with time. The symbol T is used to denote the period of the current (that is, the time required for the current to go through a complete cycle). Since

$$f \text{ is } \frac{\text{cycles}}{\text{seconds}}$$

and

$$T \text{ is } \frac{\text{seconds}}{\text{cycles}},$$

it is evident that f and T are reciprocals and

$$fT = 1. \qquad (2.12)$$

An alternating current is said to have an effective value of 1 amp when it produces the same heating effect in a given resistance as would a direct current of 1 amp. Unless there is a statement or indication to the contrary, the effective value is meant whenever an alternating current is given in amperes. It can be shown that for sine waves the effective value is $1/\sqrt{2}$ times the maximum value.

EXAMPLE: A sinusoidal current has a frequency of 60 cycles per sec and a maximum value of 1 amp. (a) What is the value of the current 0.001 sec after it is zero and begins increasing toward maximum positive? (b) How long after the current is zero and increasing toward maximum positive will it be -0.5 amp?

SOLUTION:

$$i = I_m \sin 2\pi ft, \qquad (2.10)$$

(a)
$$= 1 \sin 2\pi \times 60 \times 0.001$$
$$= 1 \sin 21.6° = 0.368 \text{ amp}.$$

(b)
$$-0.5 = 1 \sin 2\pi \times 60 \times t,$$
$$= \sin 377t.$$

$377t$ is any angle which has a sine of -0.5—that is, 210°, 330°, 570°, and so forth.

∴ i will first reach -0.5 amp when

$$377t = 210° = 3.67 \text{ radians},$$
$$t = \frac{3.67}{377} = 0.00974 \text{ sec}.$$

Problems

(7-II) A sinusoidal current has a frequency of 1000 cycles per sec and a maximum value of 5 amp. Calculate and plot one cycle of this current using a scale 1 in. = 0.0005 sec and 1 in. = 2 amp.

(8-II) A sinusoidal current has a frequency of 1150 kilocycles (kc) per sec and a maximum value of 20 amp. What is the period? How long a time elapses between zero increasing toward + maximum and + maximum? Between zero increasing toward + maximum and +17.32 amp?

8. Frequency. Frequency is an all-important quantity in electrical engineering. In various phases of the art, we work with currents ranging in frequency from zero (direct current), up to 3×10^{10} cycles per sec. For the generation, transmission, and distribution of electrical energy, except on aircraft, a frequency of 60 cycles per sec is more used than any other. Many aircraft electrical systems use

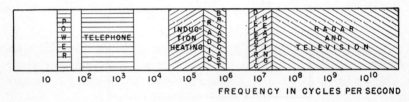

FREQUENCY IN CYCLES PER SECOND

Fig. 2.6. Frequency chart.

alternating current, the most common frequency being 400 cycles per sec. Local telephone transmission requires the use of frequencies up to about 5000 cycles per sec. For induction heating now being used in industry, 300 kc per sec is a typical frequency, and the present-day radio broadcasting stations operate at frequencies from 550 to 1500 kc per sec. Industrial dielectric heating uses frequencies such as 10 megacycles per sec. The television stations in use in 1951 operated at frequencies from 54 to 216 megacycles per sec. and radar at frequencies up to 30,000 megacycles per sec. Phenomena that are not present, or are so feeble as to escape notice at certain frequencies, become paramount at higher frequencies, and much of the progress in electrical engineering can be credited to the discovery and invention of high-frequency phenomena and apparatus.

9. Positive direction. It is obvious that in alternating current circuits, we cannot say that the current flows in one direction any more than in the other direction. We can, however, select and mark one direction as the **positive direction,** which means that at any time the current is actually in that particular direction, we will speak of it and write it as positive; otherwise, we will speak of it and write it as negative.   Thus, in Fig. 2.7, an arrow pointing to the right has been placed on the upper conductor.   This is the positive-direction arrow for the current in the circuit.   If we now say that at a certain instant the current is $+5$ amp, it means 5 amp in the direction indicated by the arrow.   At another instant, the current may be -2 amp—that is, 2 amp in the direction opposite to the arrow.   It should be obvious that unless some direction is marked as positive, then $+5$ and -2 are meaningless so far as the signs are concerned.   It is exactly like saying to a man lost in a strange city, "Go two blocks north."   His next question will very likely be, "Which way is north?"

Instead of designating the positive direction by an arrow, some books use a double-subscript method of notation.   Thus, if we mark a point a and a point b on a circuit, as in Fig. 2.7, then, to say that at a certain instant I_{ab} is 5 amp conveys a definite meaning as to

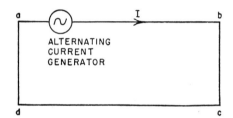

Fig. 2.7.   Simple a-c circuit.

direction as well as magnitude. I_{ab} is equal to I_{ba} in magnitude, but is opposite in direction.

The marking of positive directions is essential not only in alternating current circuits but in many direct current circuits as well.   In direct current circuits, the current will be always in one direction, but which direction may not be known when the solution of a problem is begun.   A direction is, therefore, assumed, and is marked with an arrow or by double subscripts.   As the solution proceeds, the current may be found to be either positive or negative, positive meaning that the current is actually in the arrow direction; negative, that the current is actually opposite in direction to the arrow.

10. Quantity of electricity—The coulomb.   As we have seen, current in a wire is the drift of electrons through the space lattice.   Each electron carries a certain invariable charge.   Hence, when a wire carries a steady current for a given length of time, a definite **quantity of electricity** will pass any fixed reference point on the wire, and we can, therefore, define unit quantity of electricity in terms of current and time.   The unit is called the **coulomb,** for Charles Augustus de

Coulomb, who in 1785 discovered the law of forces between charged bodies. *One coulomb is that quantity of electricity which passes a reference point on a conductor in 1 sec when the conductor carries a steady current of 1 amp.* We may state this definition in equation form as follows:

$$Q = IT, \tag{2.13}$$

where Q is quantity of electricity in coulombs.

   I is current in amperes.

   T is time in seconds.

Determinations of quantity of electricity, when a steady current flows in a complete circuit as in Fig. 2.1, can be readily made by using Equation (2.13) directly.

EXAMPLE: The current in an ordinary 100-w lamp is about 0.833 amp. What quantity of electricity passes through the filament in 1 hr when the lamp is connected to direct current mains?

SOLUTION:

$$Q = IT. \tag{2.13}$$
$$I = 0.833 \text{ amp.}$$
$$T = 1 \text{ hr} = 3600 \text{ sec.}$$
$$Q = (0.833)(3600) = 3000 \text{ coulombs.}$$

We see from this example that the coulomb is not a particularly large unit for such measurements.

In electrostatics, however, and in determining charges on particles, the coulomb is immensely larger than the quantities of electricity usually dealt with. For example, if two spheres each 1 cm diam were placed 1 m apart and given opposite charges of 1 coulomb each, they would attract each other with a force of 9×10^9 newtons, or about one million tons. No such experiment has ever been carried out, for the reason that long before the charge on the spheres amounted to anything like 1 coulomb, any known substance used to insulate them would have broken down. The charges usually used in electrostatic experiments are of the order of a few microcoulombs. The largest electrostatic charges known are those which occur on thunderclouds, which are believed to reach magnitudes of several hundred coulombs.

The charge of an electron was determined by Robert Andrews Millikan in one of the most famous experimental procedures ever devised, the "oil-drop experiment." He found the value of the electronic charge to be 1.60×10^{-19} coulomb, from which it can be seen that a quantity of electricity of 1 coulomb would be equivalent to the charge on $1/(1.60 \times 10^{-19})$, or 6.25×10^{18} electrons.

Problems

(9-II) What quantity of electricity passes a reference point on a conductor in 1 hr if the current is 200 amp?   In 0.05 sec, if the current is 0.002 amp?

(10-II) Electrons are passing a reference point on a conductor at the rate of 5×10^{21} electrons per min.   What is the current in amperes?

11. Resistance.   It was pointed out in Section 3 that one of the effects of current was to heat the conductor.   In other words, the movement of electrons through the conductor cannot take place without the expenditure of some energy, which appears in the form of heat.   The rate of expenditure of energy can be shown to be proportional to the square of the current.   That is, doubling the current would result in the rate of heating being increased to four times as much.   The property of a conductor which requires the expenditure of energy by the moving electrons is called **resistance.**   Just what takes place in the space lattice of the conductor to bring about the heating effect is not easily explainable; the most obvious thing to say would be that the moving electrons collide with the atomic nuclei and with one another, each collision resulting in the liberation of a minute quantity of heat.   Although this explanation gives a crude picture of the phenomenon that will serve our purpose for the present, it needs a great deal of modification and refinement to make it accurate.

Some simple facts about resistance, however, may be stated with certainty.   First, resistance depends upon the material used for the conductor.   Metals, particularly silver, copper, and aluminum, make the best conductors.   That is, wires made of these metals have less resistance, and they are, therefore, used in preference to others where it is desirable to conduct current with as little energy loss as possible, as in power-station bus bars and in transmission lines.   Other metals and metal alloys make much poorer conductors—that is, conductors offering much more resistance, and, therefore, well-suited for use where energy loss and heating effects are wanted, as in incandescent lamps and electric heating appliances.

Resistance also depends upon the temperature of the material.   In general, the resistance of any metal conductor increases with increasing temperature and decreases with decreasing temperature.   It is found that as the temperature approaches absolute zero ($-273°$ C), the resistance approaches zero, and in some instances, it becomes possible for a conductor to carry current without any loss of energy.   We can now begin to improve our explanation of the nature of resistance.   As the temperature is reduced, the random darting-about of the electrons becomes less and less.   At absolute zero, it stops entirely, and all that is left is the orderly drift of the electrons in the required direction when the conductor carries current.   This involves no loss in energy.   In some way then, the heating and loss in energy are the result of superimposing the drift motion upon the random motion of the electrons.

Resistance depends also upon the dimensions of the conductor. For a conductor of constant cross section, the resistance varies directly as the length.   For a conductor of constant length, the resistance varies inversely with the cross section.   Thus, if the length and cross section of a wire were each doubled, the resistance would be the same.

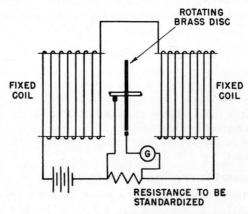

Fig. 2.8.   Lorenz apparatus for absolute measurement of resistance.

12. Unit of resistance—The ohm.   A unit of resistance can now be defined in terms of current and the rate of energy loss.   The MKS unit of resistance is called the **ohm,** and is defined as follows: *One ohm is the resistance of a conductor in which energy is lost at the rate of 1 joule per sec (1 w) when the current is 1 amp.*

Since the rate of energy loss is found to be proportional to the square of the current, the defining equation of resistance is

$$R = \frac{P}{I^2},$$ (2.14)

where R is resistance in ohms.

P is rate of energy loss in joules per second.

I is current in amperes.

The resistance of a piece of No. 10 copper wire 1000 ft long is approximately 1 ohm.   This is a convenient fact to remember as a basis for the quick calculation of the resistances of other sizes and lengths (see Chapter VI).   An aluminum wire of the same size and length would have a resistance of about 1.6 ohms, an iron wire 5.6 ohms, a nichrome alloy wire 65 ohms.

Absolute measurements of resistance are made in standard laboratories by several methods, all of which require the precise determination of the dimensions of the apparatus.   One such method was suggested by L. Lorenz in 1873.   Essentially it consists in rotating a brass disk between two very accurately constructed coils of wire that carry current from a battery (Fig. 2.8).   This arrangement is, in reality, a sort of generator, and its potential difference is balanced against the potential difference between the terminals of a resistor which is included in the battery circuit.   The resistance R may be calculated from the dimensions of the apparatus and the speed of rotation of the disk.

Problems

$\checkmark$ **(11-II)** Electrical energy is converted to heat in a certain conductor at the rate of 50 joules per sec when the current is 2.24 amp.   What is the resistance of the conductor?

(12-II) What is the resistance of a conductor which will absorb 10 w of power when the current is 100 amp?

(13-II) What current flowing in a conductor having a resistance of 50 ohms will cause heating at the rate of 500 w?

13. How energy is supplied to the free electrons.   In order that the free electrons may continue to move through the space lattice of the conductor at a constant rate, it is obvious from the law of conservation of energy that we must supply energy to them at the same rate at which they are losing energy in the resistance of the conductor.   In order to do this, we include in the circuit some device, such as a battery or generator, that can convert chemical or mechanical energy into the electrical form, so that the energy may be assimilated by the electrons.   If a battery is used, the energy comes from a chemical reaction such as

$$Zn + 2HCl = ZnCl_2 + H_2 + 166{,}000 \text{ joules per gram}$$
$$\text{molecule of zinc.}\quad (2.15)$$

This liberated energy, or some part of it at least, is supplied to the electrons nearest the battery and is passed on by these to other electrons in turn, and so around the circuit.

If a steam-turbine-driven generator is used, the energy still comes from a chemical reaction.   Fuel is burned, but instead of the energy passing directly from the chemical into the electrical form, it first appears as heat, which is converted into mechanical energy by the turbine, and this in turn is supplied to the electrons by the generator. We may think of a battery or generator as a device in which the "suitable forces," described as being *required* in Section 1, act upon the free electrons and tend to force them around the circuit. The nature of the forces themselves and how they act upon the electrons will be considered in some detail in the following chapters.

Let us make use of an analogy to get more clearly in mind the idea of energy gained and lost. Fig. 2.9*a* is our simple electric circuit and

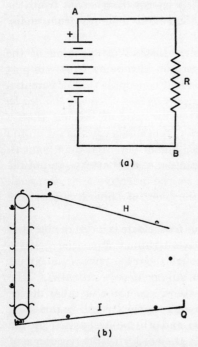

(a)

(b)

Fig. 2.9. **Mechanical analogy of rise and fall of potential.**

Fig. 2.9*b* is a mechanical hoist arrangement in which steel shot are raised by an endless-belt hoist to the platform *P*, from which they roll down the inclined planes *H* and *I* to be hoisted again. In order to make our analogy consistent with the conventional direction for current, let us suppose that it is the protons and not the electrons that move. A proton that has just been through the battery and is emerging at the positive terminal is like a shot that has just been hoisted and is lying on the platform. The proton possesses potential energy; it is capable of doing work in passing around the circuit, as the shot is capable of doing work in rolling down the inclined planes. The proton has lost all its energy by the time it arrives at the negative terminal of the battery, as the shot has lost all its energy by the time it comes to rest at the foot of the hoist. The proton loses most of its energy in passing through the coil of wire *R*, as the shot loses most of its energy when it drops from plane *H* to plane *I*. The proton possesses more energy at *A* than at *B*. The shot possesses more energy at *P* than at *Q*.

Though this analogy is useful, we must guard against a number of wrong ideas to which it might lead:

1. It is not the protons, but the electrons which actually move around the circuit. But electrons moving around the circuit in a

given direction are *equivalent* to protons moving around in the opposite direction.

2. The energy which the electrons (protons) receive in the battery is not represented by the increased velocity of the electrons (protons) themselves. The average velocity may be no greater at A than at B. The energy possessed by the electrons (protons) at any point is to be regarded as **potential** energy (energy of position) rather than **kinetic** energy (energy of velocity).

3. A particular electron (proton) does not necessarily make the trip around the circuit on the original energy it received from the battery. It may give up energy to, and receive energy from, many other electrons during the trip.

14. Potential difference—The volt. Instead of speaking of the potential energy gained or lost by a proton in moving from one part of the circuit to another, a more convenient concept is that of **potential difference.** *Potential difference is the gain or loss of energy divided by the quantity of electricity moved.* Thus, instead of saying that a proton at A (Fig. 2.9a) possesses more potential energy than a proton at B, we simply say that point A is at a higher potential than point B. A is designated as the positive $(+)$ terminal of the battery (and of the resistor also), and B is designated as the negative $(-)$ terminal. These signs indicate the **polarity** of the piece of apparatus at whose terminals they are placed.

Another way of putting it would be to say there is a rise in potential through the battery from the negative terminal B to the positive terminal A, and a fall in potential through the other part of the circuit from the positive terminal A back to the negative terminal B. The rise in potential associated with a battery, generator or other device in which energy is imparted to the moving electricity will in this book be called an **electromotive force** (emf) and will be designated by the symbol E or e. The fall in potential associated with the resistance of the remainder of the circuit in which the moving electricity loses energy will be called a **voltage drop** and will be designated by the symbol V or v.[1]

The unit of potential difference is the joule per coulomb, or **volt,** and is defined as follows: *One volt is the potential difference between two*

---

[1] Unfortunately there is no generally accepted standard notation for potential differences. Some writers use E regardless of whether a rise or a fall of potential is meant. Others use V regardless of which is meant. Others use both E and V but without regard to whether a rise or fall of potential is meant. When reading a textbook or technical paper the student will need to inform himself as to the notation used.

points on a circuit when the energy involved in moving 1 coulomb from one point to the other is 1 joule.

Potential difference is defined by the equation

$$E \text{ (or } V) = \frac{W}{Q},\qquad(2.16)$$

where E (or V) is potential difference in volts.

W is energy in joules.

Q is quantity of electricity in coulombs.

The name **electromotive force** was originally meant to imply that it is the force that causes the electricity to move—that is, causes the current. This is not strictly correct because, as we have just seen, electromotive force is not a force at all but is the energy supplied per

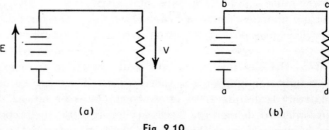

(a)   **(b)**

Fig. 2.10.

unit quantity of electricity moved. Nevertheless, it is convenient to think of electromotive force as being the cause of current, and ordinarily this viewpoint will not lead to any error. On the other hand voltage drop is usually thought of as being a consequence of current flow.

One thing further is required. We must have some means of designating the points between which the electromotive force or the voltage drop is being considered and of designating which point is at the higher potential. In this book use will be made of arrows placed alongside the circuit with the tail opposite one of the points and the tip opposite the other point. Thus in Fig. 2.10a, the arrow marked E designates the positive direction of an electromotive force (rise of potential) from the lower terminal of the battery to the upper terminal, and the arrow marked V designates the positive direction of a voltage drop (fall of potential) from the upper terminal of the resistor to the lower terminal. Double subscripts are used in many books for designating electromotive forces and voltage drops. Thus in Fig. 2.10b, E_{ab} or V_{ab} would refer to the potential difference between point a and point b, and E_{cd} and V_{cd} would refer to the potential difference between point c and point d.[1]

15. Meaning of potential difference.   Large potential differences mean large amounts of energy per unit quantity of electricity moved. This is clear from the definition of potential difference.   However, if an operation involves a very small quantity of electricity, then a large potential difference may result from the expenditure of only a little energy.   For example, by sliding across the plastic cover of an automobile seat, one can readily establish a potential difference of several hundred volts between himself and the metal parts of the car.   This may produce a startling shock upon touching the key or dash, but it is not dangerous because the quantity of electricity moved is extremely small and the energy involved is a very minute fraction of that which the battery must supply to operate the starter.

Most automobile electric systems operate at a potential difference of 6 v.   This means that for every coulomb of electricity passing through the battery, 6 joules of energy is being converted from the chemical to the electrical form and made available to operate the starter or lights or ignition or other device.   These are so designed that relatively large quantities of electricity must be moved through them in order to deliver the necessary energy for their operation. This can be done efficiently because the distances between the various parts of the system are small.

For supplying the lighting and appliance requirements of residences, businesses and small industries, the potential difference almost universally used is 115–120 v.   It is obvious that at this voltage each coulomb of electricity has received from the generator about 20 times as much energy as it would receive from the battery in an automobile electric system.   Thus it can deliver 20 times as much to the lamps and appliances or, what amounts to the same thing, a required amount of energy can be delivered by moving only 1/20 of the quantity of electricity that would be necessary in a 6-v system.   This means that smaller currents are required, smaller conductors may be used, and loads at increased distances may be served more efficiently.

---

[1] To know which point is at the higher potential it is necessary to know the system of notation being used.   Some (including this writer) would use E_{ab} to designate the positive direction of a voltage rise from point a to point b, and V_{ab} to designate the positive direction of a voltage drop from point a to point b.   Other writers use either E_{ab} or V_{ab} to designate the positive direction of a voltage drop from point a to point b.   Still others use either E_{ab} or V_{ab} to designate the positive direction of a voltage rise from point a to point b.   For a complete account of the possible conventions see "Voltage Notation Conventions," by Myril B. Reed and W. A. Lewis, in *Electrical Engineering*, January 1948.

The disadvantages of using a higher voltage are: (1) it is more expensive to insulate the conductors and apparatus and, (2) it is more hazardous.   In going from 6 to 120 v, the increase in cost of insulation is trivial and is far outweighed by the saving in conductor size.   The danger from electric shock is very definitely increased, but with proper equipment and installation methods the risk is small.

For long distance transmission of power and distribution over considerable areas, and for many special purposes, higher voltages are necessary.   Common distribution voltages are 240, 2300, 4100, 6900, and 13,000.   For long transmission lines voltages as high as 275,000 are in use in the United States, and a line designed to operate at 380,000 v was put into service in Sweden in 1951.   Potential differences of several million volts have been produced for experimental and test purposes.

As we go to higher and higher voltages, the problem of insulating the apparatus and the conductors becomes more difficult and its solution more costly.   Air, which is the cheapest and most abundant insulating material, will "break down" and become a conductor if large potential differences are established between points not too far apart.   There are other insulating substances which do not break down as readily as air, but their use to separate points of high potential difference increases the expense of the installation and as the voltage is raised, this increase outweighs the saving on cost of conductors. Thus it is seen that the highest voltage to be considered for a given line is, at least in part, an economic problem.

16. Alternating potential difference.   In direct current circuits, the polarities of batteries and generators will usually be known and will remain unchanged.   Hence an electromotive force arrow can readily be placed alongside each battery or generator with the tail opposite the negative terminal and the tip opposite the positive terminal, and the electromotive force treated as a positive quantity throughout.

In alternating current circuits the polarity of the generator or oscillator changes from instant to instant.   An alternating current generator can be thought of as imparting energy to the free electrons in its windings, momentarily raising the potential of first one terminal and then the other.   In most alternating current generators an effort is made to have the electromotive force vary according to the equation

$$e = E_m \sin 2\pi ft, \qquad (2.17)$$

where e is the instantaneous value of the electromotive force.

E_m is the maximum value of the electromotive force.

f is the frequency in cycles per second.

t is the time in seconds since the electromotive force was zero, increasing in the positive direction.

Thus in Fig. 2.11 the electromotive force designated as e would be positive for values of $2\pi ft$ from 0 to 180° and there would be a rise of potential from the lower terminal to the upper terminal.   For values of $2\pi ft$ from 180° to 360° the rise of potential would be from the upper terminal to the lower terminal and the electromotive force designated as e would be negative.   Thus instead of indicating the actual direction of the electromotive force, we see that the arrow marks a positive, or reference direction.[1]   When there is actually a rise of potential from the point designated by the tail of the arrow to the point designated by the tip, the electromotive force e is positive; otherwise the electromotive force e is negative.

Fig. 2.11.

The remarks above apply also to voltage drops, and it may be added further that since a voltage drop is to be thought of as a consequence of current flow, it is convenient (though not necessary) to place the reference arrow for a voltage drop to agree with the reference arrow for current.   Then if at a certain instant the current is positive, there is actually a drop in potential from the terminal designated by the tail of the voltage drop arrow to the terminal designated by the tip.

It can be seen that for alternating potential differences, the defining equation

$$E \text{ (or } V) = \frac{W}{Q} \tag{2.16}$$

would be meaningless because, when considered over a complete cycle, the quantity of electricity moved from one point to the other would be zero.   An alternating potential difference is said to have an effective value of one volt when it is equal to the voltage drop caused by an alternating current of 1 amp in a resistance of 1 ohm.

EXAMPLE: A quantity equivalent to 100 coulombs of positive electricity moves once around the circuit shown in Fig. 2.12, in the direction a-b-c-d.   In passing from d to a the energy supplied to the

---

[1] Strictly speaking, it is not correct to refer to the direction of an electromotive force or a voltage drop (or for that matter, a current).   A vector quantity, such as force, has direction, but a scalar quantity such as potential difference does not. So long as the discussion is limited to circuits, however, no misunderstanding is likely to arise from speaking of the direction of an electromotive force or voltage drop with reference to the circuit, and the word will be used in this way throughout the book.

charge by the battery is 1500 joules.   From a to b 250 joules is lost by the charge as heat in the resistor.   From b to c 1000 joules is con-

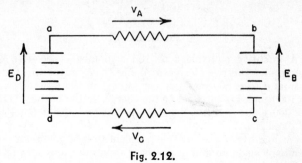

Fig. 2.12.

verted from electrical energy to chemical energy in the battery.   Find the values of E_D, V_A, E_B, V_C, V_{ab}, V_{ba}, E_{db} and V_{ac}.

SOLUTION:

$$E_D = \frac{1500}{100} = 15 \text{ v},$$

$$V_A = \frac{250}{100} = 2.5 \text{ v},$$

$$E_B = \frac{1000}{100} = 10 \text{ v}.$$

Energy lost by the charge as heat in the resistor between c and d is

$$W = 1500 - 1000 - 250 = 250 \text{ joules},$$

$$V_c = \frac{250}{100} = 2.5 \text{ v}.$$

With reference arrows as shown E_D, V_A, E_B and E_C are positive

$$V_{ab} \equiv V_A = +2.5 \text{ v},$$

$$V_{ba} \equiv -V_{ab} = -2.5 \text{ v}.$$

In passing from d to b, the net amount of energy supplied to the charge is

$$W = 1500 - 250 = 1250 \text{ joules}.$$

Therefore point b is at a higher potential than point d and

$$E_{db} = \frac{1250}{100} = +12.5 \text{ v}.$$

In passing from a to c, the net amount of energy given up by the charge is

$$W = 250 + 1000 = 1250 \text{ joules}.$$

Therefore point a is at a higher potential than point c and

$$V_{ac} = \frac{1250}{100} = +12.5 \text{ v.}$$

Problems

(14-II) A quantity equivalent to 100 coulombs of positive electricity moves once around the circuit shown in Fig. 2.12, in the direction d-c-b-a. In passing from d to c, 200 joules is lost as heat in the resistor. In passing from c to b 1000 joules is supplied to the charge by the battery. In passing from b to a, 300 joules is lost as heat in the resistor. Find V_A, V_C, E_B, E_D, V_{ba}, E_{ad}, V_{ca} and E_{db}.

(15-II) A quantity of electricity equivalent to $+50$ coulombs moves once around the circuit made up of four pieces of apparatus, as shown in Fig. 2.13, in the direction a-b-c-d. The energy supplied to the charge in passing through

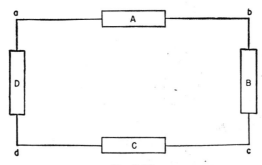

Fig. 2.13.

A is 250 joules, and in passing through B, 200 joules. In C, 150 joules is given up by the charge, and in D, 300 joules. Mark the polarities of A, B, C, and D and place E or V arrows for each. Calculate the electromotive force or voltage drop for each piece of apparatus.

(16-II) Four pieces of apparatus are connected into a circuit, as shown in Fig. 2.13. A number of free electrons equivalent to 50 coulombs moves once around the circuit in the direction a-b-c-d. In A, energy is supplied to the electrons in the amount of 600 joules. In B, energy amounting to 200 joules is given up by the electrons. In C, 300 joules is supplied to the electrons. In D, energy is given up as required by the law of conservation of energy. Redraw the circuit showing batteries or resistors instead of rectangles A, B, C, and D. Mark polarities and place E and V arrows. Calculate the electromotive force or voltage drop for each piece of apparatus.

(17-II) Four pieces of apparatus are connected as shown in Fig. 2.13, and a current of 10 amp flows in the direction a-b-c-d. In A, electrical energy is converted to heat at the rate of 60 w. In B, chemical energy is converted to electrical energy at the rate of 140 w. In C, chemical energy is converted to electrical energy at the rate of 30 w. In D, electrical energy is converted to heat at the rate required by the law of conservation of energy. Redraw the circuit, showing batteries or resistors instead of rectangles A, B, C, and D.

Mark polarities and place E and V arrows.   Calculate the electromotive force or voltage drop for each piece of apparatus.

Study Questions

1. Describe the behavior of the free electrons in conductors.

2. Reconcile the statements "electricity moves with the speed of light" and "the velocity of the free electrons in current-carrying conductors is of the order of a few hundredths of a centimeter per second."

3. How does it happen that the conventional current direction is opposite to the direction of electron flow?   Why not change the convention?

4. What is permeability?   In what particular does a substance of high permeability differ from one of low permeability?

5. Two very long parallel wires spaced S meters apart in free space, and each carrying a current of I amp in the same direction, are attracted by a force of F newtons.   What would be the effect on the force of (a) increasing the spacing to $2S$, (b) increasing the current to $2I$, (c) reversing the current in one conductor, (d) immersing the conductors in a medium of permeability $2\,\mu_0$?

6. What is an "absolute" measurement of current?   Why are such measurements necessary?   Describe the apparatus.

7. What is the significance of a current arrow on a circuit diagram?

8. What is the significance of the statement "the current in this part of the circuit is -1.23 amperes"?

9. Would it be practical to store quantities of electricity to be withdrawn gradually to furnish the current for operating electric motors or lamps?   Why?

10. Why does the filament of an incandescent lamp become white hot while the wires leading to the lamp, and which carry the same current, remain cool enough to handle?

11. Criticize these statements, and write statements which convey the intended meaning more precisely:

    (a) "Electricity is produced by generators."

    (b) "The light company charged me $6.00 for current last month."

12. Distinguish between electromotive force and voltage drop.

13. What quantity in mechanics would be analogous to potential difference?   Explain.

14. Consider the following names as to whether they might be more appropriate than "generator": (a) separator, (b) energizer, (c) electron hoist.

15. What factors do you think may have caused 6 v (rather than 0.6 or 60) to have been chosen for automobile electric systems?   120 v (rather than 12 or 1200) for lighting and appliances?

CHAPTER III

THE LAWS OF THE ELECTRIC CIRCUIT AND SOME OF THEIR APPLICATIONS

1. Power and energy in electric circuits. In the preceding chapter we developed the concepts of current, quantity of electricity, resistance and potential difference, and we defined each concept by an equation and named and defined a unit of each.

Our equation defining potential difference was

$$V = \frac{W}{Q}, \tag{2.16}$$

where V is potential difference in volts.

W is energy in joules.

Q is quantity of electricity in coulombs.

We also defined quantity of electricity by the equation

$$Q = IT, \tag{2.13}$$

where I is current in amperes.

T is time in seconds.

Substituting (2.13) in (2.16) we obtain

$$V = \frac{W}{IT},$$

or
$$W = VIT. \tag{3.1}$$

In actual practice measurements of potential difference, current and time are readily made and, by use of Equation (3.1), the energy supplied or absorbed by any part of a direct current circuit can be found.

Further, since power is defined as the time rate of doing work,

$$P = \frac{W}{T}, \tag{1.5}$$

it follows that
$$P = \frac{VIT}{T} = VI. \tag{3.2}$$

Where resistance is known, the power absorbed can be calculated directly from the defining equation

$$R = \frac{P}{I^2}, \tag{2.14}$$

or
$$P = I^2R. \tag{3.3}$$

By solving (3.2) for I, and substituting in (3.3), it can be shown that

$$P = \frac{V^2}{R}. \tag{3.4}$$

Equations (3.2), (3.3) and (3.4) are equally valid for calculation of power in direct current circuits. Which one is to be used depends simply on which quantities are known, or most easily determined.

In general, Equations (3.1), (3.2) and (3.4) are not applicable to alternating current circuits. This is because the current is changing from instant to instant in both magnitude and direction, as is the potential difference; and the time which elapses between the change in direction of the current and the change in direction of the potential difference must be taken into account in calculating power or energy. Expressions for doing this are developed in any text book on alternating currents.

2. Ohm's law. A further consequence of the definitions of resistance, potential difference, and current as formulated in the last chapter becomes evident if we equate the right-hand side of Equation (3.2) to the right-hand side of Equation (3.3) and divide through by I. Thus

$$VI = I^2R$$
or
$$V = IR \tag{3.5}$$
or
$$R = \frac{V}{I} \tag{3.6}$$
or
$$I = \frac{V}{R}. \tag{3.7}$$

This relationship is probably better known and more used than any other in electrical engineering. It is not, in general, valid for alternating current circuits, but for direct current circuits it makes possible the ready calculation of any one of the three quantities V, R or I if the other two are known.

If we consider only metal conductors at constant temperature, the potential difference will always be proportional to the current in the conductor and the resistance will therefore be constant and independent of either potential difference or current. This fact was discovered by George Simon Ohm in 1826 and is known as **Ohm's law.** The law may be concisely stated as follows: *The current in a metal*

Ohm's law

conductor which is maintained at a constant temperature is proportional to the potential difference between its terminals.

It can be seen that neither Equation (3.5), (3.6) nor (3.7) is a complete mathematical statement of Ohm's law. These equations state the relationship between potential difference, current and resistance, but say nothing about the constancy of the resistance. A complete mathematical statement of Ohm's law would be

$$R = \frac{V}{I} = \text{a constant.} \tag{3.8}$$

Strictly speaking we may use Equation (3.8) only for metal conductors at constant temperature. Actually there are many other conductors for which the proportionality of V to I is approximately constant and to which we may therefore apply Ohm's law.

Circuits which consist entirely of conductors and devices to which Ohm's law applies are called **linear circuits**. Those circuits to which Ohm's law does not apply are called **non-linear circuits** and must usually be solved by graphical methods.

3. Non-linear circuits. The filament of an ordinary incandescent lamp is a very good example of a non-linear circuit element. The cold resistance of a 100-w lamp is about 10 ohms. When first connected to 120-v mains the current will be

$$I = \frac{V}{R} = \frac{120}{10} = 12 \text{ amp.}$$

The current raises the temperature of the filament very rapidly, and its resistance increases with increased temperature. By the time the normal operating temperature of the lamp is reached, the resistance will have increased to about 144 ohms, reducing the current to

$$I = {}^{120}\!/_{144} = 0.833 \text{ amp}$$

and making the power input to the lamp

$$P = VI = 120 \times 0.833 = 100 \text{ w.}$$

At its normal operating temperature the lamp is able to dissipate energy at the rate of just 100 w, so that no further increase in temperature takes place. It can be seen that if the resistance of the filament did not increase the power input would remain

$$P = 120 \times 10 = 1200 \text{ w,}$$

and the lamp would be destroyed by its own heat before an equilibrium temperature could be reached. It is also obvious that if the cold resistance were used as the basis for calculating normal current and power, the results would be very seriously in error. If the resistance at normal operating temperature were used to calculate the current and power when operating at some voltage close to normal (say 110 or 125 v) the results would not be precise, but would be within the tolerance usually allowed in such calculations.

A number of conducting substances, notably carbon, decrease in resistance as the temperature is increased. Resistors made of metallic oxides held together with some sort of ceramic binder have the property of decreasing in resistance by as much as 4 or 5 per cent for one degree increase in temperature. Such resistors are called **thermistors** and have numerous applications based upon the fact that increasing the current raises the temperature and brings about a decrease in resistance.

There are other conductors in which the non-linearity is inherent in the nature of the material itself and exists even if the temperature remains unchanged. Such a material called *thyrite*, a carborundum-like solid, has the property of decreasing its resistance as the current through it is increased. A piece of thyrite which has a resistance of 15,000 ohms for a current of 5 milliamperes might show a resistance of only 300 ohms at a current of 5 amp. Thyrite was originally developed as a lightning arrester material and has since found many additional applications.

The contact resistance between two dissimilar substances such as a carbon brush on a copper commutator, or a copper plate on a layer of copper oxide in a rectifier, is non-linear as is the resistance of any device such as an electric arc, or a fluorescent lamp, where the carriers are gaseous ions rather than electrons. A further discussion of conduction in gases will be found in Chapter XIV.

While it is usually possible to find a way of mathematically expressing the relationship between current and potential difference in a non-linear circuit, such expressions offer little or no advantage over graphical methods for most purposes.

Problems

(**1-III**) What is the potential difference between the terminals of a 5-ohm resistance which carries a current of 20 amp?

(**2-III**) What is the current in a 0.02-ohm resistance if the potential difference across its terminals is 0.1 v?

(**3-III**) What is the resistance of a wire that has a potential difference of 2.07 v between its terminals when carrying a current of 500 amp?

(**4-III**) The following data were taken on an ordinary 40-w tungsten-filament incandescent lamp:

V (volts)	I (amp)	R (Ω)	V	I	R
5	0.105	47.6	65	0.25	268
20	0.155	129.0	80	0.275	291
35	0.19	184.0	95	0.3	316
50	0.22	227.0	115	0.325	352

Plot a curve showing potential difference (ordinate) as a function of current. Also plot a curve showing resistance (ordinate) as a function of current. At what voltage does the lamp take 0.215 amp? By what percentage must the voltage be increased to increase the current by 50 per cent?

(5-III) An experimenter measures the current taken by the lamp in Problem 4-III for a potential difference of 5 v. Assuming that Ohm's law applies in this instance, he takes no other readings, but proceeds to find the resistance of the lamp from the data he has taken and then to calculate the current that it would take at a potential difference of 115 v. What current would he find? How much in error would his result be? Why is his result in error?

(6-III) The following data were taken on a 50-cp, metallized, carbon-filament lamp:

V (volts)	I (amp)	R (Ω)	V	I	R
0	0	~			
5	0.016	312	65	0.295	220
20	0.07	286	80	0.38	210
35	0.14	250	95	0.478	199
50	0.21	238	115	0.595	193

Plot a curve showing potential difference (ordinate) as a function of current. Also plot a curve showing resistance (ordinate) as a function of current. At what voltage does this lamp take 0.4 amp? By what percentage must the voltage be increased to increase the current by 50 per cent?

(7-III) The following data were taken on a thyrite disk ¾ in. thick and 6 in. diam (thyrite is a ceramic material developed for use in lightning arresters):

V (volts)	I (ma)	V	I
0	0		
50	3.2	200	42
100	9.8	250	82
150	22.4	300	147

Plot a curve showing potential difference (ordinate) as a function of current. Also plot a curve showing resistance (ordinate) as a function of voltage. For what voltage will the resistance be 10,000 ohms? At how many times this voltage will the resistance be ¼ as much?

(8-III) The following data were taken on a small thermistor (thermally sensitive resistor):

I (ma)	V (volts)	I	V
1	15	6	9.4
2	13.4	7	8.8
3	11.9	8	8.3
4	10.8	9	7.9
5	10	10	7.4

Plot a curve showing the potential difference (ordinate) as a function of current. Also plot a curve showing resistance (ordinate) as a function of current. At what current will the resistance be 5000 ohms? By what per cent does the voltage decrease if the current is increased by 100 per cent from 2.5 milliamperes?

(9-III) The voltage drop across a resistor is 50 v, and the current through it is 5 amp. What is the power absorbed by the resistor?

(10-III) The current through a 10-ohm resistor is 5 amp. What power is absorbed?

(11-III) The voltage drop across a 10-ohm resistor is 50 v. How much power is absorbed?

√ (12-III) What should be the resistance of an electric heater that is to absorb 600 w when connected to 120-v mains?

(13-III) A heater absorbs 500 w from 230-v mains. What power would it take from 208-v mains?

√ (14-III) An electric heater absorbs 1000 w from 120-v mains. By how much should its resistance be increased to reduce the power to 900 w?

(15-III) An electric heater takes 450 w from mains of a certain voltage. If the voltage is increased 10 per cent, the current through the heater is 5 amp. What is the original voltage?

√ (16-III) Plot curves showing power (ordinate) as a function of voltage for each of the lamps for which data is given in Problems 4-III and 6-III. At what voltage does the carbon-filament lamp take 50 w? By what percentage must the voltage be increased in order to increase the power by 10 per cent? At what voltage does the tungsten-filament lamp take 30 w? By what percentage must the voltage be increased in order to increase the power by 10 per cent?

(17-III) A watt-hour meter is installed on the premises of nearly every electric power and light consumer, to measure the energy used. In one type commonly used, the disk makes 2 rev per w-hr. If a customer having such a meter finds the disk making 19 rev in 1 min, at what rate (in watts) in energy being used?

(18-III) A certain lighting installation consists of twenty 200-w lamps, ten 100-w lamps and four 40-w lamps. If energy costs 4 cents per kw-hr, what would be the monthly bill for operating this installation 6 hr per day?

(19-III) A direct-current motor takes a current of 5.8 amp when operating at a voltage of 119.5. If energy costs 5 cents per kw-hr, what would be the cost per hour of operating this motor?

(20-III) If the motor of Problem 19-III operates at an efficiency of 81.2 per cent, what is its horsepower output?

(21-III) The cost of operating an electric grill is 9 cents per hr with energy at 3.5 cents per kw-hr. The operating voltage is 230. What current does the grill take? What is the resistance of the heating element?

(22-III) An electric water heater is required to raise the temperature of 15 gal of water per hr from 50° F to 180° F. The supply voltage is 230. Determine the watt rating and resistance of the heating element.

4. Series circuits—Kirchhoff's voltage law.

An electric circuit may contain more than one source of emf and more than one conductor, each with its own particular resistance. If all the parts are

arranged to form a single complete loop, as in Fig. 3.1, they are said
to comprise a **series circuit**. In the battery in Fig. 3.1, energy is
being imparted to the electrons, whereas in each of the resistances,
energy is being given up by the electrons and dissipated in the form
of heat.   Let us consider what happens as a certain group of electrons,
whose combined charges total Q coulombs, pass once around the
circuit.   Let the energy gained by the electrons in passing through
the battery be W, and let the energy lost in the various resistances

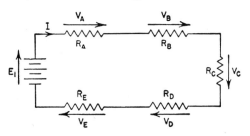

Fig. 3.1.   Series circuit.

be W_a, W_b, W_c, W_d, and W_e, respectively.   **Then, from the law of**
conservation of energy

$$W = W_a + W_b + W_c + W_d + W_e. \tag{3.9}$$

Dividing by the quantity of electricity Q, we get

$$\frac{W}{Q} = \frac{W_a}{Q} + \frac{W_b}{Q} + \frac{W_c}{Q} + \frac{W_d}{Q} + \frac{W_e}{Q}. \tag{3.10}$$

But W/Q is, by definition, the electromotive force of the **battery,**
W_a/Q is the voltage drop across resistance R_a, W_b/Q is the voltage
drop across resistance R_b, and so forth.

$$\therefore\ E_1 = V_a + V_b + V_c + V_d + V_e. \tag{3.11}$$

Or, substituting for V_a, V_b, and so forth, their equivalents IR_a, IR_b,
and so forth, according to Equation 3.5, we get

$$E_1 = IR_a + IR_b + IR_c + IR_d + IR_e. \tag{3.12}$$

This relationship is known as **Kirchhoff's voltage law** and may be
stated as follows: *Around any complete circuit, the algebraic sum of the
electromotive forces equals the algebraic sum of the voltage drops.*

Attention is called to the fact that the sum that has to be taken
is, in each case, the algebraic sum.   This means that the sign as well
as the magnitude of each electromotive force, and each voltage drop
must be considered.   In the circuit of Fig. 3.1, the signs are all posi-

tive, and the algebraic sum is no different from the arithmetic sum. In general, however, this will not be true, as we shall see in the following sections.

EXAMPLE: The battery in Fig. 3.1 has an electromotive force of 30 v, and the resistances R_a, R_b, and so forth, are each 6 ohms. What is the current and what is the voltage drop across each resistance?

SOLUTION: By Kirchhoff's voltage law, we have

$$30 = 6I + 6I + 6I + 6I + 6I = 30I,$$

from which we get

$$I = 1 \text{ amp.}$$

By Ohm's law, the voltage drops V_a, V_b, and so forth, are each

$$V = IR = 1 \times 6 = 6 \text{ v.}$$

Problems

(**23-III**) The college class bells are operated by relays placed in the various buildings and connected in series with a battery in the Electrical Engineering Building. There are 18 relays, each having a resistance of 30 ohms, and the resistance of the connecting lines is 44 ohms. It requires a current of 40 milliamperes to operate the relays. What should be the electromotive force of the battery? What is the voltage drop across the terminals of each relay? What is the voltage drop in the line?

(**24-III**) The lamps of street-lighting circuits are usually connected in series and the current maintained constant at 6.6 amp. How many lamps, each having a resistance of 7.2 ohms at rated current and connected by lines having a total resistance of 24 ohms, can be operated from a generator which supplies an electromotive force of 5000 v? What is the power taken by each lamp? What is the power loss in the line? What is the power output of the generator?

(**25-III**) Three resistances of 7, 10, and 12 ohms, respectively, are connected in series, and the group connected to a battery having an electromotive force of 200 v. What is the current in the circuit? What is the voltage drop across each resistance?

(**26-III**) A battery of unknown electromotive force and resistances of 8, 11, and 14 ohms, respectively, are connected in series. The voltage drop across the 8-ohm resistance is 15 v. What is the current? What is the electromotive force of the battery? What is the voltage drop across each of the other resistors?

(**27-III**) How much resistance must be put in series with a coil connected to a generator which has an electromotive force of 110 v in order to reduce the current from 2.18 to 1.84 amp?

(**28-III**) The tungsten-filament lamp described in Problem 4-III and the carbon-filament lamp described in Problem 6-III are connected in series across the terminals of a 200-v generator. Find the current and the voltage drop across each lamp. *Suggestion:* Plot curve showing the sum of the voltage drops for various values of current.

(**29-III**) The thermistor of Problem 8-III is connected in series with a 3000-ohm wire-wound (linear) resistor and a potential difference of 25 v is applied to the circuit. What is the voltage drop at the terminals of the thermistor? What would happen to the drop across the thermistor if the circuit potential difference were increased to 30 v? (*Suggestion:* Plot curve showing the sum of the voltage drops for various values of current.)

5. Equivalent resistance of a series circuit. Since the current is the same through all parts of a series circuit, we may factor out I in Equation (3.12) thus:

$$E = I(R_a + R_b + R_c + R_d + R_e). \tag{3.13}$$

There is some resistance,

$$R_0 = R_a + R_b + R_c + R_d + R_e, \tag{3.14}$$

that will exactly replace the five resistances in series by permitting exactly the same current to flow when connected to the same electromotive force. This resistance R_0 is called the total resistance or the **equivalent resistance** of the series circuit. The rule for calculating it may be stated as follows: *The equivalent resistance of a series circuit is the sum of the individual resistances.*

Problems

(**30-III**) What is the equivalent resistance of a circuit consisting of three coils in series, the resistances of the individual coils being 60.5, 1.45, and 910 ohms, respectively?

(**31-III**) What is the equivalent resistance of the street-lighting circuit in Problem 24-III?

(**32-III**) The thyrite disk described in Problem 7-III and a 4000-ohm wire-wound (linear) resistor are connected in series across the terminals of a 200-v generator. What is the equivalent resistance at this particular voltage? *Suggestion:* Plot a curve showing sum of the voltage across the thyrite and voltage across the linear resistor for various values of current.

6. Internal resistance of batteries and generators. Any battery or generator has a certain amount of resistance within itself. This internal resistance must be considered in many problems, particularly if the total resistance of the circuit is low. The internal resistance R_b is in series with whatever additional resistance R_x is placed in the circuit, as in Fig. 3.2. The voltage drop V across the external resistance is called the **terminal voltage** of the battery, and in general, it will be less than the battery emf except when the battery is being charged. Note that the terminals of the battery are M and P. The point N is not accessible. Applying Kirchhoff's voltage law we have

$$E = IR_x + IR_b \tag{3.15}$$

or

$$E = V + IR_b. \tag{3.16}$$

The internal resistance of a battery is ordinarily not constant, but depends somewhat on the condition of the battery and the current that is flowing. It may, however, be treated as constant in problems that do not involve the use of the battery over long periods of time.

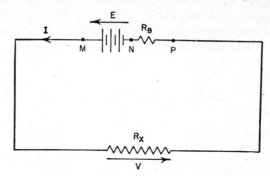

Fig. 3.2.   Battery internal resistance.

EXAMPLE: A battery has an electromotive force of 6 v and will deliver a current of 5 amp through a resistance of 1 ohm connected to its terminals. What is the internal resistance of the battery?

SOLUTION: By Kirchhoff's voltage law, we have

$$6 = 5R_b + (5 \times 1),$$
$$5R_b = 6 - 5 = 1,$$
$$R_b = 0.2 \text{ ohm.}$$

Problems

(33-III) The terminal voltage of a battery is found to be 30.65 v when an external resistance of 2 ohms is connected to its terminals. The electromotive force of the battery is 32 v. What is its internal resistance?

(34-III) A storage battery having an electromotive force of 6 v and an internal resistance of 0.006 ohm is connected to an external circuit having a resistance of 0.04 ohm. What is the terminal voltage of the battery?

(35-III) A battery whose electromotive force is 18 v will maintain a current of 8.8 amp through a resistance of 1.95 ohms connected to its terminals. What is the internal resistance of the battery? What current will it supply if the external circuit resistance is reduced to 1.14 ohms?

(36-III) A battery which gives 32.5 amp on short circuit (that is, external resistance equal to zero) will supply a current of 7.5 amp to a resistance of 1.2 ohms connected to its terminals. What is the electromotive force of the battery? What is its internal resistance?

7. Battery charging. We may further illustrate the use of Kirchhoff's voltage law by considering the charging of storage batteries. Charging is usually done by connecting the battery to a direct current generator, or other source of electromotive force in such manner that current will flow into the battery at its positive terminal—that is, opposite the normal direction in which current would flow if the battery were discharging. In Fig. 3.3, E_G and E_B represent the electromotive forces of the generator and battery respectively. R_G and R_B are the internal resistances of the generator and of the battery, and R_x is the resistance of a rheostat placed in the circuit to limit the current to the proper value. Current will be assumed to flow out the positive

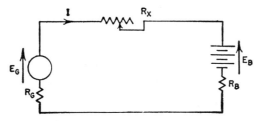

Fig. 3.3. Battery charging circuit.

terminal of the generator and into the positive terminal of the battery. Applying Kirchhoff's voltage law to this circuit, we have

$$E_G - E_B = IR_G + IR_x + IR_B. \tag{3.17}$$

As we trace clockwise around the circuit, E_G is positive, but E_B is negative, since we are going oppositely to the arrow. $E_G - E_B$ is the "algebraic sum of the electromotive forces" called for in the law. All of the voltage drops are positive because we trace through each resistor in the direction of the current. Had we traced counterclockwise around the circuit, we would have had

$$E_B - E_G = -IR_x - IR_G - IR_B. \tag{3.18}$$

Inspection will show that Equation (3.18) can be obtained by multiplying Equation (3.17) by -1. Since it is always legitimate to do this, it makes no difference in which direction we trace the circuit.

Our procedure, then, in applying Kirchhoff's voltage law to such a circuit, may be summarized as follows:

1. Place arrows to represent all electromotive forces and voltage drops. Remember electromotive force arrows are to point from negative to positive, and voltage drop arrows are to point in the direction of the current.

2. Beginning at any point, trace once around the circuit, putting down electromotive forces as positive if the arrow is in the direction traced; negative if the arrow is opposite to the direction traced.

3. Trace around the circuit once again in the same direction, this time to collect the voltage drops, putting down the voltage drop as positive if the arrow is in the direction traced; negative if the arrow is opposite to the direction traced.

EXAMPLE: A battery having an electromotive force of 119 v is to be charged from a generator having an electromotive force of 130 v, the connections being as in Fig. 3.3. The resistance of the battery is 0.111 ohm, and the resistance of the generator is 0.052 ohm. A rheostat having a resistance of 0.937 ohm is included in the circuit. Find the current, the rate at which mechanical energy is being converted into electrical energy in the generator, the power loss in the generator resistance, the power loss in the rheostat, the power loss in the battery resistance, and the rate at which electrical energy is being converted into chemical energy in the battery.

SOLUTION: By Kirchhoff's voltage law, we have

$$130 - 119 = 0.111I + 0.052I + 0.937I,$$
$$11 = 1.1I,$$
$$I = 10 \text{ amp.}$$

Rate of conversion of mechanical energy to electrical energy in the generator is

$$P = E_G I = 130 \times 10 = 1300 \text{ w.}$$

Power lost as heat in the generator resistance is

$$P = I^2 R_G = (10)^2 \times 0.052 = 5.2 \text{ w.}$$

Power lost as heat in the rheostat is

$$P = I^2 R_x = (10)^2 \times 0.937 = 93.7 \text{ w.}$$

Power lost as heat in the internal resistance of the battery is

$$P = I^2 R_b = (10)^2 \times 0.111 = 11.1 \text{ w.}$$

Rate of conversion from electrical to chemical energy in the battery is

$$P = E_B I = 119 \times 10 = 1190 \text{ w.}$$

To check our calculations, we may see whether the electrical power developed by the generator is all accounted for:

$$1300 = 5.2 + 93.7 + 11.1 + 1190,$$
$$1300 = 1300.$$

Problems

(**37-III**) A battery having an electromotive force of 60 v is being charged from a generator having an electromotive force of 90 v, the connections being made as in Fig. 3.3. The internal resistance of the battery (designated by R_B) is 0.78 ohm and the internal resistance of the generator (designated by R_G) is 0.1 ohm. What value shall the resistance R_x have in order that the charging rate shall be 15 amp?

(**38-III**) (a) What is the electrical power developed by the generator in Problem 37-III? (b) How much of this is lost as heat in the internal resistance of the generator? (c) In the resistance R_x? (d) In the internal resistance of the battery? (e) At what rate is electrical energy being converted into chemical energy in the battery? (f) What is the efficiency of this method of charging [(e) divided by (a)]?

(**39-III**) In Problem 37-III, what would happen if the battery were accidentally connected into the circuit with its terminals reversed? Calculate the current for this connection, if R_x is 1 ohm.

(**40-III**) How many 6-v automobile batteries, each having an internal resistance of 0.03 ohm, can be put in series to charge at a 10-amp rate from a 120-v, direct current generator having negligible internal resistance?

(**41-III**) What should be the electromotive force of an automobile-charging generator to charge the battery at a 25-amp rate? Assume the electromotive force of the battery is 6.1 v, $R_B = 0.037$ ohm, $R_G = 0.1$ ohm, and resistance of connecting wire is 0.15 ohm.

8. Power transmission. Kirchhoff's voltage law and the rules for calculating power may be further illustrated by consideration of a few

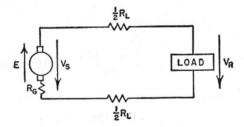

Fig. 3.4. Power transmission.

problems in the electrical transmission of energy. Fig. 3.4 shows a generator connected to a transmission line, over which energy is delivered to the **load,** some distance away, and consisting of lamps, motors, heating appliances, and so forth. The resistance of each wire of the line is designated as $\frac{1}{2}R_L$, or the total line resistance by R_L. The subscripts S and R refer to the sending end (where the generator is located) and the receiving end (where the load is located), respectively. Instead of working with the emf of the generator and taking into account the voltage drop in its internal resistance, we shall find it more convenient to work with its terminal voltage, which is also, of course, the terminal voltage at the sending end of the line.　As typical of the problems that may have to be solved, we may take the following examples:

EXAMPLE 1: Power is transmitted over a line having a resistance of 1.07 ohms to a load requiring 1 kw.　The voltage at the receiving end is to be 120.　Calculate the current, the power loss in the line, and the voltage at the sending end.

SOLUTION: Applying the power equation to the load,

$$I = \frac{P_R}{V_R} = \frac{1000}{120} = 8.33 \text{ amp.}$$

Applying the power equation to the line resistance,

$$P_{\text{loss}} = I^2R = (8.33)^2 \times 1.07 = 74.2 \text{ w.}$$

Applying Kirchhoff's voltage law around the circuit,

$$0 = V_R - V_S + IR_L,$$
$$V_S = V_R + IR = 120 + (8.33 \times 1.07) = 128.9 \text{ v.}$$

EXAMPLE 2: Power is to be transmitted over a line to a load which requires 60 amp at a voltage of not less than 115.　The voltage at the sending end is 125.　What is the maximum resistance which the line may have?　What is the power lost in the line?　What is the efficiency of transmission?

SOLUTION: By Kirchhoff's voltage law,

$$0 = V_R - V_S + IR_L,$$
$$R_L = \frac{V_S - V_R}{I} = \frac{125 - 115}{60} = 0.166 \text{ ohm.}$$

Power lost in line is

$$I^2R_L = (60)^2 \times 0.166 = 600 \text{ w.}$$

Power input to line at sending end is

$$P_S = V_S I = 125 \times 60 = 7500 \text{ w.}$$

Power output of line at receiving end is

$$P_R = V_R I = 115 \times 60 = 6900 \text{ w.}$$

Efficiency of line is

$$\frac{\text{Output}}{\text{Input}} = \frac{6900}{7500} = 0.92 \text{ or 92 per cent.}$$

Problems

(42-III) A generator delivers 1500 w to the sending end of a transmission line. The electromotive force of the generator is 125 v, and voltage at the receiving end is to be 113 v. Determine the current, the voltage drop in line, and the power received by the load.

(43-III) How much power can be delivered over a line having a resistance of 1.5 ohms if the voltage drop in the line resistance is not to exceed 5 per cent of the voltage at the load, which is to be 250 v? What will be the sending-end voltage?

(44-III) The power lost in a line must not exceed 10 per cent of the power supplied to the line. The power required at the receiving end is 5000 w, and the potential difference at the sending end is 250 v. What is the maximum value the line resistance may have? What will be the voltage at the receiving end?

(45-III) The power delivered to the sending end of a line is 808 w, and that taken from the sending end is 727 w. The line resistance is 2 ohms. What is the current? What is the voltage drop at the load? What is the electromotive force at the generator?

(46-III) Two transmission lines have the same resistance and deliver the same power to the load, but line B operates at twice the receiving end voltage of line A. The loss in line A is 600 w. What is the loss in line B?

(47-III) Two transmission lines A and B operate at the same receiving-end voltage, and the loss in each line is to be the same. Line B has twice as much resistance as line A. If the power delivered to the load by line A is 4000 w, how much power can be delivered by line B?

(48-III) Two transmission lines A and B have the same resistance and are to operate so that the loss in each line is the same. The receiving end voltage of line A is twice that of line B. The power delivered to the load by line A is 4000 w. How much power can be delivered to the load by line B?

(49-III) Two transmission lines A and B operate at the same receiving end voltage and deliver the same power to the load, but line B has twice the resistance of line A. The efficiency of line A is 80 per cent. What is the efficiency of line B?

(50-III) The power input to a transmission line is 3600 w. The sending-end voltage is 240, and the receiving-end voltage is 226. Calculate the current, power output of the line, line loss and efficiency.

(51-III) The power received by the load at the end of a transmission line is 1115 w. The potential difference at the sending end is 160 v, and the line resistance is 0.835 ohm. Find the current, the potential difference at the load, and the line loss. *Note:* This problem requires the solution of a quadratic equation. Obtain both roots and find both possible values of current, potential difference, line loss, and load resistance. Which would be the more practical set of values?

(52-III) The sending-end voltage of a transmission line is maintained constant at 125 v. The resistance of the line is 1 ohm. The load resistance is first set at infinity (open circuit) and gradually reduced to zero (short circuit). Calculate and plot the receiving-end power against load resistance for load resistances of infinity, 100 ohms, 10 ohms, 2 ohms, 1 ohm, 0.5 ohm, 0.1 ohm, 0.01 ohm, and zero. For what load resistance is receiving-end power a maximum? What is receiving-end power when V_R is maximum? When I is maximum?

9. Parallel circuits—Kirchhoff's current law. An electric circuit that contains a number of conductors, each with its own particular resistance, arranged as in Fig. 3.5, is known as a **parallel circuit.** Each of the conductors, the resistance of which is designated as R_A, R_B, and R_C, offers a possible path through which current may flow. The electrons arriving at point n split up into three streams, one stream taking the path through R_A, another through R_B, and the third through R_C. At the point m, the streams reunite and continue on around the circuit. We may say the same thing in another way: the current I_0 splits into three currents at the point m, and these three

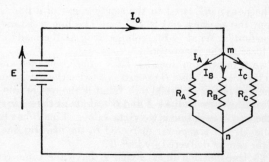

Fig. 3.5.   Parallel circuit.

currents I_A, I_B, and I_C reunite at point n to again make up the current I_0. Now, unless electrons can accumulate at point m or point n, the rate at which electrons leave such a point must be exactly equal to the rate at which they enter it. There is no evidence that electrons do accumulate at the points m and n, and we are, therefore, forced to the conclusion that they enter a point and leave it at the same rate. Stated in terms of currents, this is **Kirchhoff's current law**: *At any junction point, the algebraic sum of the currents entering the point equals the algebraic sum of the currents leaving the point.*

Stated in equation form, we would have, for either junction in Fig. 3.5,

$$I_0 = I_A + I_B + I_C. \tag{3.19}$$

EXAMPLE: In the circuit shown in Fig. 3.5, I_A is 5 amp, I_B is -6 amp, and I_C is 11 amp. Find the current I_0.

SOLUTION:

$$I_0 = 5 + (-6) + 11 = 10 \text{ amp.}$$

10. Equivalent resistance of a parallel circuit—Conductance. We may apply Kirchhoff's voltage law to the circuit shown in Fig. 3.5 to obtain the following equations:

$$E = I_A R_A, \tag{3.20}$$

from which
$$I_A = \frac{E}{R_A}.$$

$$E = I_B R_B, \tag{3.21}$$

from which
$$I_B = \frac{E}{R_B}.$$

$$E = I_C R_C, \tag{3.22}$$

from which
$$I_C = \frac{E}{R_C}.$$

We may then substitute these values of I_A, I_B, and I_C into Equation (3.19) to obtain

$$I_0 = \frac{E}{R_A} + \frac{E}{R_B} + \frac{E}{R_C}. \tag{3.23}$$

Let R_0 be a single resistance which will replace all of the individual resistances in the sense that it will permit the same current to flow when connected to the battery, so that

$$I_0 = \frac{E}{R_0}. \tag{3.24}$$

Equating the right-hand side of Equation (3.24) to the right-hand side of Equation (3.23) and dividing through by E, we have

$$\frac{1}{R_0} = \frac{1}{R_A} + \frac{1}{R_B} + \frac{1}{R_C}. \tag{3.25}$$

The resistance R_0 is called the *group resistance* or the *equivalent resistance* of the parallel circuit.   The rule for calculating it may be stated in words as follows: *The equivalent resistance of a parallel circuit is the reciprocal of the sum of the reciprocals of the individual resistances.*   Each term in Equation (3.25) is of the form $1/R$, and is called a **conductance.**

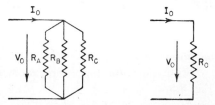

Fig. 3.6.   Equivalent of a parallel circuit.

Thus, $1/R_0$ is the conductance of the parallel group, $1/R_A$ is the conductance of conductor A, and so forth.   The symbol for conductance is G, and its unit is the **mho** (ohm spelled backward).   Conductance of any conductor may be found by taking the reciprocal of its resistance, or more directly, by taking the ratio of current to potential difference. Resistance was shown to be

$$R = \frac{V}{I},$$ (3.6)

and we now define conductance as

$$G = \frac{I}{V}.$$ (3.26)

Equation (3.25) may now be rewritten as

$$G_0 = G_A + G_B + G_C,$$ (3.27)

and our procedure for finding the equivalent resistance of a group of parallel conductors may be restated thus: Find the conductance of each branch; add the individual conductances to find the group conductance; take the reciprocal of the group conductance to find the equivalent resistance.

EXAMPLE 1: Three conductors that are connected in parallel have resistances of 10, 20, and 30 ohms, respectively. What is the conductance of each branch? What is the group conductance? What is the equivalent resistance?

SOLUTION:

$$G_A = \frac{1}{R_A} = \frac{1}{10} = 0.1 \text{ mho.}$$

$$G_B = \frac{1}{R_B} = \frac{1}{20} = 0.05 \text{ mho.}$$

$$G_C = \frac{1}{R_C} = \frac{1}{30} = 0.0333 \text{ mho.}$$

$$G_0 = G_A + G_B + G_C$$
$$= 0.1 + 0.05 + 0.033 = 0.183 \text{ mho.}$$

$$R_0 = \frac{1}{G_0} = \frac{1}{0.183} = 5.46 \text{ ohms.}$$

EXAMPLE 2: How would a current of 15 amp divide among the branches of the circuit in the foregoing problem?

SOLUTION: Our first step will be to find the voltage drop across the group.

$$V_0 = I_0 R_0$$
$$= 15 \times 5.46 = 81.9 \text{ v.}$$

The divided currents may then be found by Ohm's law:

$$I_A = \frac{81.9}{10} = 8.19 \text{ amp.}$$

$$I_B = \frac{81.9}{20} = 4.09 \text{ amp.}$$

$$I_C = \frac{81.9}{30} = 2.73 \text{ amp.}$$

We can check the correctness of our work by applying Kirchhoff's current law:

$$I_0 = I_A + I_B + I_C$$
$$15 = 8.19 + 4.09 + 2.73 = 15.01.$$

Instead of dividing the voltage by resistance to find current, we may multiply the voltage by conductance:

$$I_A = G_A V = 0.1 \times 81.9 = 8.19 \text{ amp.}$$
$$I_B = G_B V = 0.05 \times 81.9 = 4.09 \text{ amp.}$$
$$I_C = G_C V = 0.0333 \times 81.9 = 2.73 \text{ amp.}$$
$$I_0 = G_0 V = 0.183 \times 81.9 = 15 \text{ amp.}$$

Problems

(53-III) Conductors of 3, 5, and 8 ohms resistance, respectively, are connected in parallel. What is the conductance of each conductor? What is the resistance of the group? What is the group conductance?

(54-III) Conductors of 5, 11, 13, and 21 ohms resistance, respectively, are connected in parallel, and a current of 10 amp flows in the 13-ohm conductor. What is the current in each of the others, and what is the total current?

(55-III) The total current through a group made up of a 10-ohm, a 15-ohm, and a 30-ohm conductor in parallel is 10 amp. What is the current in each conductor?

(56-III) A 12-ohm and a 17-ohm conductor are in parallel, and a third conductor is to be added to make the group resistance 5 ohms. What should be the resistance of the third conductor?

(57-III) Three conductances of 0.003, 0.005, and 0.0075 mho, respectively, are connected in parallel across a potential difference of 100 v. What is the current in each conductance and in the line?

(58-III) Two parallel conductors carry currents of 12.5 and 15.5 amp, respectively, and the conductance of the first is 0.023 mho. What is the conductance of the other conductor? What is the resistance of the two conductors in parallel?

(59-III) Derive an equation for calculating power in terms of conductance and voltage drop. Using this equation, find the power for each conductance of Problem 57-III.

(**60-III**) Show that if two resistances R_A and R_B are in parallel the equivalent resistance is given by

$$R_0 = \frac{R_A R_B}{R_A + R_B} \tag{3.28}$$

(**61-III**) Derive the corresponding expression for equivalent resistance of three resistances R_A, R_B, and R_C connected in parallel.

(**62-III**) The tungsten-filament lamp described in Problem 4-III and the carbon-filament lamp described in Problem 6-III are connected in parallel, and a total current of 0.3 amp is sent through the group. What is the voltage drop? What is the current through each lamp? Recalculate for a total current of 0.7 amp. *Suggestion:* Plot a curve showing the sum of the currents for various values of voltage.

(**63-III**) The thyrite disk described in Problem 7-III and a 4000-ohm wire-wound (linear) resistor are connected in parallel, and a current of 60 milliamperes is sent through the group. What is the voltage drop? What is the current in each conductor? (See the suggestion in Problem 62-III.)

11. Series-parallel circuits. There is a great variety of possible ways in which conductors may be connected to form what may be termed series-parallel, or parallel-series, circuits. There are no additional laws or rules to learn in dealing with such circuits. It is only necessary to remember and intelligently apply Ohm's law, the two laws of Kirchhoff, and the rules for finding equivalent resistance of series and parallel groups. It may be well to point out, however, that the laws of Kirchhoff are more broadly applicable than might be inferred from what has been said heretofore concerning them.

Kirchhoff's voltage law can be applied, not only to simple series loops, but to any loop or circuit through which the student can trace his way back to the starting point. This loop may be part of a more extensive circuit, and it is not necessary that the current be the same in every part of the loop. It is necessary, though, to remember that it is the *algebraic sum* of the voltage drops that must be taken and, therefore, in tracing, strict attention must be paid to whether a particular voltage drop is in the direction traced or in the opposite direction.

Kirchhoff's current law can be applied to any junction point, no matter how extensive the circuit. One of the simplest possible series-parallel circuits is shown in Fig. 3.7. Two branches of resistance R_2 and R_3, respectively, are connected in parallel, and a third conductor of resistance R_1 is connected in series with this group. This arrangement is then connected to the terminals of the battery. It should be obvious that the current in each of the parallel branches will be different from the current in R_1. These currents are designated I_1, I_2, and I_3, and the directions selected as positive are marked by arrows. Positive directions for the voltage drops are also selected (the same as the current direction in each case) and designated V_1 and V_2. The voltage drop across each parallel branch is, of course, the same.

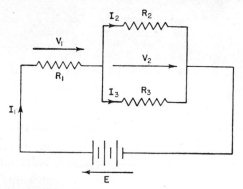

Fig. 3.7.   Series-parallel circuit.

Let us assume first that the electromotive force of the battery and the three resistances are known, and that we have to find the current in each part of the circuit and the voltage drops. Our first step will be to find the equivalent resistance of the parallel group, and thus, in

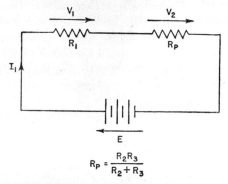

$$R_P = \frac{R_2 R_3}{R_2 + R_3}$$

Fig. 3.8.   Equivalent of a series-parallel circuit.

effect, to reduce the circuit to that shown in Fig. 3.8. We then find the equivalent resistance of this circuit, or else apply Kirchhoff's voltage law directly and find the current. We can then find the voltage drops V_1 and V_2, and knowing V_2, we can find the branch currents I_2 and I_3.

EXAMPLE: In the circuit shown in Fig. 3.7, let $E = 22$ v, $R_1 = 10$ ohms, $R_2 = 20$ ohms, and $R_3 = 30$ ohms.

Then, $$R_P = \frac{20 \times 30}{20 + 30} = 12 \text{ ohms.}$$

$$R_0 = 10 + 12 = 22 \text{ ohms.}$$

By Kirchhoff's voltage law,

$$22 = 22I_1.$$
$$I_1 = 1 \text{ amp.}$$

Then, $$V_1 = 1 \times 10 = 10 \text{ v.}$$
$$V_2 = 1 \times 12 = 12 \text{ v.}$$
$$I_2 = {}^{12}\!/_{20} = 0.6 \text{ amp.}$$
$$I_3 = {}^{12}\!/_{30} = 0.4 \text{ amp.}$$

Let us now assume that, instead of the emf and all of the resistances being known, we know one or more currents, one or more resistances, one or more voltage drops, and that we have to solve for the remaining currents, resistances, and voltage drops. In such problems, it is not expedient to try to reduce the network to a single equivalent resistance, but rather to apply Ohm's law and Kirchhoff's laws as needed, proceeding a step at a time until the required results are found. In general, we must start with that part of the network about which the most information is given. If we know the resistance and current, or current and voltage drop, or voltage drop and resistance for a certain branch, then that is the logical starting point. In other problems, the first step may be to apply Kirchhoff's current law at some junction point immediately, or Kirchhoff's voltage law around some loop.

EXAMPLE: Suppose in the circuit of Fig. 3.7, V_1 is 28 v, R_2 is 8 ohms, I_2 is 3 amp, and I_3 is 4 amp. We are to find R_1, R_3, I_1, V_2, and E.

SOLUTION: From Kirchhoff's current law,

$$I_1 = 3 + 4 = 7 \text{ amp.}$$

From Ohm's law,

$$V_2 = 3 \times 8 = 24 \text{ v.}$$
$$R_3 = {}^{24}\!/_4 = 6 \text{ ohms.}$$
$$R_1 = {}^{28}\!/_7 = 4 \text{ ohms.}$$

From Kirchhoff's voltage law,

$$E = 28 + 24 = 52 \text{ v.}$$

Problems

✓ (64-III) How many different values of resistance can be obtained with three resistors of 10, 20 and 30 ohms respectively by connecting them in various ways? Show diagrams and calculate resistances.

(65-III) How many different values of resistance can be obtained with four 10-ohm resistors by connecting them in different ways? Show diagram and calculate resistances.

  ✓ **(66-III)** The resistances of the branches of the network shown in Fig. 3.7 are $R_1 = 5$ ohms, $R_2 = 8$ ohms, and $R_3 = 12$ ohms. The electromotive force of the battery is 50 v. Calculate all the currents and voltage drops.

(67-III) In the network shown in Fig. 3.7, E is 40 v, R_1 is 2 ohms, R_2 is 4 ohms, and I_1 is 8 amp. Calculate the other voltage drops, resistances, and currents.

(68-III) In the network shown in Fig. 3.7, E is 75 v, V_1 is 40 v, R_1 is 5 ohms, and I_2 is 2 amp. Calculate the other voltage drops, resistances, and currents.

(69-III) In the network shown in Fig. 3.7, E is 21 v, I_1 is 7 amp, I_2 is 5 amp, and R_3 is 5 ohms. Calculate the other voltage drops, resistances, and currents.

(70-III) The resistances of the branches of the network in Fig. 3.9 are $R_1 = 11$ ohms, $R_2 = 17$ ohms, $R_3 = 12$ ohms, $R_4 = 30$ ohms, $R_5 = 24$ ohms,

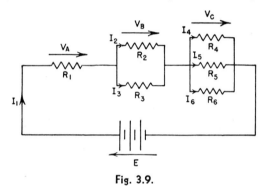

Fig. 3.9.

and $R_6 = 55$ ohms. The electromotive force of the battery is 100 v. Solve for all currents and voltage drops, and power in each part of the circuit.

(71-III) In the network in Fig. 3.10a, the resistances are $R_1 = 5$ ohms, $R_2 = 6$ ohms, $R_3 = 7$ ohms, $R_4 = 3$ ohms, $R_5 = 4$ ohms, and $R_7 = 1$ ohm. The battery electromotive force is 10 v. Find currents and voltage drops. *Suggestion:* Reduce the network by successive steps as shown in Fig. 3.10b, c, d, e, and f.

(72-III) In the network shown in Fig. 3.9, E is 80 v, V_A is 20 v, R_1 is 5 ohms, R_2 is 11 ohms, I_3 is 1 amp, R_4 is 44 ohms, and I_5 is 2 amp. Determine the other voltage drops, resistances, and currents.

(73-III) In the network shown in Fig. 3.9, E is 60 v, I_1 is 6 amp, I_4 is 2 amp, I_5 is 3 amp, R_2 is 7 ohms, R_3 is 5 ohms, and R_6 is 12 ohms. Find the other voltage drops, currents, and resistances.

(74-III) In the network of Fig. 3.10a, $V_3 = 35$ v, $V_1 = 25$ v, $V_4 = 10$ v, $R_5 = 3$ ohms, $I_2 = 9$ amp, $R_3 = 8$ ohms, and $R_7 = 7$ ohms. Find the other currents, resistances, and voltage drops.

  ✓ **(75-III)** A lamp bank is used as a rheostat, as shown in Fig. 3.11, to regulate the current through a 20-ohm coil. There are 10 lamps in the bank, each having a resistance of 240 ohms, and the current is changed by changing the number of lamps in parallel. The voltage drop across the entire circuit

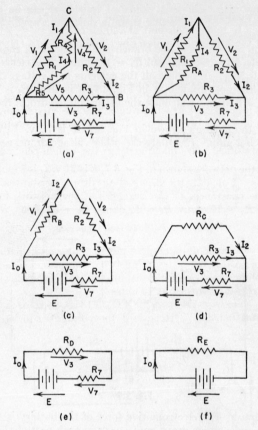

Fig. 3.10.   Reduction of a series-parallel circuit.

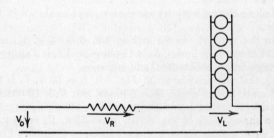

Fig. 3.11.   Lamp bank used as a rheostat.

is 115 v.   Over what range may the current be varied?   Assume the resistance of each lamp to remain constant at 240 ohms.

(**76-III**) For the arrangement described in Problem 75-III, plot the following curves, using as abscissa the number of lamps in parallel: (a) current, (b) V_R, and (c) V_L.

(**77-III**) A slide-wire rheostat having a maximum resistance of 2800 ohms variable in 2-ohm steps is connected so as to control the last lamp of the bank shown in Fig. 3.11.   Over what range may the current now be varied? Can the current be set at exactly 2 amp?   Explain how to do this.

(**78-III**) Fig. 3.12 shows a special rheostat, or "load rack," used in the machinery laboratories.   By manipulating the single-pole, double-throw

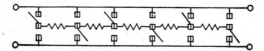

Fig. 3.12.   A "load rack" rheostat.

switches, all the resistance units may be put in series, all in parallel, or they may be put into a great many series-parallel combinations.   If each unit has a resistance of 25 ohms, what range of resistance may be obtained with a 10-unit rack?   Can the resistance be set at 10 ohms?

(**79-III**) The slide-wire rheostat in Fig. 3.13 is used as a three-point rheostat, or "potentiometer."   It permits the voltage V_3 to be varied from

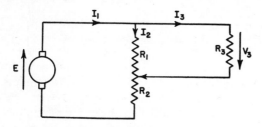

Fig. 3.13.   A three-point rheostat.

zero to maximum, which is a wider range than could be obtained by using the same rheostat in series with R_3 and the generator.   What is the current in each part of the network if $E = 100$ v, $R_1 = R_2 = 400$ ohms, and $R_3 = 800$ ohms. What is V_3?   What power is consumed in each part of the circuit?

(**80-III**) Recalculate Problem 79-III for R_3 equal to 80 ohms.

12. Parallel circuits containing sources of electromotive force.

Strictly speaking, we never have electromotive forces in parallel.   We have sources of electromotive force, such as batteries and generators in parallel, but every such device has its own internal resistance, inseparable from its electromotive force.   Let us consider a circuit such as that shown in Fig. 3.14, comprising two batteries with electromotive forces E_A and E_B, and internal resistances R_A and R_B, respectively, connected in parallel, and a third resistance R_C connected to the battery terminals. An inspection of Fig. 3.14 should make it evident that neither the electromotive forces nor the internal resistances of the battery are in parallel. For the special case where the batteries are identical—that is, have identical electromotive forces and identical internal resistances, it may be considered that a connection exists as shown by the dotted line p-q, thus connecting the electromotive forces in parallel and the internal resistances in parallel. In that case, the two batteries would be equivalent to a single battery having the same electromotive force as E_A or E_B and an internal resistance equal to $\frac{1}{2}R_A$ or $\frac{1}{2}R_B$.

In general, however, batteries are not identical, and it is necessary to use Kirchhoff's laws. Let us assume that we know the electromotive forces and resistances involved in the circuit shown in Fig. 3.14

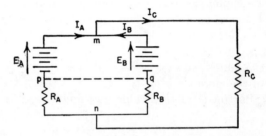

Fig. 3.14.   Batteries in parallel.

and that we are required to find the current in each branch. These currents are designated I_A, I_B, and I_C. A direction is selected as positive for each current, and marked by an arrow. Since we have no way of knowing in advance in which direction the currents will flow, the directions selected as positive may or may not be the actual current directions.

At the junction point m, Kirchhoff's current law gives

$$I_A + I_B = I_C. \tag{3.29}$$

At the junction point n also, we might apply the current law, but we would get

$$I_C = I_A + I_B, \tag{3.30}$$

which is obviously the same relationship already expressed by (3.29). Therefore, it is of no use to us. There are no other junction points, so we turn to Kirchhoff's voltage law. There are three possible loops which we may trace. The loop containing the two batteries gives

$$E_A - E_B = I_A R_A - I_B R_B. \tag{3.31}$$

The loop containing the battery A and resistance R_C gives

$$E_A = I_A R_A + I_C R_C. \tag{3.32}$$

The loop containing the battery B and the resistance R_C gives

$$E_B = I_B R_B + I_C R_C. \tag{3.33}$$

Upon studying these equations, we see that (3.32) might be obtained by adding (3.31) and (3.33). It is, therefore, not an independent relationship and is useless if we use (3.31) and (3.33). Kirchhoff's laws, then, have enabled us to get three independent relationships among the electromotive forces, resistances, and currents. These relationships are represented by Equations (3.29), (3.31) and (3.33). No one of these equations taken by itself will yield a solution. The three must be solved as a set of independent simultaneous equations to obtain the required currents.

EXAMPLE: In the circuit of Fig. 3.14, E_A is 12 v, E_B is 10 v, R_A is 4 ohms, R_B is 2 ohms, and R_C is 8 ohms. Calculate the current in each branch of the circuit.

SOLUTION: Putting numerical values in Equations (3.31) and (3.33), we have

$$12 - 10 = 4I_A - 2I_B, \tag{3.31}$$
$$10 = 2I_B + 8I_C. \tag{3.33}$$

Solving, $4I_A = 2 + 2I_B,$

$$I_A = 0.5 + 0.5I_B \quad \text{(from (3.31)).}$$
$$8I_C = 10 - 2I_B,$$
$$I_C = 1.25 - 0.25I_B \quad \text{(from (3.33)).}$$

Substituting in (3.29),

$$0.5 + 0.5I_B + I_B = 1.25 - 0.25I_B,$$
$$1.75I_B = 0.75,$$
$$I_B = 0.428 \text{ amp.}$$

Substituting in (3.31),

$$I_A = 0.5 + (0.5 \times 0.428) = 0.714 \text{ amp.}$$

Substituting in (3.33),

$$I_C = 1.25 - (0.25 \times 0.428) = 1.143 \text{ amp.}$$

To check the solution, substitute results in (3.29):

$$0.714 + 0.428 = 1.143,$$
$$1.142 = 1.143.$$

Problems

(81-III) Calculate the currents in each branch of the circuit used in the foregoing example if E_B is 6 v and the other values are unchanged.

(82-III) Calculate the currents in each branch of the circuit used in the foregoing example if R_C is 4 ohms and the other values are unchanged.

(83-III) Obtain the literal solution for the current in each branch of the circuit shown in Fig. 3.14 from Equations (3.29), (3.31), and (3.33).

(84-III) Show that if the two batteries in Fig. 3.14 are identical ($E_A = E_B$, $R_A = R_B$), they may be replaced by a single battery of electromotive force $E = E_A = E_B$ and an internal resistance $R = \frac{1}{2}R_A = \frac{1}{2}R_B$. *Suggestion:* Show that the current I_C will be the same if the replacement be made.

(85-III) The network shown in Fig. 3.15 is set up in the laboratory for a study of Kirchhoff's laws. The numerical values are as follows: $E_G = 120$ v,

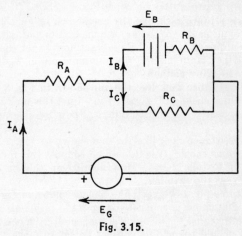

Fig. 3.15.

$E_B = 30$ v, $R_A = 12$ ohms, $R_B = 8$ ohms and $R_C = 20$ ohms. Find the current in each branch of the network.

(86-III) The following numerical values are given for the network of Fig. 3.15. $E_G = 75$ v, $E_B = 25$ v, $R_A = 30$ ohms, $R_B = 15$ ohms, $R_C = 5$ ohms. Find the current in each branch of the network.

(87-III) In studying the network shown in Fig. 3.15, it is desired to cause the current I_B to reverse in direction by varying the magnitude of E_G, all the other quantities remaining fixed. If E_G can be varied from 50 to 100 v, and E_B is fixed at 10 v, what relationship should exist among the resistances R_A, R_B and R_C in order to have I_B reverse at $E_G = 75$ v? Which resistance appears to be of the least significance? (*Suggestion:* Make a literal solution for the current I_B).

(88-III) It is desired to replace the network in Fig. 3.16a with the network in Fig. 3.16b, so choosing R_Y that the battery current will be the same as before. Calculate R_Y.

(89-III) It is desired to replace the network in Fig. 3.16a with the network in Fig. 3.16b, so choosing R_Y that the current in the 20-ohm resistor will be the same as before. Calculate R_Y.

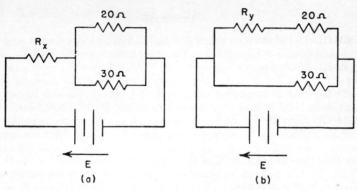

Fig. 3.16.

(90-III) A resistance rack like the one shown in Fig. 3.12 is made up of 10 units of 30 ohms each. What are the maximum and minimum resistances which may be obtained? Show by diagram how to set the switches in each case. What is the maximum and the minimum power when the rack is connected directly to 120-v mains?

(91-III) A resistance rack like the one shown in Fig. 3.12 is made up of 25 units of 30 ohms each. It is desired to adjust this rack for a resistance of 80 ohms. How nearly can this be done? Show by diagram how to set the switches.

(92-III) A resistance rack like the one shown in Fig. 3.12 is made up of 25 units of 30 ohms each. It is desired to connect this rack to 120-v mains and to adjust it to take 2 kw. How nearly can this be done? Show by diagram how to set the switches.

(93-III) A three-point rheostat, like the one shown in Fig. 3.13 and having a resistance of 200 ohms, is connected across the terminals of a 110-v generator. A resistance equal to 200 ohms is connected from one line to the sliding contact. How should the sliding contact be set to make the voltage across the resistance 100 v?

(94-III) A three-point rheostat, like the one shown in Fig. 3.13 and having a resistance of 600 ohms, is connected across the terminals of a 100-v generator. A resistance of 400 ohms is connected from one line to the sliding contact. How should the sliding contact be set to make the power absorbed in the resistance equal to 25 w? What would be the power lost in the rheostat when so set?

(95-III) A generator supplies power to two loads, as shown in Fig. 3.17. The resistances of the lines are as shown. Load No. 1 takes 8 amp, and load No. 2 takes 6 amp. The voltage at the generator (V_S) is 120 v. Find the

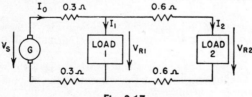

Fig. 3.17.

voltage at each load, the power taken by each load, power lost in the lines, and power supplied by the generator.

(**96-III**) The generator in Fig. 3.17 supplies 2500 w to the line at a voltage of 135.   Load No. 1 takes 1300 w.   Find the power taken by load No. 2 and the voltage at each load.

(**97-III**) Load No. 2 in Fig. 3.17 requires 1000 w at 115 v.   Load No. 1 normally requires 1000 w at 115 v, but can operate satisfactorily at any voltage from 115 to 130, and the power it takes varies directly as the voltage. Assuming that the requirements of load No. 2 are to be met exactly, find the voltage at load No. 1, the power taken by load No. 1, and the sending-end voltage.

(**98-III**) Two generators supply power to a single load, as shown in Fig. 3.18.   The resistances of the lines are as shown.   The terminal voltage

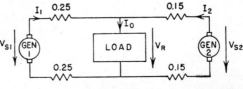

Fig. 3.18.

of generator No. 1 is 235 v and of generator No. 2, 225 v.   The load current (I_0) is 50 amp.   Find the voltage at the load, the power received by the load, the current supplied by each generator, the power supplied by each generator, and the total line loss.

(**99-III**) Two generators supply power to a single load, as shown in Fig. 3.18.   The resistances of the lines are as shown.   The power absorbed by the load is 12,000 w, and the voltage across the load is 225 v.   The terminal voltage of generator No. 1 is 235 v.   Calculate the terminal voltage of generator No. 2, the current supplied by each generator, the power supplied by each generator, and the total line loss.

(**100-III**) Two generators supply power to a single load, as shown in Fig. 3.18.   The resistances of the lines are as shown.   The power absorbed by the load is 12,000 w, and the voltage at the load is 225 v.   Find the terminal voltage of each generator in order that each shall supply the same current.

(**101-III**) In electric power distribution, the three-wire system is widely used, both for direct and alternating current.   The third wire, usually

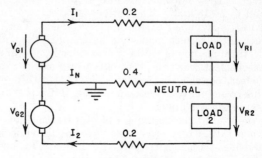

Fig. 3.19.   Three-wire power system.

grounded, is called the neutral.   A simple three-wire, direct current system, using two generators is shown in Fig. 3.19.   Each generator has a terminal voltage of 120 v.   The line resistances are as shown.   Calculate the current in the neutral, and the voltage across each load if
>   (a) $I_1 = 36$ amp and $I_2 = 24$ amp.
>   (b) $I_1 = 24$ amp and $I_2 = 36$ amp.
>   (c) $I_1 = 30$ amp and $I_2 = 30$ amp.

(102-III) Each generator in the three-wire system shown in Fig. 3.19 has a terminal voltage of 120.   The line resistances are as shown, and the current I_2 is 30 amp.   Calculate and plot curves showing V_{R_1} and V_{R_2} as functions of I_1 (abscissa) as I_1 is increased from 0 to 60 amp in steps of 10 amp.

(103-III) Power in the amount of 5 kw is to be transmitted over the three-wire line shown in Fig. 3.19.   The line resistances are as shown, and the voltage across each load is to be 115 v.   Calculate the total line loss (a) if the entire 5 kw is required by load No. 1 and (b) if the 5 kw is equally divided between the two loads.

Study Questions

1. During the life of a tungsten-filament lamp, metal is gradually evaporated from the filament, decreasing its cross section.   How would this affect the luminous output of a lamp operated at constant voltage?   Of a lamp operated at constant current?   Neglect the effect of the evaporated metal blackening the bulb.

2. One element of a circuit is non-linear, showing an increase of resistance with increase of current.   What might be done to give linear characteristics to the circuit as a whole?

3. The measurement of the electromotive force of a battery is not a valid test of its condition.   For instance, a 6-v battery might be found to have an electromotive force of 6.0 v exactly and still be incapable of delivering any appreciable current.   Explain.

4. A storage battery is connected into a circuit as in Fig. 3.3.   The polarity of the battery is not known and there is no means of determining the actual direction of the current, but it is observed that the terminal voltage of the battery decreases when the circuit is closed.   Is the battery connected for charge or discharge?

5. Two batteries having different electromotive forces but equal internal resistances are connected in parallel (+ to + and − to −).   What will happen?

6. A storage battery is connected into a circuit as in Fig. 3.3 and the current is found to be 18 amp.   The battery is taken out of the circuit and reconnected with its terminals in the opposite order.   The current is now 21 amp.   Which is the correct connection for charging the battery?

7. The electrical method of power transmission is, of course, not the only method.   A mechanical gear train transmits power and the shipping of coal by rail is, in effect, power transmission.   List as many alternative methods as you can think of and for each method, indicate if it is practical or might be practical under certain conditions.

8. When the load at the receiving end of a transmission line has grown to the point where satisfactory service can no longer be rendered, one solution is to operate the line at a higher voltage.   For instance, the operating voltage of a certain line might be increased from 120 v to 2400 v. (a) What would be the indications that such a change was necessary? (b) How would increasing the operating voltage remedy the situation?

9. Would it be practical to connect two rheostats in parallel to secure more precise control of current? What should be the relative resistances for the best results?

10. What advantage would there be in operating lamps in series (as is usually done for street lighting) rather than in parallel (as is usually done for interior lighting)? What disadvantages?

11. Kirchhoff's voltage law is based upon the principle of conservation of energy. Upon what principle might Kirchhoff's current law be said to be based?

12. A number of lamps are operated in parallel from a generator of constant emf. What would be the effect on these lamps of connecting another lamp in parallel? What would be the effect on the generator?

13. A number of lamps are operated in series from a generator of constant electromotive force. What would be the effect on these lamps of connecting another lamp in series? What would be the effect on the generator?

14. A generator is so modified that it maintains a constant current regardless of the load resistance. A number of lamps in parallel are operated from this generator. What would be the effect on these lamps of adding another lamp in parallel? What would be the effect on the generator?

15. A generator is so modified that it supplies a constant current regardless of the load resistance. A number of lamps in series are operated from this generator. What would be the effect on these lamps of adding another lamp in series? What would be the effect on the generator?

CHAPTER IV

ELECTRICAL NETWORKS

1. Terminology. Any arrangement of batteries, generators, resistances, and other circuit elements may be termed an **electrical network.** The terms *circuit* and *network* are used synonymously in much of electrical literature, the tendency being to refer to simpler arrangements as circuits and to the more complicated ones as *networks.* Any of the circuits, so-called, in Figs. 3.1 to 3.19 might, however, be

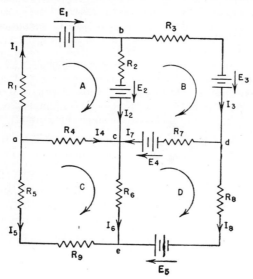

Fig. 4.1. Four-mesh electrical network.

properly referred to as networks. Some of the terminology pertaining to networks has already been introduced in the last chapter. Referring to Fig. 4.1, we should now be able to see that there are five junction points *a, b, c, d,* and *e*. A part of the network that connects one junction point with another is called a **branch.** In Fig. 4.1, there are eight branches *ab, ac, ae, bc, bd, dc, de,* and *ec*. The most elementary of the many closed loops which we can trace out in a network are called **meshes.** In Fig. 4.1, there are four meshes, designated *A, B, C,* and *D*.

73

The sources of electromotive force in a network may be either direct or alternating. The resistances may be either linear or nonlinear (see Chapter III), and they may be bilateral or unilateral. A bilateral resistance is one that is independent of the direction of the current, whereas a unilateral resistance depends upon the direction in which current flows through it. In subsequent chapters, we will consider sources of emf and resistance elements in some detail, and furthermore, we shall find that there are additional network elements which have to be introduced. For the present, we will consider networks that are made up entirely of batteries or other sources of direct emf, and linear, bilateral resistances.

2. The method of branch currents. The problem that arises most commonly in the study of networks is that of determining the currents in the various parts of the network when the electromotive forces and resistances are known. The method ordinarily used for representing the currents is that of branch currents, already introduced and used in the preceding chapters. A different current must be designated for each branch of the network, and a direction selected as positive for each current. In Fig. 4.1, the branch currents are I_1, I_2, I_3, I_4, I_5, I_6, I_7, and I_8, with directions as indicated by the arrows. It must be emphasized that it is a waste of time, and actually a hindrance, to speculate on the probable direction of each current and try to decide in advance what its actual direction will be. In a network that is at all complicated, it is impossible to determine current direction by inspection. Furthermore, as was pointed out in Chapter II, the arrows are not intended to represent actual direction of the current, but to indicate which direction is to be referred to as positive. The arrows in Fig. 4.1 were, accordingly, placed on the different branches arbitrarily as to direction.

The direction of the electromotive force arrow which is placed beside each battery, on the other hand, is not arbitrary. In each case we know which are the positive and negative terminals of the battery, and we make the emf arrow point in the direction of rise of potential (from negative toward positive). The electromotive forces of the batteries in Fig. 4.1 are designated E_1, E_2, E_3, E_4, and E_5. The resistances are numbered from 1 to 9. Now, assuming that we know all electromotive forces and all resistances, there are eight unknown currents to be found, and to do this we have to have eight independent equations. These we must obtain by application of Kirchhoff's laws.

Taking the current law first, we apply it at the junction points to obtain:

$$\text{At } a \qquad 0 = I_1 + I_4 + I_5. \tag{4.1}$$

$$\text{At } b \qquad I_1 = I_2 + I_3. \tag{4.2}$$

$$\text{At } c \qquad I_2 + I_4 + I_7 = I_6. \tag{4.3}$$

$$\text{At } d \qquad I_3 = I_7 + I_8. \tag{4.4}$$

$$\text{At } e \qquad I_5 + I_6 + I_8 = 0 \tag{4.5}$$

Of these five equations, one is not independent. For example, by adding Equations (4.1), (4.2), (4.4) and (4.5) we may obtain Equation (4.3). Any one of the five equations may be obtained by combining the others, and consequently, we have to discard one of the five as not independent. In general, we can obtain as many independent equations by use of Kirchhoff's current law as there are junction points in the network, less one.

This leaves four other equations to be obtained by the use of Kirchhoff's voltage law. Unless there is some special reason for doing otherwise, the best procedure is to apply the voltage law to each mesh of the network. This gives, around mesh A,

$$E_1 + E_2 = R_1 I_1 + R_2 I_2 - R_4 I_4. \tag{4.6}$$

Around mesh B,

$$E_3 + E_4 - E_2 = R_3 I_3 + R_7 I_7 - R_2 I_2. \tag{4.7}$$

Around mesh C,

$$0 = R_4 I_4 + R_6 I_6 - R_9 I_5 - R_5 I_5. \tag{4.8}$$

Around mesh D,

$$E_5 - E_4 = R_8 I_8 - R_6 I_6 - R_7 I_7. \tag{4.9}$$

Kirchhoff's voltage law could, of course, be applied to a number of other closed loops in Fig. 4.1; for example, around the loop that encircles all the meshes, we would have

$$E_1 + E_3 + E_5 = R_1 I_1 + R_3 I_3 + R_8 I_8 - R_9 I_5 - R_5 I_5. \tag{4.10}$$

It can be seen, however, that Equation (4.10) might be obtained by adding Equations (4.6), (4.7), (4.8) and (4.9), and is not, therefore, an independent equation. It might be used as such if one of the first four were omitted, but the use of loops other than meshes always brings up the question of whether or not the equation obtained is independent. One rule is that an equation obtained by Kirchhoff's voltage law must, in order to be independent, contain at least one term that does not appear in any equation already obtained. A very simple way to be sure of having a new term in each equation is to apply the voltage law to meshes only.

We now have the eight independent equations required. We may proceed with their solution in a number of different ways. Generally speaking, it is good procedure to begin by substituting for some of the currents that appear in the voltage Equations (4.6), (4.7), (4.8), and (4.9) their equivalents as found from the current Equations (4.1), (4.2), (4.4), and (4.5). Thus, we may substitute

$$-I_1 - I_5 \text{ for } I_4 \qquad \text{[from (4.1)].}$$
$$I_1 - I_3 \text{ for } I_2 \qquad \text{[from (4.2)].}$$
$$I_3 - I_8 \text{ for } I_7 \qquad \text{[from (4.4)].}$$
$$-I_5 - I_8 \text{ for } I_6 \qquad \text{[from (4.5)].}$$

Making the substitutions, we obtain

$$E_1 + E_2 = R_1 I_1 + R_2(I_1 - I_3) - R_4(-I_1 - I_5). \qquad (4.6)$$
$$E_3 + E_4 - E_2 = R_3 I_3 + R_7(I_3 - I_8) - R_2(I_1 - I_3). \qquad (4.7)$$
$$0 = R_4(-I_1 - I_5) + R_6(-I_5 - I_8) - R_9 I_5 - R_5 I_5. \qquad (4.8)$$
$$E_5 - E_4 = R_8 I_8 - R_6(-I_5 - I_8) - R_7(I_3 - I_8). \qquad (4.9)$$

In short order, we have reduced the number of equations (and corresponding number of unknown currents) from eight to four.

Some students prefer to make these substitutions before even applying Kirchhoff's voltage law. Thus, in place of designating the current in branch ac as I_4, we might designate it $(-I_1 - I_5)$, and so forth. When Kirchhoff's voltage law was applied, we would find that the resulting equations then contained only the four unknown currents I_1, I_3, I_5, and I_8.

We then single out one of these unknowns and proceed to eliminate it from the system of equations by any of the common means learned in algebra, thereby reducing the number of unknowns and equations to three. Another unknown is then eliminated in like manner, and so forth, until finally, we are left with a single equation and a single unknown, which is then found. Then comes the process of substituting this back into the various equations to find the other currents. Or we may use determinants, which is a somewhat more systematic way of accomplishing the same purpose. This part of the work is tedious and slow by any method, and of course becomes more so as the complexity of the network increases and a greater number of unknown currents has to be found.

EXAMPLE: The following data are furnished on the network in Fig. 4.1.

$$E_1 = 18 \text{ v}, \quad R_1 = 6 \text{ ohms}, \quad R_6 = 13 \text{ ohms},$$
$$E_2 = 5 \text{ v}, \quad R_2 = 3 \text{ ohms}, \quad R_7 = 8 \text{ ohms},$$
$$E_3 = 11 \text{ v}, \quad R_3 = 9 \text{ ohms}, \quad R_8 = 12 \text{ ohms},$$
$$E_4 = 7 \text{ v}, \quad R_4 = 17 \text{ ohms}, \quad R_9 = 2 \text{ ohms}.$$
$$E_5 = 15 \text{ v}, \quad R_5 = 4 \text{ ohms},$$

SOLUTION: Replacing the symbols with numerical values in Equations (4.6) to (4.9), we have

$$18 + 5 = 6I_1 + 3(I_1 - I_3) - 17(-I_1 - I_5) \tag{4.6}$$
$$11 + 7 - 5 = 9I_3 + 8(I_3 - I_8) - 3(I_1 - I_3). \tag{4.7}$$
$$0 = 17(-I_1 - I_5) + 13(-I_5 - I_8) - 2I_5 - 4I_5. \tag{4.8}$$
$$15 - 7 = 12I_8 - 13(-I_5 - I_8) - 8(I_3 - I_8). \tag{4.9}$$

Collecting terms,

$$23 = 26I_1 - 3I_3 + 17I_5. \tag{4.6}$$
$$13 = -3I_1 + 20I_3 - 8I_8. \tag{4.7}$$
$$0 = -17I_1 - 36I_5 - 13I_8. \tag{4.8}$$
$$8 = -8I_3 + 13I_5 + 33I_8. \tag{4.9}$$

Eliminating I_8 between Equations (4.7) and (4.8) we get

$$21.12 = 12.13I_1 + 32.5I_3 + 36I_5. \tag{4.11}$$

Eliminating I_8 between Equations (4.8) and (4.9), we get

$$8 = -43.15I_1 - 8I_3 - 78.37I_5. \tag{4.12}$$

Eliminating I_5 between Equations (4.6) and (4.11), we get

$$27.59 = 42.94I_1 - 38.85I_3. \tag{4.13}$$

Eliminating I_5 between Equations (4.6) and (4.12), we get

$$114 = 76.61I_1 - 21.83I_3. \tag{4.14}$$

Eliminating I_3 between Equations (4.13) and (4.14), we get

$$175.31 = 93.6I_1,$$
$$I_1 = 1.873 \text{ amp.}$$

Substituting this value of I_1 in (4.14)

$$114 = 143.68 - 21.83I_3,$$
$$I_3 = 1.358 \text{ amp.}$$

Substituting these values in (4.6)

$$23 = 48.70 - 4.074 + 17I_5,$$
$$I_5 = -1.272 \text{ amp.}$$

Substituting in (4.7),

$$13 = 5.62 + 27.16 - 8I_8,$$
$$I_8 = 1.067 \text{ amp.}$$

Substituting in (4.1),

$$I_4 = -1.873 - (-1.272) = -0.601 \text{ amp.}$$

Substituting in (4.2),

$$I_2 = 1.873 - 1.358 = 0.515 \text{ amp.}$$

Substituting in (4.4),

$$I_7 = 1.358 - 1.067 = 0.291 \text{ amp.}$$

Substituting in (4.5),

$$I_6 = -(-1.272) - 1.067 = 0.205 \text{ amp.}$$

To check our work, we may substitute our current values into any of the network equations. Upon substituting, these equations should reduce to identities.
Substituting in (4.3),

$$I_2 + I_4 + I_7 = I_6,$$
$$0.515 + (-0.601) + 0.291 = 0.205,$$
$$0.806 = 0.806.$$

Substituting in (4.10),

$$E_1 + E_3 + E_5 = R_1I_1 + R_3I_3 + R_8I_8 - (R_9 + R_5)I_5,$$
$$18 + 11 + 15 = (6 \times 1.873) + (9 \times 1.358) + (12 \times 1.067)$$
$$- (6 \times -1.272)$$
$$44 = 43.89.$$

3. Solution by determinants. The solution of the simultaneous equations resulting from the application of Kirchhoff's laws to a network may be systematized by the use of determinants and any unknown current can be written at once as the quotient of two determinants.[1] Thus, for the group of equations 4.6–4.9 obtained in the last article, the unknown current I_1 is **given** by

---

[1] See any college algebra text.

$$I_1 = \frac{\begin{vmatrix} 23 & -3 & 17 & 0 \\ 13 & 20 & 0 & -8 \\ 0 & 0 & -36 & -13 \\ 8 & -8 & 13 & 33 \end{vmatrix}}{\begin{vmatrix} 26 & -3 & 17 & 0 \\ -3 & 20 & 0 & -8 \\ -17 & 0 & -36 & -13 \\ 0 & -8 & 13 & 33 \end{vmatrix}}.$$

Developing the numerator along the third row, we get

$$\text{numerator} = -36 \begin{vmatrix} 23 & -3 & 0 \\ 13 & 20 & -8 \\ 8 & -8 & 33 \end{vmatrix} + 13 \begin{vmatrix} 23 & -3 & 17 \\ 13 & 20 & 0 \\ 8 & -8 & 13 \end{vmatrix}$$
$$= -546{,}732 + 25{,}987 = -520{,}745.$$

Developing the denominator along the first column, we get

$$\text{denominator} = 26 \begin{vmatrix} 20 & 0 & -8 \\ 0 & -36 & -13 \\ -8 & 13 & 33 \end{vmatrix} + 3 \begin{vmatrix} -3 & 17 & 0 \\ 0 & -36 & -13 \\ -8 & 13 & 33 \end{vmatrix}$$
$$- 17 \begin{vmatrix} -3 & 17 & 0 \\ 20 & 0 & -8 \\ -8 & 13 & 33 \end{vmatrix}.$$
$$= -469{,}976 + 14{,}475 + 177{,}548 = -277{,}953$$
$$I_1 = \frac{-520{,}745}{-277{,}953} = 1.873 \text{ amp.}$$

The denominator or determinant of the system is the same, whichever current is being found, and need be calculated only once. Thus, the number of determinants that have to be evaluated is equal to the number of unknown currents to be found, plus one.

4. Method of mesh currents. Instead of designating the branch currents, an alternative method is to designate a different current for each mesh of the network. Thus, in the four-mesh network of Fig. 4.1, we may designate mesh currents I_A, I_B, I_C and I_D for meshes A, B, C and D, respectively. The directions selected as positive are designated by the curved arrows within the meshes.

It is obvious that in a single-mesh network, the mesh current and the branch current would either be identical, or one would be the negative of the other, depending upon the directions selected as positive. In a network of two or more meshes, any particular branch may be part of one mesh only, if it forms part of the outside contour of the network, or it may be common to two or more meshes. If the branch is part of one mesh only, the branch current will be identical with the mesh current (or the negative of it). If the branch is common to two or more meshes, the branch current will be the algebraic sum of the mesh currents. Thus, for the network of Fig. 4.1,

$$I_1 = I_A, \tag{4.15}$$
$$I_3 = I_B, \tag{4.16}$$
$$I_5 = -I_C. \tag{4.17}$$
$$I_8 = I_D. \tag{4.18}$$
$$I_2 = I_A - I_B. \tag{4.19}$$
$$I_4 = I_C - I_A. \tag{4.20}$$
$$I_6 = I_C - I_D. \tag{4.21}$$
$$I_7 = I_B - I_D. \tag{4.22}$$

One advantage of using mesh currents is that the number of unknowns in a network problem is thereby reduced. For the network of Fig. 4.1, there would be eight branch currents to be found but only four mesh currents. Since there are four meshes, four independent equations may be written by applying Kirchhoff's voltage law, and these are sufficient. If branch currents are required, they can be calculated from the mesh currents by using Equations (4.15) to (4.22).

In applying Kirchhoff's voltage law, two voltage drops will be taken into account in every branch that is common to two meshes, provided the branch has a resistance other than zero. This fact should be obvious when it is considered that the current in any such branch is made up of two mesh currents. The voltage drops due to the mesh currents are to be considered algebraically. Thus, if one traces around a particular mesh in the direction selected as positive for the current in that mesh, the voltage drops caused by that current would all be written as positive. But the voltage drops caused by currents in adjoining meshes might be either positive or negative according to whether, in the common branch, the positive direction of the current in the adjoining mesh agrees with the direction of tracing the mesh under consideration. Since an electromotive force is not considered a consequence of current flow, an electromotive force will appear only once in any voltage equation. For the network of Fig. 4.1 the voltage equations will be as follows:

$$E_1 + E_2 = I_A R_1 + I_A R_2 - I_B R_2 + I_A R_4 - I_C R_4. \tag{4.23}$$
$$-E_2 + E_3 + E_4 = I_B R_2 - I_A R_2 + I_B R_3 + I_B R_7 - I_D R_7. \tag{4.24}$$
$$0 = I_C R_9 + I_C R_5 + I_C R_4 - I_A R_4 + I_C R_6 - I_D R_6. \tag{4.25}$$
$$-E_4 + E_5 = I_D R_8 + I_D R_6 - I_C R_6 + I_D R_7 - I_B R_7. \tag{4.26}$$

Collecting terms and arranging in alphabetical order, we get

$$E_1 + E_2 = I_A(R_1 + R_2 + R_4) - I_B R_2 - I_C R_4. \quad (4.27)$$
$$-E_2 + E_3 + E_4 = -I_A R_2 + I_B(R_2 + R_3 + R_7) - I_D R_7. \quad (4.28)$$
$$0 = -I_A R_4 + I_C(R_9 + R_5 + R_4 + R_6) - I_D R_6. \quad (4.29)$$
$$-E_4 + E_5 = -I_B R_7 - I_C R_6 + I_D(R_8 + R_6 + R_7). \quad (4.30)$$

After a little practice, the equations may be written in this form immediately.

If we now substitute into Equations (4.27) to (4.30) the numerical values used for the electromotive forces and resistances in the previous example, we have

$$23 = 26I_A - 3I_B - 17I_C. \quad (4.31)$$
$$13 = -3I_A + 20I_B - 8I_D. \quad (4.32)$$
$$0 = -17I_A + 36I_C - 13I_D. \quad (4.33)$$
$$8 = -8I_B - 13I_C + 33I_D. \quad (4.34)$$

These equations are identical to Equations (4.6) to (4.9), except that instead of the branch currents I_1, I_3, I_5, and I_8, we have the mesh currents I_A, I_B, $-I_C$ and I_D. The solution could now be carried out by either of the methods demonstrated in the previous example, and the numerical values of the four mesh currents determined.

Problems

(1-IV) In the network shown in Fig. 4.2, E_1 is 12 v, E_2 is 8 v, and E_3 is 4 v. R_1 is 2 ohms, R_2 is 7 ohms, R_3 is 3 ohms, R_4 is 8 ohms, R_5 is 5 ohms, and R_6 is 4 ohms. Find the current in each branch of the network.

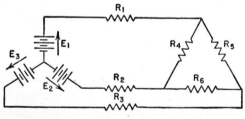

Fig. 4.2.

(2-IV) In the network shown in Fig. 4.2, E_1 is 4 v, E_2 is 12 v, and E_3 is 8 v. R_1 is 11 ohms, R_2 is 9 ohms, R_3 is 5 ohms, R_4 is 15 ohms, R_5 is 2 ohms, and R_6 is 6 ohms. Find the current in each branch of the network.

(3-IV) In the network shown in Fig. 4.3, E_1 is 16 v, E_2 is 5 v, R_1 is 30 ohms, R_2 is 22 ohms, R_3 is 45 ohms, R_4 is 35 ohms, R_5 is 75 ohms, and R_6 is 10 ohms. Find the current in each branch of the network.

(**4-IV**) In the network shown in Fig. 4.3, E_1 is 5 v, E_2 is 20 v, R_1 is 5 ohms, R_2 is 7 ohms, R_3 is 10 ohms, R_4 is 3 ohms, R_5 is 8 ohms, and R_6 is 12 ohms. Find the current in each part of the network.

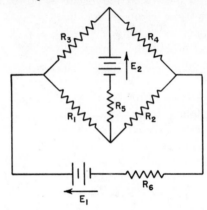

Fig. 4.3.

(**5-IV**) In the network shown in Fig. 4.1,

$E_1 = 10$ v,	$R_1 = 100$ ohms,	$R_6 = 90$ ohms,
$E_2 = 20$ v,	$R_2 = 50$ ohms,	$R_7 = 120$ ohms,
$E_3 = 30$ v,	$R_3 = 150$ ohms,	$R_8 = 180$ ohms,
$E_4 = 40$ v,	$R_4 = 200$ ohms,	$R_9 = 30$ ohms.
$E_5 = 50$ v,	$R_5 = 40$ ohms,	

Calculate the current in each part of the network.

(**6-IV**) In the network shown in Fig. 4.4, the resistances R_1 and R_2 are each 2 ohms; R_3 and R_4 are each 50 ohms; R_5, R_6, and R_7 are each 3 ohms; R_8 is

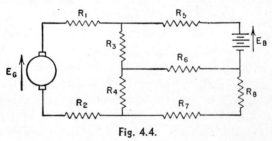

Fig. 4.4.

50 ohms; E_G is 600 v; and E_B is 550 v. Calculate the current in each branch of the network.

(**7-IV**) In the network shown in Fig. 4.4, the resistances R_1 and R_2 are each 5 ohms; R_3 and R_4 are each 100 ohms; R_5, R_6, and R_7 are each 10 ohms; R_8 is 75 ohms; and E_G is 200 v. Find the value of E_B which will make the current zero through the resistance R_5.

5. Theorems which aid in the simplification of networks. It is evident from what has been said that the straightforward solution of network problems by the application of Kirchhoff's laws becomes very laborious, even for networks that are comparatively simple. For the complicated networks that occur in power and communications systems, the time required for the solution of problems by Kirchhoff's laws makes this method of attack impractical. One alternative is to set up the system in miniature and solve the problems experimentally. Such a miniature system is known as a **calculating board,** and is an invaluable aid, particularly in solution of power-system problems.

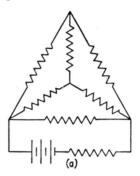

The other alternative is to devise ways and means of reducing the complicated network to a simpler one. We have already shown that we could find single equivalent resistances which could be put in place of groups of resistances in series or in parallel, and by this procedure alone it is often possible to reduce formidable-looking networks to very simple ones. However, there are many networks, such as the one shown in Fig. 4.5a, in which the resistances are neither in series nor parallel. There are others in which the presence of one or more sources of emf makes it impossible to apply the series- and parallel-circuit rules, as in the network of Fig. 4.5b. We shall now consider some theorems that lead to the simplification of such networks.

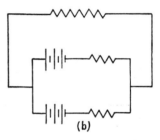

Fig. 4.5. Circuits which cannot be simplified by use of the series- and parallel-circuit rules.

6. The delta-wye transformation. It is always possible to find three resistances R_A, R_B, and R_C which, if they be connected in **wye,** as in Fig. 4.6a, will be exactly equivalent to three other resistances R_X, R_Y, and R_Z, which are connected in **delta,** as in Fig. 4.6b. By *equivalent,* we mean that the resistance, as measured between corresponding terminals, is the same for either arrangement. To prove this theorem, let us begin by writing down the resistances which we would expect to find between the various pairs of terminals. For the wye,

$$R_{12} = R_A + R_B. \tag{4.35}$$
$$R_{23} = R_B + R_C. \tag{4.36}$$
$$R_{31} = R_C + R_A. \tag{4 37}$$

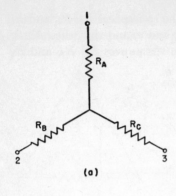

(a)

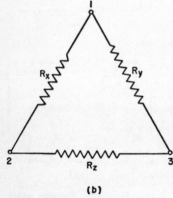

(b)

Fig. 4.6. Wye and delta networks. Any delta network may be replaced by an equivalent wye network and vice versa.

For the delta,

$$R_{12} = \frac{R_X(R_Y + R_Z)}{R_X + (R_Y + R_Z)}. \quad (4.38)$$

$$R_{23} = \frac{R_Z(R_X + R_Y)}{R_Z + (R_X + R_Y)}. \quad (4.39)$$

$$R_{31} = \frac{R_Y(R_Z + R_X)}{R_Y + (R_Z + R_X)}. \quad (4.40)$$

Then, for equivalence,

$$R_A + R_B = \frac{R_X(R_Y + R_Z)}{R_X + (R_Y + R_Z)}. \quad (4.41)$$

$$R_B + R_C = \frac{R_Z(R_X + R_Y)}{R_Z + (R_X + R_Y)}. \quad (4.42)$$

$$R_C + R_A = \frac{R_Y(R_Z + R_X)}{R_Y + (R_Z + R_X)}. \quad (4.43)$$

Solving for R_A, R_B and R_C, we find

$$R_A = \frac{R_X R_Y}{R_X + R_Y + R_Z}. \quad (4.44)$$

$$R_B = \frac{R_X R_Z}{R_X + R_Y + R_Z}. \quad (4.45)$$

$$R_C = \frac{R_Y R_Z}{R_X + R_Y + R_Z}. \quad (4.46)$$

The wye arrangement made up of R_A, R_B, and R_C is equivalent to the delta provided R_A, R_B, and R_C are given the values calculated by Equations (4.44), (4.45) and (4.46). It is important to note that in each of these equations, the two resistances in the numerator of the right-hand side are the two that are connected to the same terminal as is the wye resistance being calculated.

The usefulness of this theorem becomes apparent when it is noticed how many networks include one or more groups of resistances that form deltas.

EXAMPLE: The resistances in Fig. 4.7a are as follows:

$$R_1 = 40 \text{ ohms}, R_3 = 10 \text{ ohms, and } R_5 = 50 \text{ ohms}.$$
$$R_2 = 20 \text{ ohms}, R_4 = 30 \text{ ohms, and } R_0 = 5 \text{ ohms}.$$

The emf of the battery is 15 v, and it is required to find the currents in the various branches.

SOLUTION: It is seen (Fig. 4.7b) that the resistances R_2, R_4, and R_5 form a delta with corners at points m, n, and o, and that these three resistances may be replaced by the three resistances R_6, R_7, and R_8

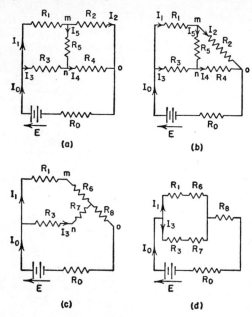

Fig. 4.7.

which form a wye, as shown in Fig. 4.7c. We calculate R_6, R_7, and R_8 by Equations (4.44), (4.45), and (4.46).

$$R_6 = \frac{R_2 R_5}{R_2 + R_4 + R_5} = \frac{20 \times 50}{20 + 30 + 50} = 10 \text{ ohms.}$$

$$R_7 = \frac{R_4 R_5}{R_2 + R_4 + R_5} = \frac{30 \times 50}{20 + 30 + 50} = 15 \text{ ohms.}$$

$$R_8 = \frac{R_2 R_4}{R_2 + R_4 + R_5} = \frac{20 \times 30}{20 + 30 + 50} = 6 \text{ ohms.}$$

We have thus reduced a three-mesh network to an ordinary series-parallel circuit (4.7d), and we proceed with the solution as follows:

$$R_{parallel} = \frac{(R_1 + R_6)(R_3 + R_7)}{(R_1 + R_6) + (R_3 + R_7)} = \frac{(40 + 10)(10 + 15)}{(40 + 10) + (10 + 15)}$$
$$= 16.67 \text{ ohms.}$$

$$R_{circuit} = R_{parallel} + R_8 + R_0 = 16.67 + 6 + 5 = 27.67 \text{ ohms.}$$

$$I_0 = \frac{E}{R_{circuit}} = \frac{15}{27.67} = 0.542 \text{ amp.}$$

$V_{parallel} = I_0 R_{parallel} = 0.542 \times 16.67 = 9.04$ v.

$$I_1 = \frac{V_{parallel}}{R_1 + R_6} = \frac{9.04}{40 + 10} = 0.1805 \text{ amp.}$$

$$I_3 = \frac{V_{parallel}}{R_3 + R_7} = \frac{9.04}{10 + 15} = 0.361 \text{ amp.}$$

I_1 and I_3 are the currents through the resistances R_1 and R_3, respectively, and are the same in the original network (Fig. 4.7a) as in its series-parallel equivalent. We can now find I_5 by applying Kirchhoff's voltage law around the mesh consisting of R_1, R_5, and R_3.

$$0 = R_1 I_1 + R_5 I_5 - R_3 I_3,$$
$$0 = (40 \times 0.1805) + (50 I_5) - (10 \times 0.361), \qquad (4.47)$$
$$50 I_5 = -3.61,$$
$$I_5 = -0.0722 \text{ amp.}$$

Then, by Kirchhoff's current law,

$$I_1 = I_5 + I_2, \qquad (4.48)$$
$$I_2 = I_1 - I_5 = 0.1805 - (-0.0722) = 0.253 \text{ amp.}$$
$$I_3 + I_5 = I_4,$$
$$I_4 = 0.361 - 0.0722 = 0.289 \text{ amp.}$$

To check the results, we apply Kirchhoff's voltage law around the loop containing the battery, R_1, R_2, and R_0,

$$E = R_1 I_1 + R_2 I_2 + R_0 I_0, \qquad (4.49)$$
$$15 = (40 \times 0.1805) + (20 \times 0.253) + (5 \times 0.542),$$
$$15 = 14.99.$$

Problems

(8-IV) Show that the set of wye-connected resistances R_A, R_B, and R_C (Fig. 4.6a) may be replaced by the set of delta-connected resistances R_X, R_Y, and R_Z according to the equations

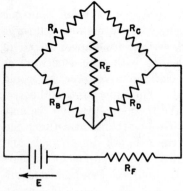

$$R_X = \frac{R_A R_B + R_B R_C + R_C R_A}{R_C}.$$

$$R_Y = \frac{R_A R_B + R_B R_C + R_C R_A}{R_B}.$$

$$R_Z = \frac{R_A R_B + R_B R_C + R_C R_A}{R_A}.$$

Fig. 4.8.

(9-IV) In the network shown in Fig. 4.8, $R_A = 50$ ohms, $R_C = 500$ ohms, $R_B = 250$ ohms, $R_D = 2000$ ohms. $R_E = 200$ ohms, $R_F = 100$ ohms, and

$E = 5$ v.   Reduce the network to the simplest possible equivalent circuit, using a delta-wye transformation and parallel-circuit rule.

   (10-IV) In the network shown in Fig. 4.8, and using the data given in Problem 9-IV, calculate the current in the resistance R_E.

   (11-IV) Use the delta-wye transformation theorem to reduce the network in Fig. 4.2 to a two-mesh network.

   (12-IV) In the network in Fig. 4.9, $R_1 = 500$ ohms, $R_2 = 400$ ohms, $R_4 = 50$ ohms, $R_5 = 1000$ ohms, $R_3 = 800$ ohms, $R_6 = 1000$ ohms, $R_7 = 900$ ohms, and $R_8 = 20$ ohms.   The electromotive force of the battery is 15 v. Reduce the network to the simplest possible equivalent circuit, using the delta-wye transformation and parallel-circuit rule as necessary.

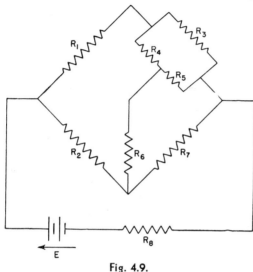

Fig. 4.9.

   (13-IV) Reduce the network in Fig. 4.1 as far as possible by use of the delta-wye transformation.

7. The superposition theorem.

The presence of more than one source of emf in a network often prevents us from making delta-wye transformations and from considering certain resistances to be in parallel.   If there were some way of dealing with such a network as though it contained only one source of electromotive force, we would be free to simplify it as far as we wished.   The superposition theorem permits us to do just that.   In effect, the theorem says that we may consider the sources of electromotive force to act one at a time, find the current in any specified branch of the network due to each, and then "superimpose," or add algebraically, these component currents to find the current in that branch if all the sources of emf acted simultaneously.   When the current due to a particular source of electromotive force is being found, all the other electromotive forces are considered to be zero for the time being. All branches of the circuit remain intact; the sources of electromotive force are not disconnected: they are merely treated as though their electromotive forces had become zero.

EXAMPLE: Let us consider the network shown in Fig. 4.10a. If E_A were zero, we could consider R_A and R_C to be in parallel and this group in series with R_B (Fig. 4.10b). If E_B were zero, we could consider R_C and R_B in parallel and in series with R_A (Fig. 4.10c).

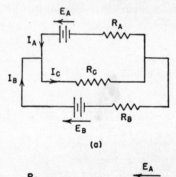

(a)

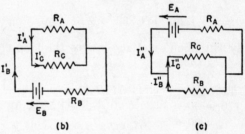

(b)   (c)

Fig. 4.10.

Suppose $E_B = 120$ v, $E_A = 30$ v, $R_A = 5$ ohms, $R_C = 15$ ohms, and $R_B = 20$ ohms, and that we are to find all currents.

SOLUTION: In Fig. 4.10b,

$$R_{parallel} = \frac{R_A R_C}{R_A + R_C} = \frac{5 \times 15}{5 + 15} = 3.75 \text{ ohms.}$$

$$R_{circuit} = 3.75 + 20 = 23.75 \text{ ohms.}$$

$$I_{B}' = \frac{E_B}{R_{circuit}} = \frac{120}{23.75} = 5.05 \text{ amp.}$$

$$V_{parallel} = R_{parallel} \times I_{B}' = 3.75 \times 5.05 = 18.95 \text{ v.}$$

$$I_{A}' = -\frac{V_{parallel}}{R_A} = -\frac{18.95}{5} = -3.79 \text{ amp.}$$

$$I_{C}' = \frac{V_{parallel}}{R_C} = \frac{18.95}{15} = 1.262 \text{ amp.}$$

In Fig. 4.10c,

$$R_{parallel} = \frac{15 \times 20}{15 + 20} = 8.58 \text{ ohms.}$$

$$R_{circuit} = 8.58 + 5 = 13.58 \text{ ohms.}$$

$$I_A'' = \frac{E_A}{R_{circuit}} = \frac{30}{13.58} = 2.21 \text{ amp.}$$

$$V_{parallel} = 8.58 \times 2.21 = 18.95 \text{ v.}$$

$$I_C'' = \frac{18.95}{15} = 1.263 \text{ amp.}$$

$$I_B'' = -\frac{18.95}{20} = -0.947 \text{ amp.}$$

Then, superimposing the results,

$$I_A = I_A' + I_A'' \tag{4.50}$$
$$= (-3.79) + 2.21 = -1.58 \text{ amp.}$$
$$I_B = I_B' + I_B'' \tag{4.51}$$
$$= 5.05 + (-0.947) = 4.1 \text{ amp.}$$
$$I_C = I_C' + I_C'' \tag{4.52}$$
$$= 1.262 + 1.263 = 2.52 \text{ amp.}$$

To check, apply Kirchhoff's voltage law to the loop containing both batteries:

$$E_B - E_A = I_B R_B - I_A R_A, \tag{4.53}$$
$$120 - 30 = (4.1 \times 20) - (-1.58 \times 5),$$
$$90 = 89.9.$$

Problems

(**14-IV**) Use the superposition theorem to find the current in each branch of the network shown in Fig. 4.11. E_A is 9 v, E_B is 15 v, R_A is 2.5 ohms, R_B is 3.25 ohms, and R_C is 5 ohms.

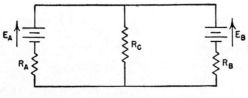

Fig. 4.11.

(**15-IV**) Use the superposition theorem to find the current in each branch of the network shown in Fig. 4.12. E_A is 20 v, E_B is 30 v, E_C is 40 v, R_A is 15 ohms, R_B is 10 ohms, and R_C is 20 ohms.

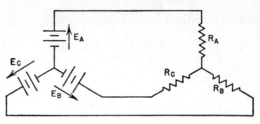

Fig. 4.12.

(**16-IV**) Use the superposition theorem and the wye-delta transformation to solve Problem 1-IV.

8. Thevenin's theorem. It often happens that we wish to study the effect in a network of changing some one resistance, all the other resistances and electromotive forces remaining unchanged. It would be convenient to be able to reduce the entire network, except for the one resistance, down to the simplest equivalent circuit possible. By doing so, we would greatly reduce the amount of work which we would have to do each time a new value was assigned to the one resistance. This simplification is made possible by Thevenin's theorem, which says that: *Any two-terminal network, made up of linear resistances and sources of electromotive force, can be replaced by a single source of electromotive force, E_x, having an internal resistance R_x, E_x being the potential difference between the network terminals at open circuit, and R_x being the resistance between the network terminals at open circuit with all emf's in the network reduced to zero.*

EXAMPLE: In Fig. 4.13a, there is shown a network consisting of a battery and four resistors R_1, R_2, R_3, and R_4. The resistance of R_4 is to be varied, and we wish to know how the current in R_4 will vary with its resistance.

SOLUTION: To apply Thevenin's theorem, we separate R_4 from the rest of the network, as in Fig. 4.13b. A and B, then, are the terminals of the network which we are to replace by the equivalent emf E_x and resistance R_x shown in Fig. 4.13c.

Suppose $E = 5$ v and $R_1 = R_2 = R_3 = 10$ ohms. First, find the potential difference between terminals A and B at open circuit. Since there is no current in R_3, this potential difference will obviously be the same as that across R_2, which is

$$\frac{E}{R_1 + R_2} R_2 = \frac{5}{10 + 10} 10 = 2.5 \text{ v.}$$

This is the E_x for the equivalent circuit. We next find the resistance between terminals A and B when E is set equal to zero. R_1 and R_2

are then in parallel, and their combined resistance is

$$\frac{R_1 R_2}{R_1 + R_2} = \frac{10 \times 10}{10 + 10} = 5 \text{ ohms,}$$

and the total resistance is

$$R_{parallel} + R_3 = 5 + 10 = 15 \text{ ohms.}$$

This is the R_X for the equivalent circuit.

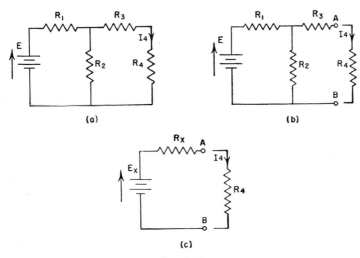

Fig. 4.13.

To check these results, we may calculate from the equivalent circuit, Fig. 4.13c, the current which would flow if R_4 were connected to its terminals and given a certain value, say 5 ohms:

$$I_4 = \frac{E_X}{R_X + 5} = \frac{2.5}{15 + 5} = 0.125 \text{ amp.}$$

Calculating I_4 from the original circuit, Fig. 45a, we also find $I_4 = 0.125$ amp.

Problems

(17-IV) Calculate the current in R_4 in the preceding example as R_4 is varied from zero to 50 ohms.

(18-IV) Use Thevenin's theorem to replace the network shown in Fig. 4.11, maintaining the identity of R_C. E_A is 15 v, E_B is 9 v, R_A is 2.5 ohms, and R_B is 3.25 ohms.   Calculate the current in R_C as R_C is varied from zero to 10 ohms.

(19-IV) Use Thevenin's theorem to replace the network shown in Fig. 4.12, maintaining the identity of R_A. E_A is 20 v, E_B is 30 v, E_C is 40 v, R_B is 10 ohms, and R_C is 20 ohms. Calculate the current in R_A as R_A is varied from zero to 100 ohms.

(20-IV) Use Thevenin's theorem to replace the network shown in Fig. 4.14, maintaining the identity of R. The battery electromotive force is 50 v. Calculate the current in R as R is varied from 0 to 100 ohms.

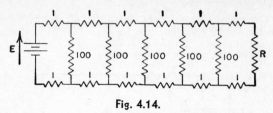

Fig. 4.14.

(21-IV) It is desired to replace the series-parallel network in Fig. 4.15a with that shown in Fig. 4.15b. The 5-ohm resistance is to be retained in the upper branch and resistances R_A and R_B are to be chosen so that (1) the total current I_0 is the same, and (2) the ratio of I_1 to I_2 is the same. Find R_A and R_B.

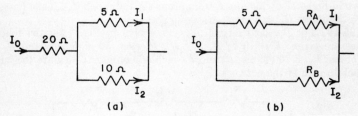

Fig. 4.15.

(22-IV) Develop a general equation for replacing a network, in which R_X is in series with a parallel group made up of R_Y and R_Z, with a network in which R_A and R_C are in series and in parallel with this group is R_B. The conditions are the same as called for in Problem 21-IV.

(23-IV) It is sometimes convenient in network problems to work with a current source rather than an electromotive force source. Norton's theorem

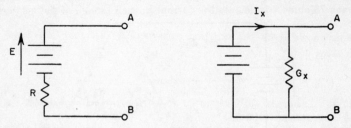

Fig. 4.16.

states that any two-terminal network made up of electromotive force sources and linear resistances can be replaced by a single source of current, I_X, in parallel with a conductance G_X, where I_X is the short-circuit current at the network terminals and G_X is the conductance measured at the network terminals at open circuit with all the electromotive forces in the network reduced to zero. Calculate the values of I_X and G_X so that the network in Fig. 4.16b will exactly replace that in Fig. 4.16a, if E is 10 v and R is 2 ohms. Check the equivalence by supposing various resistances to be connected to the terminals A-B.

(24-IV) The reciprocity theorem states that if, in any network made up of linear resistances, an electromotive force of E volts in branch X causes a current of I amp in branch Y, then an electromotive force of E volts in branch

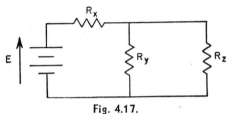

Fig. 4.17.

Y will cause a current of I amp in branch X. Verify this for the network shown in Fig. 4.17 by moving E from branch X to branch Y. Take $E = 10$ v, $R_X = 20$ ohms, $R_Y = 5$ ohms, $R_Z = 30$ ohms.

(25-IV) For the lattice-type network shown in Fig. 4.18, the following values are given: $E = 10$ v; R_1, R_3, R_4, R_6 each 50 ohms; R_2 and R_5 each 100 ohms; $R_7 = 200$ ohms; R_8 and R_9 each 500 ohms. Calculate the current in each branch of the network.

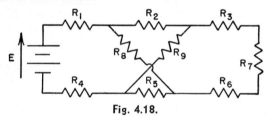

Fig. 4.18.

(26-IV) For the network shown in Fig. 4.19, the following values are given: $E = 15$ v; R_1, R_2, R_3, R_4, R_5, and R_6 are each 15 ohms; R_7, R_8, and R_9 are each 75 ohms. Calculate the current in each branch of the network.

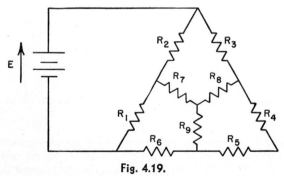

Fig. 4.19.

(**27-IV**) The battery in the network shown in Fig. 4.20 has an electromotive force of 10 v. Calculate the voltage drop in (a) the 20Ω resistance, (b) the 30Ω resistance, (c) the 40Ω resistance.

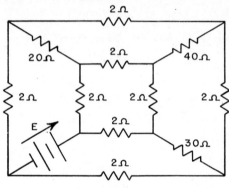

Fig. 4.20.

(**28-IV**) Six identical pieces of wire each having a resistance of 6 ohms are welded together to form a cube. Calculate the resistance of the cube: (a) between corners which lie on an edge; (b) between corners which lie on the diagonal of a face; (c) between corners which lie on a diagonal of the cube.

(**29-IV**) Two resistances of 30 ohms and 50 ohms, respectively, are connected in series, and this group is connected in parallel with a resistance of 70 ohms and with a series group made up of a battery having an electromotive force of 15 v and a resistance of 20 ohms. A resistance of 100 ohms is now connected from the junction of the 30-ohm and 50-ohm resistances to the junction point of the battery and the 20-ohm resistance. There is no direct connection from the 20-ohm resistance to the 30-ohm resistance. Calculate the current in the 70-ohm resistance.

(**30-IV**) The following data is furnished for the network shown in Fig. 4.21: $E = 30$ v; $R_1 = 15$ ohms; $R_2 = 25$ ohms; R_4, R_5 and R_6 are each 30 ohms; $R_3 = 55$ ohms. Calculate a value of R_7 for which the current through R_5 will be independent of the value of R_5.

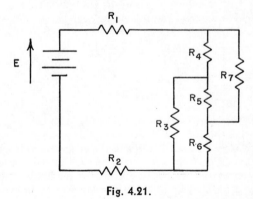

Fig. 4.21.

(31-IV) For the network shown in Fig. 4.22 the resistances are as follows:
$R_1 = 73.2$ ohms, $R_2 = 19.5$ ohms, $R_3 = 56.4$ ohms, $R_4 = 91.1$ ohms,
$R_5 = 66.2$ ohms, $R_6 = 11.9$ ohms, $R_7 = 33.3$ ohms, $R_8 = 85.6$ ohms,
$R_9 = 90.5$ ohms. $E_1 = 17.6$ v, and $E_2 = 8.8$ v. Calculate the current
in R_9.

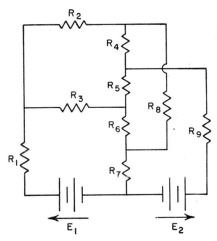

Fig. 4.22.

(32-IV) The power system shown in Fig. 4.23 comprises two generators and
two loads, connected by lines with resistances as shown. The voltage at the
terminals of each generator is maintained constant at 130 v. The current
I_1 taken by load No. 1 is 50 amp, and the current I_2 taken by load No. 2 is
40 amp. Calculate the voltage at each load, the current supplied by each
generator, and the current in the middle line section.

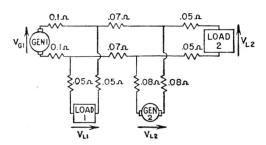

Fig. 4.23.

(33-IV) (a) The power system shown in Fig. 4.24 is made up of five loads
and a single generator connected by lines with resistances as shown. The
current taken by each load is 15 amp and the generator voltage is maintained
constant at 250 v. Calculate the voltage at each of the five loads.

(b) The power system shown in Fig. 4.24 is made up of five loads and a
single generator connected by lines with resistances as shown. The current

taken by each load is 15 amp and the voltage at load No. 4 is maintained constant at 225 v. Calculate the voltage at each of the other four loads and at the generator.

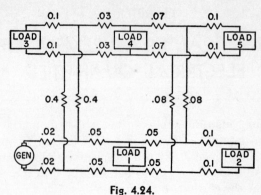

Fig. 4.24.

CHAPTER V

PRACTICAL MEASUREMENT OF ELECTRICAL QUANTITIES

1. Indicating instruments. Current and potential difference are most often determined by reading them directly from the scales of indicating instruments, known respectively as **ammeters** and **voltmeters.** An ammeter is connected directly into the circuit, as in Fig. 5.1, so that the current to be measured or a certain fraction of it passes through the instrument itself. It is thus in *series* with the other parts of the circuit. It must, therefore, be capable of carrying this current without injury to itself and without abnormally increasing the resistance of the circuit into which it is inserted.

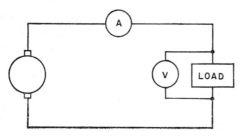

Fig. 5.1.   Ammeter and voltmeter connections.

A voltmeter is used by connecting its terminals to the two points between which it is desired to measure the potential difference. It is thus in *parallel* with the circuit or some part of the circuit. The voltmeter in Fig. 5.1 measures the potential difference at the terminals of the load. To be used in this way, a voltmeter must have enough resistance so that it will not be injured by the current that flows through it, and so that it will not materially affect the current in the circuit to which it is connected.

The basic principle of the ammeter and of the voltmeter is the same. The moving element is actuated by current in either case. In the ammeter, the element is actuated by the current we wish to measure, or a certain fraction of that current. In the voltmeter, the moving element is actuated by a current which is proportional to the potential difference we wish to measure. Since the current through the instrument is

$$I_V = \frac{V}{R},$$ (5.1)

where I_V is current through the instrument.

V is the potential difference to be measured.

R is the resistance of the instrument itself.

For accurate measurements in direct current circuits, meters of the D'Arsonval type are generally used. These depend upon the forces acting upon the sides of a movable coil carrying the current, and situated in the field of a permanent magnet. For alternating current measurements, the **iron-vane** type is most used. It depends upon the forces which act upon a light, movable piece of iron in the field of a fixed coil that carries the current. The **electrodynamometer** type is suitable for either direct current or alternating current measurements, and depends upon the forces that act between fixed and movable coils, both of which carry current.

In each of these types, the moving element is caused to rotate by a **torque,** or moment, resulting from the forces mentioned above. This is known as the **deflecting torque** and is always dependent upon current, but not always directly proportional to it. As the coil rotates, it tightens a spiral spring, or twists a suspension strip, thereby setting up a **restoring torque** that tends to restore the coil to its original position. When a current is passed through the meter, the movable element will rotate, carrying the pointer over the scale, until the restoring torque becomes equal to the deflecting torque for that particular current. This represents a condition of equilibrium, and the movable element and pointer will come to rest in a certain position and indicating a certain figure on the scale. It is evident that the position of rest depends as much upon the spring as upon the electrical element of the meter.

Any voltmeter or ammeter is a **secondary** instrument; it reads voltage or current correctly only because it has been **calibrated**— that is, its scale has been made by applying known voltages to its terminals or passing known currents through it, and marking on the scale the position taken by the pointer for each voltage or current. Calibrating of one meter can be done by comparing it with another similar meter already calibrated, but it should be evident that this procedure eventually leads back to an absolute determination in a standards laboratory.

2. The D'Arsonval principle. The element of a D'Arsonval type meter is shown in Fig. 5.2. The U-shaped permanent magnet is fitted with specially designed pole pieces, between which is mounted a cylindrical iron core. In the uniform air gap thus formed the magnetic field is radially directed, and the forces that act on the sides of the moving coil are always perpendicular to the radius of the coil. The coil is rectangular in form and may consist of from 20 or 30, up to several hundred, turns of small-diameter wire. It is fitted with steel pivots top and bottom, which work in jeweled bearings

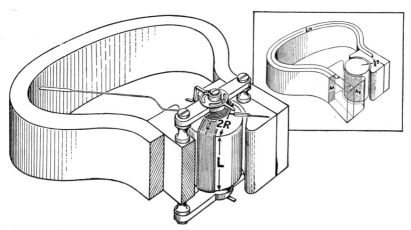

Fig. 5.2. Permanent-magnet moving-coil movement utilizing the D'Arsonval principle. (Courtesy Weston Electrical Instrument Corporation.)

mounted on supporting bridges which, in turn, are carried on the pole pieces. Spiral springs serve the double purpose of furnishing the restoring torque and making the connections to the coil.

The force on each coil side is given by

$$f = NBLI, \tag{5.2}$$

where f is the force in newtons.

N is the number of turns on the coil.

B is the flux density in webers per square meter (a constant which depends on the permanent magnet).

L is the length of the coil side in meters.

I is the current in amperes.

The deflecting torque for any coil position under the pole pieces is

$$T_d = 2Rf = 2NBLRI, \tag{5.3}$$

where T_d is the deflecting torque in newton-meters.

2R is the breadth of the coil in meters.

The restoring torque is

$$T_r = K\theta, \tag{5.4}$$

where T_r is the restoring torque in newton-meters.

     K is the spring constant in newton-meters per degree of turn.

     θ is the angle in degrees the coil has rotated from zero position.

For the moving system to be in equilibrium,

$$T_d = T_r, \tag{5.5}$$
$$2NBLRI = K\theta, \tag{5.6}$$

$$I = \frac{K\theta}{2NBLR}. \tag{5.7}$$

For any particular instrument, $K, N, B, L,$ and R are constants and may all be combined into a single constant K'. Doing this, we have

$$I = K'\theta. \tag{5.8}$$

Thus, we have shown the deflection to be proportional to the current, and, consequently, that the scale of the meter will be uniform.

The constant K' can be calculated as indicated above, or it can be determined experimentally by observing the deflection that occurs when a known current is sent through the coil.

EXAMPLE 1: A D'Arsonval instrument is designed to have a coil of 30 turns mounted in a magnetic field of 0.1 weber per sq m flux density. The coil is 3 cm long and 2 cm broad; the spring constant is to be 5×10^{-7} newton-meter per degree. The scale covers 60 degrees of arc, divided into 100 equal parts. What will be the current per degree? The current per scale division? The current required for full-scale deflection?

SOLUTION: The deflecting torque T_d by Equation (5.3) is

$$(30)(0.1)(3 \times 10^{-2})(2 \times 10^{-2})I \text{ newton-meters} = 18 \times 10^{-4}I.$$

The restoring torque T_r by Equation (5.4) is

$$5 \times 10^{-7}\theta \text{ newton-meter.}$$

For equilibrium at 1°,

$$18 \times 10^{-4}I = (5 \times 10^{-7})(1),$$
$$I = 2.78 \times 10^{-4} \text{ amp.}$$

For equilibrium at 1 scale division,

$$18 \times 10^{-4}I = (5 \times 10^{-7})^{60}\!\!/_{100},$$
$$I = 1.666 \times 10^{-4} \text{ amp.}$$

For equilibrium at full scale,

$$18 \times 10^{-4}I = (5 \times 10^{-7})60,$$
$$I = 1.666 \times 10^{-2}, \text{ or } 16.66 \text{ milliamperes (ma.)}$$

EXAMPLE 2: On test, the instrument described in Example 1 shows a deflection of 95 scale divisions for a current of 16.66 ma. What is the actual current for full-scale deflection? What could account for the difference between the calculated and the actual value?

SOLUTION: Current for full-scale deflection is

$$\frac{16.66}{95} \times 100 = 17.52 \text{ ma.}$$

The difference is due to the flux density of the permanent magnet or the constant of the spring differing somewhat from the design values.

Problems

(1-V) A D'Arsonval instrument has a 50-turn coil, 1.5 cm long by 1 cm broad, mounted in a magnetic field in which the flux density is 0.1 weber per sq m. The scale covers 65 degrees of arc divided into 50 equal parts. What should be the spring constant (newton-meters per degree) so that the current for full-scale deflection will be 10 ma?

(2-V) A D'Arsonval instrument has been designed to be deflected full scale by a current of 10 ma. What would be the effect on the current for full-scale deflection of: (a) Increasing the strength of the magnet by 10 per cent? (b) Increasing the number of turns on the coil by 10 per cent? (c) Increasing the strength of the spring by 10 per cent?

(3-V) What differences in design might be expected as between instrument A with a current of 1 ma for full-scale deflection, and instrument B with a current of 10 ma for full-scale deflection?

3. Ammeters. In a practical current-measuring instrument of the permanent-magnet moving-coil type, a **shunt** or by-pass, is nearly always provided, so that only a fraction of the current to be measured flows through the moving coil, the remainder taking the parallel path through the shunt. The resistance of the shunt must, of course, be properly adjusted, taking into account the current

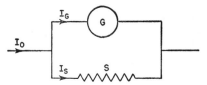

Fig. 5.3. A shunt in parallel with the moving element of an ammeter.

to be measured, the current required for full-scale deflection of the movable coil, and the resistance of the movable coil itself. In milliammeters and low-range ammeters, the shunts are usually built into the instrument itself. For the measurement of larger currents, however, external shunts are used and connected to the meter by special leads. If desired, the meter may be placed some distance from the shunt. In Fig. 5.3, G represents the meter element and S the shunt. The resistance of the meter element including the movable coil, springs, leads, and so forth, is designated R_G, and the resistance of the shunt is designated R_S. The current to be measured is I_0 and the currents through the meter element and the shunt are I_G and I_S, respectively. By Kirchhoff's laws,

$$I_0 = I_G + I_S. \tag{5.9}$$
$$I_G R_G = I_S R_S. \tag{5.10}$$

These equations enable us to make the necessary calculations of shunt resistance.

EXAMPLE: The resistance of a meter element of the permanent-magnet moving-coil type is 1.6 ohms, and it is deflected full scale by a current of 25 ma. What should be the resistance of a shunt to give this instrument a range of 0 to 200 ma?

SOLUTION: The shunt (when I_0 is 200 ma) must carry a current of

$$I_S = I_0 - I_G = 200 - 25 = 175 \text{ ma}$$
$$= 0.175 \text{ amp.}$$

The voltage drop across the shunt and meter in parallel must be

$$I_G R_G = 0.025 \times 1.6 = 0.04 \text{ v} = I_S R_S.$$

The resistance of the shunt must, therefore, be

$$R_S = \frac{0.04}{0.175} = 0.228 \text{ ohm.}$$

Problems

(4-V) The movable coil of a milliammeter has a resistance of 60 ohms and is deflected full scale by a current of 1 ma. Calculate the shunt resistance to make the range of the meter (a) 0 to 5 ma. (b) 0 to 10 ma. (c) 0 to 25 ma.

(5-V) The resistance of a meter element can be adjusted by putting additional resistance in series in order to make it work with a certain shunt. How much resistance should be connected in series with a milliammeter which requires 10 ma for full-scale deflection in order that it may be used with a 0.5-ohm shunt to measure currents over a range 0 to 500 ma? The resistance of the milliammeter is 7.5 ohms.

(6-V) The moving coil of an ammeter has a resistance of 2.14 ohms including leads. The current for full-scale deflection is 26.7 ma. What should be the shunt resistance if the range of the meter is to be 0 to 100 ma? 0 to 1 amp? 0 to 5 amp? 0 to 100 amp? 0 to 1000 amp?

(7-V) What should be the resistance of the moving coil of an ammeter which requires 30 ma for full-scale deflection so that it may be used with a shunt having a resistance of 0.0005 ohm for a range of 0 to 100 amp?

(8-V) A millivoltmeter may be used in conjunction with a number of different shunts for the measurement of current by designing all the shunts to have a voltage drop of, say, 50 mv across their terminals when they carry

their rated current, and the meter to give full-scale deflection when the drop
across its terminals is 50 mv.   On this basis, what should be the resistance of a
1-amp shunt?   A 10-amp shunt?   A 50-amp shunt?   A 500-amp shunt?
Neglect the current through the meter coil.

(**9-V**) The shunts in the three-range ammeters used in the college laboratories are arranged as is shown in Fig. 5.4.   The ranges are 0 to 1 amp, 0 to
2.5 amp, and 0 to 10 amp, as marked.   If the moving element is deflected
full scale when the potential difference across its terminals is 50 mv, what
should be the resistance of each part of the shunt?   Neglect the current
through the meter coil.

(**10-V**) Recalculate the shunt resistances in Problem 8-V, taking into
account the current through the meter coil.   Assume that the meter resistance (including leads) is 1 ohm.

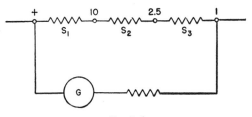

Fig. 5.4.

(**11-V**) Recalculate the shunt resistances in Problem 9-V, taking into
account the current through the meter coil.   Assume that the current for full-
scale deflection is 50 ma.

(**12-V**) An ammeter having a resistance of 1.11 ohms is used with an
external shunt to measure currents in the range 0 to 500 amp.   The shunt
resistance is 0.0001 ohm, and the leads which connect the shunt to the meter
have a resistance of 0.05 ohm.   Assuming the meter now reads correctly for a
current of 500 amperes through the shunt, what would be the effect of changing the lead resistance to 0.1 ohm?

(**13-V**) The emf of a No. 6 dry cell is 1.5 v, and its resistance is 0.05 ohm.
What current would flow if the cell were shorted by a copper strap of negligible
resistance?   What current would be read by a 0 to 30 ammeter having a
resistance of 0.0015 ohm inserted in the strap?

4. Voltmeters.   In a voltmeter, it is necessary to have in series
with the meter element enough resistance
so that when the greatest voltage to be
measured is applied to the meter terminals, exactly enough current to give full-
scale deflection will flow through the meter
element.   The necessary series resistance

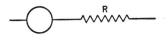

**Fig. 5.5.   Resistance in series
with the moving element of a
voltmeter.**

is usually mounted inside the meter case, but all or part of it may be
placed in a separate unit, known as a **multiplier**.   Additional series-
resistance units, or multipliers, are used when it is desired to measure
voltages beyond the nominal range of the instrument.

EXAMPLE: A meter element of the permanent-magnet, moving-coil type has a resistance of 5 ohms and requires 1 ma for full-scale deflection. What series resistance should be used to give the instrument a range of 0 to 15 v?

SOLUTION: To get a current of 1 ma through the meter with 15 v applied, the total resistance must be

$$R = \frac{V}{I} = \frac{15}{0.001} = 15000 \text{ ohms.}$$

We need, therefore, to add

$$15000 - 5 = 14995 \text{ ohms.}$$

Problems

(14-V) The three-range voltmeters used in the college laboratories are arranged as shown in Fig. 5.6. The ranges are 0 to 3 v, 0 to 15 v, and 0 to 50 v, as marked. If the current for full-scale deflection is 10 ma, what should be

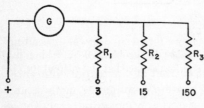

Fig. 5.6.

the resistance of R_1, R_2, and R_3? The resistance of the moving element is 5 ohms.

(15-V) It is desired to rebuild a 0 to 1.5-scale voltmeter to measure voltage from 0 to 75 mv. On going into the meter, it is found that the movement itself has a resistance of 2 ohms and that it is in series with a wire-wound resistance of 1480 ohms. How may the change be made?

(16-V) A 0 to 3 voltmeter has a resistance of 2910 ohms. Design a multiplier to be used with this meter so that its range is increased from 0 to 3 to 0 to 75. By what number will the readings then have to be multiplied?

(17-V) Two voltmeters, one having a resistance of 13,500 ohms and the other a resistance of 15,200 ohms, are connected in series across a 115-v line. Both are 0 to 150 range. Calculate the reading of each meter.

(18-V) A 0 to 15-scale voltmeter having a resistance of 1290 ohms is connected in series with a resistance of 10,000 ohms across the terminals of a d-c generator, and shows a reading of 12 v. What is the terminal voltage of the generator?

(19-V) Resistances of 10,000, 20,000, and 40,000 ohms are connected in series and a difference of potential of 150 v is applied. What is the voltage across each resistor? What voltage would be measured across each resistor if a 0 to 150-scale voltmeter having a resistance of 15,000 ohms were used?

5. Measurement of resistance by the voltmeter-ammeter method.

Since resistance is the ratio of potential difference to current, its measurement is readily accomplished by taking readings with voltmeter and ammeter and using Equation (3.6)

$$R = \frac{V}{I},$$

to calculate resistance. The accuracy which may be attained by this method depends, of course, on the accuracy with which the potential difference and current can be measured. Besides the inaccuracies that are inherent in the meters themselves, there is always an error in the measurement of the current or voltage owing to the presence of the other meter. The method gives fairly accurate results in the measurement of resistances that are neither extremely small nor extremely large—in the range, say, from 1 to 100 ohms. If measurement of resistances outside this range is attempted, or if better accuracy is wanted, corrections may be applied as explained in Section 7.

6. Measurement of Power. Power measurements in d-c circuits involve the use of a voltmeter and an ammeter to obtain potential difference between the terminals of the circuit and the current through it. Power is then found by Equation (3.2)

$$P = VI.$$

This method is subject to the same errors mentioned in the preceding section, which are discussed more fully below.

7. Simultaneous measurement of current and potential difference. Measurements of resistance by the voltmeter-ammeter method and measurements of power require the determination simultaneously of potential difference and current. The meters may be arranged either as in Fig. 5.7a or 5.7b. In neither case, however, will both the voltmeter and the ammeter give correct indications: the reading of one or the other is affected by the presence of the other meter.

If connected as in Fig. 5.7a, the voltmeter reads the potential difference across R, but the ammeter reads the sum of the current through R and the current through the voltmeter. If the resistance of the voltmeter is known, the current through it may be calculated by dividing its reading by its resistance. The true current through R is then found by subtracting the calculated current through the voltmeter from the reading of the ammeter. If the resistance of R is very small compared with the resistance of the voltmeter, the correction will, obviously, be very small and may ordinarily be neglected. If, however, the resistance of the voltmeter and the resistance of R are nearly equal, the correction will be approximately 50 per cent of the measured current. This connection is, therefore, best adapted to measurements of resistance or power when the resistance of R is small compared to the resistance of the voltmeter.

If connected as in Fig. 5.7b, the ammeter reads the current through R, but the voltmeter reads the potential difference across R and the ammeter in series. If the resistances of the ammeter and of the connection between the ammeter and R are known, the potential difference across them may be calculated by multiplying resistance by current. The true potential difference across R is then found by subtracting the potential difference calculated from the reading of the voltmeter. If the resistance of the ammeter and of the connecting wire is small compared to the resistance of R, the correction may be negligible. On the other hand, if the resistance of the connecting wire and ammeter were equal to the resistance of R, the correction would amount to approximately 50 per cent of the measured potential difference. This connection is to be recommended only

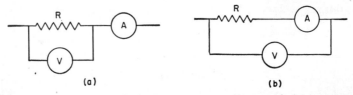

Fig. 5.7. Connections for simultaneous measurement of voltage and current.

if the resistance of R is large as compared to the resistance of the ammeter connection.

The above recommendations as to which connection is preferable apply only to approximate measurements. If corrections are to be made, the best connection to use depends upon which meter resistance is most accurately known. This will generally be the resistance of the voltmeter, making the connection as in Fig. 5.7a the best choice.

Problems

(**20-V**) A resistance of the order of 0.01 ohm is to be measured by the voltmeter-ammeter method. There are available a 0 to 25 ammeter having a resistance of 0.004 ohm including the connecting wire, and a 0 to 1 voltmeter having a resistance of 100 ohms. When connected as in Fig. 5.7a, the readings are $V = 0.39$ v, $I = 20$ amp. Find the approximate resistance, the current taken by the voltmeter, the true current through R, the corrected resistance, error in ohms, and percentage of error.

(**21-V**) The resistance described in Problem 20-V is remeasured, using the same instruments connected as in Fig. 5.7b. The readings are $V = 0.353$ v, $I = 15$ amp. Find the approximate resistance, potential difference across ammeter and connecting wire, true potential difference across R, corrected resistance, error in ohms, and percentage of error.

(**22-V**) A resistance of the order of 10,000 ohms is measured by the voltmeter-ammeter method, using a 0 to 150-scale voltmeter having a resistance of 15,000 ohms, and a 0 to 25-scale milliammeter having a resistance of 10 ohms.

With the meters connected as in Fig. 5.7a, the readings are $V = 60$ v, $I = 10.64$ ma.   Connected as in Fig. 5.7b, the readings are $V = 90$ v, $I = 9.99$ ma. For each set of readings, calculate approximate resistance, true resistance, error in ohms, and percentage of error.

(**23-V**) A 0 to 150-scale voltmeter having a resistance of 13,500 ohms and a 0 to 10-scale ammeter having a resistance of 0.0045 ohm are connected as in Fig. 5.7a to measure the power taken by a resistor.   The readings are $V = 145$ v, $I = 1.55$ amp.   What is the approximate power, power taken by voltmeter, true power, error in watts, and percentage of error?

(**24-V**) A 0 to 5-scale voltmeter having a resistance of 508 ohms and a 0 to 10-scale ammeter having a resistance of 0.05 ohm are connected as in Fig. 5.7b to determine the power taken by a resistor.   If the voltmeter reads 3.63 v and the ammeter reads 9.11 amp, find the approximate power, power taken by ammeter, true power, error in watts, and percentage of error.

8. Measurement of resistance by the voltmeter method—The ohmmeter.   A voltmeter of known resistance may be used in con-

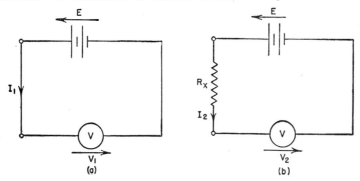

Fig. 5.8.   Voltmeter method of measuring resistance.

junction with a source of electromotive force to measure resistance. Suppose we first connect the voltmeter which has a resistance R_G to the terminals of a battery, as in Fig. 5.8a.   The voltmeter will draw a small current I_1 and will read the voltage drop across itself, which is

$$V_1 = I_1 R_G = E. \qquad (5.11)$$

Neglecting the small voltage drop in the internal resistance of the battery, the voltmeter reading is equal to the battery electromotive force.

Now, suppose we connect a resistance R_X in series with the voltmeter, as in Fig. 5.8b.   The current will decrease to some new value I_2 because of the increased circuit resistance, and the reading of the voltmeter will also decrease to some new value

$$V_2 = I_2 R_G. \qquad (5.12)$$

Now, assuming that the electromotive force of the battery is equal to

V_1 and that it remains constant, we can see that

$$I_2 = \frac{V_1}{R_G + R_x}. \tag{5.13}$$

Substituting (5.13) in (5.12), we have

$$V_2 = \frac{V_1 R_G}{R_G + R_x}, \tag{5.14}$$

and solving for R_x, we have

$$R_x = \frac{V_1 - V_2}{V_2} R_G. \tag{5.15}$$

By using Equation (5.14), we can calculate the values of V_2 that correspond to certain values of R_x, and so obtain the necessary data to mark off an ohm scale for the voltmeter. A voltmeter thus adapted to read ohms directly is known as an **ohmmeter.** An ohmmeter, as a rule, does not read resistance with the precision obtainable by the voltmeter-ammeter method or by the Wheatstone bridge. However, the ohmmeter is much easier to use, and resistances can be determined rapidly and with a fair degree of accuracy. This makes it the favorite instrument of the radio serviceman.

EXAMPLE 1: A voltmeter having a resistance of 15,000 ohms reads 120 v when connected to a certain battery. An unknown resistance is now connected in series with the voltmeter and battery and the reading drops to 112.5 v. What is the unknown resistance?

SOLUTION:

$$R_x = \frac{120 - 112.5}{112.5} \times 15000 = 1000 \text{ ohms}.$$

EXAMPLE 2: If it is desired to make an ohm scale for the voltmeter in the above example, where should the 1000-ohm mark be placed? Under what circumstances would the instrument give correct ohm readings?

SOLUTION: From Example 1, it is obvious that the 1000-ohm mark should coincide with the 112.5-v mark on the volt scale. The ohm readings would be correct only if the instrument were used with a 120-v battery, since the calculations were based on that value of V_1.

Problems

(25-V) A voltmeter having a resistance of 300 ohms reads 3 v across two dry cells that are connected in series. An unknown resistance is connected in series with the voltmeter and battery, and the reading becomes 1.65 v. What is the unknown resistance?

(**26-V**) Calculate an ohm scale for the voltmeter-and-battery combination described in Example 1. Try ohm values from zero to infinity. What are the practical limits between which resistances can be measured? What establishes these limits?

(**27-V**) Calculate an ohm scale for the voltmeter-and-battery combination described in Problem 25-V. Try ohm values from zero to infinity. What are the practical limits between which resistances can be measured? What establishes these limits?

9. The D'Arsonval galvanometer. The sensitivity of the permanent-magnet, moving-coil type of meter can be greatly increased by increasing the number of turns in the coil and suspending the coil between the poles of the permanent magnet rather than mounting it in bearings. Such an instrument, known as a **galvanometer,** usually

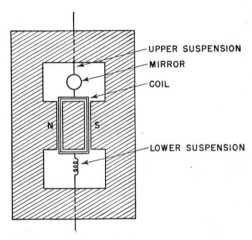

Fig. 5.9.   Wall-type D'Arsonval galvanometer.

has a scale marked off in arbitrary divisions rather than in amperes or volts. Galvanometers are used not only for measuring small currents and voltages, but also as indicators to show when the current in a certain part of a network has been adjusted to zero, as in bridge and potentiometer networks. For this use, the instrument need not be calibrated. When it is to be used for measurements of current or voltage, the usual procedure is to determine its constant (in amperes or volts per scale division) experimentally, as described in Section 2. Readings are then taken in scale divisions, and the required current or voltage is found by multiplying the reading by the constant.

Galvanometers are made in portable form, and also for wall or pedestal mounting. The latter can be made extremely sensitive, but are also extremely delicate, requiring great care in leveling, protection from vibration, and so forth.   The suspension strip, which supports the coil in the wall-type instrument, and which also serves as a connection, is commonly of gold or bronze, two or three thousandths of an inch thick and five inches long.   This strip is twisted as the coil rotates and furnishes the restoring torque.   The other connection to the coil is made through the spiral strip attached to its lower end.

In place of a pointer, a mirror is mounted upon the coil, and reflects a scale mounted some distance in front of the galvanometer. The observer looks at the mirror through a telescope mounted just below the scale and reads the scale division which coincides with a hairline in the eyepiece of the telescope.   Thus, in effect, a beam of light serves as the pointer, which can be quite long and at the same time, weightless.

In portable galvanometers, the suspension strip is much shorter and is held in tension by a flat spring, making the instrument as rugged as the ordinary voltmeter or ammeter.   The light-beam pointer of the wall-type instrument is here replaced by a short metal pointer attached to the coil.

Problems

(28-V) To determine the constant of a wall-type galvanometer having a resistance of 200 ohms, it is connected to a dry cell (emf = 1.5 v) through a series resistance of 0.8 megohm.   A deflection of 180 scale divisions is obtained. What is the constant in microamperes per scale division?

(29-V) The galvanometer of Problem 28-V is connected in series with an unknown resistance to the terminals of a 100-v battery.   A deflection of 14.5 scale divisions is obtained.   What is the unknown resistance?

(30-V) A wall-type galvanometer having a resistance of 1750 ohms is shunted by a resistance of 1000 ohms.   This parallel circuit is then connected in series with a 2-megohm resistance to the terminals of a 1.5-v dry cell, and a deflection of 22 scale divisions is obtained.   What is the constant of the galvanometer and shunt combination?   What would be the constant of the galvanometer used without the shunt?

10. Use of polarity marks.   The direction in which energy flows in a circuit can be determined by reference to the polarity markings on the voltmeter and ammeter.

The actual direction of current in a conductor can be told by using an ammeter having polarity marks on its terminals.   For the meter to read up-scale, current must flow in at its positive (+) terminal and out at its negative (−) terminal.

Likewise, the actual direction of a potential difference can be told by using a voltmeter with polarity markings.   For the meter to read up-scale, its positive terminal must be at a higher potential than its negative terminal.   In other words, if the meter reads up-scale, there is a positive voltage drop from the point to which its positive terminal is connected to the point to which its negative terminal is connected.

By using both an ammeter and a voltmeter having polarity markings, it is possible to determine the direction of power (that is, the direction in which energy flows) in a circuit.   This is important in testing electrical machinery, since a machine may sometimes operate as either motor or generator, and it is impossible to tell from external appearances which it is.   The rule may be stated as follows: *If the meters show there is a voltage drop across a circuit or any part of a circuit in the same direction as the current, then electrical energy is being absorbed.   If the meters show there is a voltage drop in the opposite direction to current, then electrical energy is being generated.*

EXAMPLE: In Fig. 5.10, the ammeter and voltmeter, connected as shown, both read up-scale.   Is the apparatus absorbing or delivering electrical energy?

SOLUTION: Since the ammeter is reading up-scale, current is flowing in at its positive terminal—that is, in the direction of the arrow. Since the voltmeter is reading up-scale, there is a voltage drop from its positive to its negative terminal —that is, in the direction of the arrow.   Since the voltage drop across the apparatus is the same as the direction of current through it, it is absorbing energy.

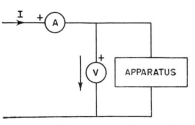

Fig. 5.10.   Determination of energy flow by use of polarity marks.

Problem

(31-V) In each of the diagrams in Fig. 5.11, the ammeter and voltmeter both read up-scale as connected.   For each diagram, state in which direction current flows, which is direction of voltage drop, and whether the apparatus absorbs or delivers electrical energy.

11. Soft-iron ammeters and voltmeters.   The forces that act upon small vanes of soft iron in a magnetic field may be directed so as to furnish the deflecting torque for current-and-voltage-measuring instruments.   These are known as **soft-iron** or **iron-vane** instruments. In the Weston design, there are two such vanes, one fixed, the other attached to the shaft of the meter.   Both vanes are bent into arcs, and the fixed vane is given a peculiar tongue shape, but the movable vane is rectangular, as shown in Fig. 5.12.

In the magnetic field of the coil, the vanes are similarly magnetized and repel each other, one component of the force being in such direction (owing to the shape of the fixed vane) as to tend to rotate the shaft. In the Thomson design, the vanes are mounted

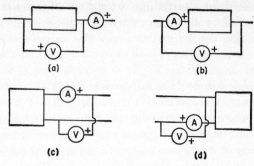

Fig. 5.11.

obliquely on the shaft, as in Fig. 5.13, and tend to move in such manner as to make the long axis of the vane line up with the magnetic field. To better carry out this design, the coil is mounted with its axis inclined from the vertical, for which reason this instrument is often referred to as the *inclined-coil type*.

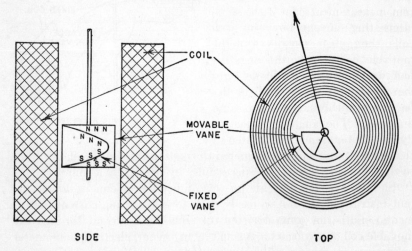

Fig. 5.12.   Iron vane movement—Weston design.

The fixed coil, which produces the magnetic field, is circular in form, and for a voltmeter consists of many turns of small-diameter wire, with additional resistance, as necessary, in series with it. For an ammeter, the coil consists of a relatively small number of turns of larger-diameter wire. No shunt is necessary, and current ranges up to 100 amp or more are available. This construction gives a very rugged and trouble-free instrument, which, however, is less sensitive and accurate than the permanent-magnet, moving-coil type. It is particularly suited for alternating current measurements. When the magnetic field of the coil reverses during the negative half cycle of the current or voltage, the magnetization of the vanes also reverses, and the deflecting torque is always such as to tend to rotate the shaft in the same direction.

The deflecting torque in a soft-iron meter does not vary directly with the current. Consequently, the scale will not be uniform, but will be so compressed near its lower end as to make reading difficult for the first 20 to 30 per cent of its current or voltage range. For this reason, the range of a soft-iron meter should always be selected so that the desired readings can be taken well up the scale.

12. Electrodynamometer instruments. Movable-coil instruments in which the magnetic field is produced by a fixed coil instead of a permanent magnet are called **electrodynamometer** instruments. Such instruments are obviously suited to both direct current and alternating current measurements, for if the same alternating current flows in both coils, then when it reverses in the movable coil during the negative half cycle, the magnetic field reverses simultaneously, and the deflecting torque remains in the same direction. The range of the electrodynamometer ammeter is limited to

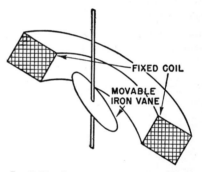

Fig. 5.13. Iron vane movement—Thomson design.

FIXED COIL

MOVABLE IRON VANE

that current that can be conducted through the movable coil, or rather to that current that can be successfully by-passed by a shunt.

Shunting, which presents no very difficult problems in direct current instruments, is not so easily done for alternating current instruments, and is not often resorted to. Since the current through the movable coil of a voltmeter is small in any event, electrodynamometer voltmeters are more readily constructed.

One important use of electrodynamometer ammeters and voltmeters is to serve as transfer standards from direct current to alternating current measurements. An electrodynamometer instrument can be calibrated by comparison with direct current standards and thus, itself, become a standard for calibrating alternating current instruments.   Although iron-vane type instruments could conceivably be used as transfer standards, the accuracy would be decidedly lower.

The most familiar electrodynamometer instrument is the **wattmeter.**   In direct current circuits, power is usually found by taking the product of current and potential difference.   In alternating current circuits, however, this method can be used only in special cases, and in general, power must be measured by the use of a wattmeter.   To adapt an electrodynamometer instrument for use as a wattmeter, the fixed coil is made with a few turns of large-diameter wire and is connected into the circuit as an ammeter would be.   The magnetic field which it produces is, therefore, proportional to the current in the circuit.   The movable coil, in series with a suitable resistance, is con-

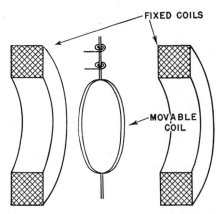

Fig. 5.14.   Electrodynamometer movement.

nected across the circuit, or across the terminals of the piece of apparatus in which the power is to be measured.   The current in the movable coil is, therefore, proportional to potential difference, and the deflecting torque is proportional to the product of current and potential difference—that is, to power.

The connections for using a wattmeter are shown in Fig. 5.15. It is evident that the remarks in Section 7, concerning the simultaneous measurement of current and potential difference, apply here.   In Fig. 5.15a, the fixed coil or **current coil,** carries a current in excess of that in the load by an amount equal to the potential-coil current, and the power read is, therefore, in excess of the power taken by the load by an amount equal to the I^2R loss in the potential coil. In Fig. 5.15b, the potential difference impressed on the movable-coil or **potential-coil** circuit is in excess of the potential difference at the load by an amount equal to the drop in the current coil.   The power read is, therefore, in excess of the power taken by the load by an amount equal to the I^2R loss in the current coil.   The possibility of the wattmeter reading the power taken by voltmeters and ammeters must also be taken into account.

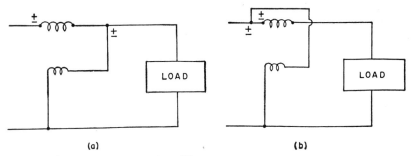

(a)   (b)

Fig. 5.15.   Wattmeter connections.

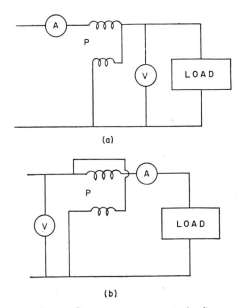

(a)

(b)

Fig. 5.16.   Connections for simultaneous measurement of voltage, current, and power.

The polarity marks on wattmeter terminals may be considered to be equivalent to those on a voltmeter and ammeter used to measure power, and the direction of energy flow may be determined in the same way.

EXAMPLE: A wattmeter, voltmeter, and ammeter are connected as in Fig. 5.16a to determine the power, voltage, and current taken by the load. The meter readings are as follows: $P = 95.2$ w, $V = 117$ v, $I = 0.812$ amp. The resistance of the wattmeter potential circuit is 4500 ohms; of the wattmeter current coil, 0.04 ohm; of the voltmeter, 7500 ohms; of the ammeter, 0.05 ohm. Find the true power, voltage, and current of the load.

SOLUTION: The voltage at the load is that read by the voltmeter, which is 117.

The current at the load is less than that read by the ammeter owing to the presence of the voltmeter and wattmeter potential coil.

$$I_L = I_A - I_P - I_V.$$
$$I_P = {}^{117}\!/_{4500} = 0.026 \text{ amp.}$$
$$I_V = {}^{117}\!/_{7500} = 0.0156 \text{ amp.}$$
$$I_L = 0.812 - 0.026 - 0.0156 = 0.771 \text{ amp.}$$

The power at the load is less than that read by the wattmeter by an amount equal to the power loss in the voltmeter and in the wattmeter potential coil.

$$P_L = 95.2 - (0.026)^2 \times 4500 - (0.0156)^2 \times 7500$$
$$= 90.3 \text{ w.}$$

Problem

(32-V) The instruments in the foregoing example are reconnected as in Fig. 5.16b. The meter readings are now $P = 90.3$ w, $V = 117$ v, $I = 0.77$ amp. Find the true power, voltage, and current of the load. If no corrections were to be made, which connection would be preferable?

13. The Wheatstone bridge. Measurement of resistance is often carried out by means of an arrangement known as a **Wheatstone**

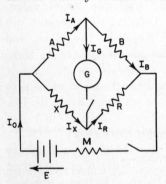

Fig. 5.17. Wheatstone bridge.

bridge. Four resistances, a battery, and a galvanometer are connected as in Fig. 5.17. Three of the resistances, A, B, and R, are known, the fourth is the unknown resistance X. At least one of the known resistances must be adjustable. In practice, A and B, which are called **ratio arms**, are usually adjustable to either 1, 10, 100, or 1000 ohms, and R, which is called the **rheostat arm**, is adjustable from 0.1 to 9999.9 ohms in 0.1-ohm steps. It is seen that the bridge constitutes a three-mesh network, and any problem concerning it depends upon the solution of Kirchhoff's law equations as follows:

$$I_A = I_B + I_G, \tag{5.16}$$
$$I_X + I_G = I_R, \tag{5.17}$$
$$I_0 = I_A + I_X, \tag{5.18}$$
$$E = I_0 M + I_R R + I_X X, \tag{5.19}$$
$$0 = I_A A + I_G G - I_X X, \tag{5.20}$$
$$0 = I_B B - I_R R - I_G G, \tag{5.21}$$

where M and G are the resistances of the battery branch and the galvanometer branch, respectively.

To use the bridge, the ratio arms and rheostat arm are adjusted so that the galvanometer shows no deflection, indicating that the current I_G is zero. The above equations may then be modified as follows:

$$I_A = I_B. \tag{5.22}$$
$$I_R = I_X. \tag{5.23}$$
$$I_0 = I_A + I_R. \tag{5.24}$$
$$E = I_0 M + I_R R + I_X X. \tag{5.25}$$
$$I_A A = I_X X. \tag{5.26}$$
$$I_B B = I_R R. \tag{5.27}$$

Substituting I_A for I_B and I_X for I_R in **(5.27)**,

$$I_A B = I_X R. \tag{5.28}$$

Dividing (5.26) by (5.28),

$$\frac{A}{B} = \frac{X}{R},$$

or

$$X = \frac{A}{B} R. \tag{5.29}$$

It is essential in using a Wheatstone bridge to choose suitable values for the ratio-arm resistances A and B. Usually, the operator will have some idea of the magnitude of the unknown resistance, and he should choose A and B so that X can be determined to three significant figures.

EXAMPLE: A resistance believed to be between 1 and 10 ohms is to be measured. Assuming that A or B can be set at either 1, 10, 100, or 1000, and that R can be set at any value from 1 to 10,000 in 1-ohm steps, what values of A and B will be the most satisfactory?

SOLUTION: Suppose we consider first $A = 1$, $B = 1$. Then, to balance the bridge, R must be set equal to X. Since R can be varied only in 1-ohm steps, it will be impossible to balance the bridge unless X happens to be an integral number of ohms. X can be determined only to one significant figure, which is not satisfactory.

Now, suppose we make $A = 1$, $B = 100$. To balance the bridge,

R must now be set at $100X$. It may still be impossible to balance the bridge exactly, but our nearest value of R will be, say, 973, and we can determine X to three significant figures, which usually is sufficient. Ratios of $A = 10$, $B = 1000$, or $A = 1$, $B = 1000$ would also be satisfactory.

In case the operator has no idea at all of the magnitude of X, the best procedure is to choose some ratio at random, say, $A = 10$, $B = 10$, and then in succession to try the minimum and the maximum values of R. If both these settings of R deflect the galvanometer in the same direction, then there is no setting of R that will balance the bridge, and some other ratio must be tried. When a ratio has been found which permits the galvanometer current to be reversed by going from a minimum to a maximum setting of R, the next step is to vary R by 1000-ohm steps, leaving it finally on the 1000-ohm step just below the one which reverses the galvanometer current. This procedure is then repeated, using 100-ohm steps, and so forth, until balance is obtained.

It is seen that the Wheatstone bridge measures a resistance in terms of other resistances, and the accuracy of the method is, therefore, limited by the accuracy of the resistances A, B, and R, and by the sensitivity of the galvanometer. Problems concerning accuracy usually call for a general solution of the bridge equations.

Problems

(33-V) A Wheatstone bridge connected as in Fig. 5.17 is balanced when $A = 10$ ohms, $B = 1000$ ohms, and $R = 7932$ ohms. What is the value of X?

(34-V) (a) If A had been set at 1 ohm and the maximum setting of R is 9999 ohms, could the bridge in Problem 33-V have been balanced? Why? (b) Would $A = 1000$, $B = 1000$ have served as well as the ratio that was used in Problem 33-V? How precisely could X have been measured?

(35-V) What is the theoretical range of resistances that may be measured with a bridge that permits A or B to be set at either 1, 10, 100, or 1000 ohms, and R at any value from 1 to 9999? Would the practical range be the same? Why?

(36-V) What would be the best choice of ratio for measuring resistances known to lie between 1 and 10 ohms? 10 and 100 ohms? 100 and 1000 ohms? 1000 and 10,000 ohms? 10,000 and 100,000 ohms?

14. The Kelvin bridge. Resistances below 1 ohm cannot be measured with sufficient accuracy by the Wheatstone bridge because the resistance of the leads used to connect them into the bridge network introduces considerable error. The Kelvin bridge obviates this difficulty and makes possible the accurate measurement of resistances as low as 0.0001 ohm.

The resistance to be measured, X, is connected into a series circuit shown by the heavy line in Fig. 5.18, containing also an adjustable standard of low resistance R, a battery, and a rheostat. The current in this circuit is much higher than that in any part of a Wheatstone bridge network, and may amount to several amperes. The network is completed by the ratio resistances A, B, C, and D and the galvanometer. The part of the standard of low resistance to the left of the slider is designated as R, the remainder as R'. In use, the ratio resistances and the standard of low resistance are adjusted to make

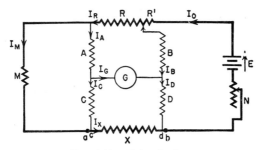

Fig. 5.18.   Kelvin bridge.

the galvanometer current zero, always keeping $A = B$ and $C = D$. The connections from C and D are joined to the resistance to be measured at points c and d, which are inside the terminals a and b, at which the resistance is connected into the main circuit. Thus, the resistance measured does not include the lead resistance nor the contact resistance at a and b. The effect of contact resistance at points c and d is negligible because the ratio resistances, with which it is in series, are of the order of several hundred ohms. The equations for the general solution of the network are as follows:

$$I_0 = I_R + I_B. \tag{5.30}$$
$$I_B + I_G = I_D. \tag{5.31}$$
$$I_D + I_X = I_0. \tag{5.32}$$
$$I_R = I_A + I_M. \tag{5.33}$$
$$I_A = I_G + I_C. \tag{5.34}$$
$$E = I_0R' + I_0N + I_BB + I_DD. \tag{5.35}$$
$$0 = I_RR + I_AA + I_GG - I_BB. \tag{5.36}$$
$$0 = I_GG + I_DD - I_XX - I_CC. \tag{5.37}$$
$$0 = I_AA + I_CC - I_MM. \tag{5.38}$$

For the special case of the bridge balanced ($I_G = 0$), Equations (5.31), (5.34), (5.36) and (5.37) are modified as follows:

$$I_B = I_D. \tag{5.39}$$
$$I_A = I_C. \tag{5.40}$$
$$0 = I_R R + I_A A - I_B B. \tag{5.41}$$
$$0 = I_D D - I_X X - I_C C. \tag{5.42}$$

Adding Equations (5.30) and (5.32) gives

$$I_D + I_X = I_R + I_B, \tag{5.43}$$

and since $I_B = I_D$ (5.39), we have

$$I_X = I_R. \tag{5.44}$$

Substituting A for B in Equation 5.41 and transposing,

$$I_R R = (I_B - I_A)A. \tag{5.45}$$

Substituting I_R for I_X, I_A for I_C, I_B for I_D, and C for D in Equation (5.42) and transposing,

$$I_R X = (I_B - I_A)C. \tag{5.46}$$

Dividing (5.45) by (5.46), we obtain

$$\frac{R}{X} = \frac{A}{C},$$

or
$$X = R\frac{C}{A}. \tag{5.47}$$

Problems

(**37-V**) A Kelvin bridge is balanced when $A = B = 100$ ohms, $C = D = 1000$ ohms, and $R = 0.00852$ ohm. What is the value of X?

(**38-V**) What is the theoretical range of a Kelvin bridge with provisions for making A, B, C, or D either 100, 550, or 1000 ohms, and R any value from 0.0001 to 0.01 ohm?

15. The potentiometer. A potential difference may be measured by comparing it with a known potential difference by use of a device known as a **potentiometer.** A simple form of the potentiometer, shown in Fig. 5.19, consists of a long, uniform resistance wire W along which a sliding contact may be moved. A steady current I_W is sent through the wire by the auxiliary battery B, the current being adjustable by means of the rheostat R. A double-pole, double-throw (dpdt) switch makes it possible to connect either the known potential difference, E_S, or the potential difference to be measured, V_X. A galvanometer G serves as an indicator to show when a balance is attained. In practice, the known potential difference is usually the electromotive force of a Weston standard cell, described in Chapter XIII. To use the potentiometer, the current I_W is adjusted to any convenient value by means of the rheostat R, and the dpdt switch is thrown to the standard cell. The slider is then adjusted until the current $I_G = 0$ (indicated by no deflection of the galvanometer), and the distance L_S from the point p to the slider is noted. Around the

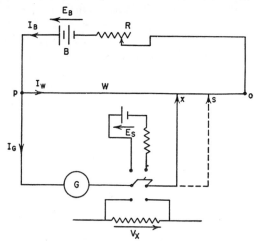

Fig. 5.19. Potentiometer.

mesh containing the standard cell, we may then apply Kirchhoff's voltage law to obtain

$$E_S = I_W K_W L_S, \tag{5.48}$$

where E_S is the emf of the standard cell in volts.

I_W is the current in the slide wire in amperes.

K_W is the resistance per unit length of slide wire.

L_S is the distance from point p to the slider.

The dpdt switch is now thrown to the unknown potential difference, and the slider again is adjusted until $I_G = 0$. Then, by Kirchhoff's voltage law

$$0 = I_W K_W L_X - V_X, \tag{5.49}$$

where L_X is the new distance from point p to the slider.

V_X is the unknown potential difference in volts.

Dividing (5.48) by (5.49), we get

$$\frac{E_S}{V_X} = \frac{L_S}{L_X},$$

or

$$V_X = E_S \frac{L_X}{L_S}. \tag{5.50}$$

It should be noted that no current flows in the potentiometer network from the circuit under test when balance is obtained. This eliminates one error that is always present if a voltmeter is used, and enables one, for example, to measure the true emf of a cell. The circuit is not modified by the introduction of the potentiometer, as it would be by the introduction of a voltmeter.

It may be that the random setting of the current I_B will not permit I_G to be made zero by moving the sliding contact. In this case, I_B must be increased until the potential difference between p and o is at least as great as the potential difference to be measured. The particular value of I_B is of no interest, nor is it necessary to know K_W. It is essential, however, that I_B remain constant during both settings of the slider and that the wire be perfectly uniform in resistance per unit length.

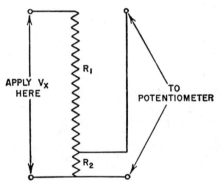

Fig. 5.20. Voltbox.

The potentiometer wire may be marked off in volts instead of units of length, thus making the scale direct-reading. If this is done, it is obvious that the marking will be correct for only one particular value of I_W, and the procedure as given above must be modified. The sliding contact is first set at the scale reading that corresponds to the emf of the standard cell, and the rheostat is adjusted until the current $I_G = 0$. The potentiometer is then said to be standardized, and is direct-reading so long as the current I_W does not change. In using a standard cell, the operator must take precautions to insure that the current through it never exceeds 0.0001 amp; otherwise, the cell will be ruined as a standard. This makes it necessary to insert a large resistance, say, 10,000 ohms, in series with the cell and to keep it there until an approximate balance is obtained. The resistance may then be cut out, and the balance perfected.

The range of the potentiometer is limited to potential differences of the order of 1 to 3 v. It may be increased, however, by using an accessory known as a **volt box.** A volt box is simply a series arrangement, as shown in Fig. 5.20, of two accurately known resistances. The voltage to be measured is applied to both resistances in series, and since the potentiometer, when balanced, draws no current, the current will be the same in R_1 and R_2. Therefore, the voltage drops will be proportional to the resistances, and the voltage applied to the potentiometer will be

$$\frac{R_2}{R_1 + R_2} V_x. \tag{5.51}$$

A potentiometer may be used in conjunction with a standard resistance to measure current. The current to be measured is sent through the standard resistance, and the potential difference between its terminals is then measured by means of the potentiometer.

Problems

(39-V) A potentiometer wire is 1 m long and has a resistance of 20 ohms. If the auxiliary battery has an emf of 6 v and the rheostat is adjusted to 40 ohms, what is the current in the wire? What range of voltages may be balanced against the drop in the wire? How would you design a scale to make the wire read directly in volts? At what distance from the zero end would balance be obtained for a standard cell having an emf of 1.0183 v?

(40-V) What should be the resistance of a potentiometer wire to give a drop of 2 v at a current of 1.5 ma? What rheostat resistance would be needed if the battery consisted of 2 dry cells in series? Does the accuracy of the instrument depend upon knowing the rheostat resistance and the emf of the battery accurately?

(41-V) A volt box has a total resistance of 100,000 ohms and is tapped at 2000 ohms. By what factor should the potentiometer readings be multiplied?

(42-V) Could the volt box described in Problem 41-V be used in conjunction with a 0 to 3-scale voltmeter having a resistance of 300 ohms? What would be the multiplying factor if this were done?

Additional Problems

(43-V) A D'Arsonval type voltmeter has a range 0 to 300 v and a resistance of 60,000 ohms, 5 ohms of which is the resistance of the coil itself. It is desired to convert this instrument into an ammeter of range 0 to 50. Explain what must be done, show diagrams of connections before and after the change, and make all necessary calculations.

(44-V) A D'Arsonval type ammeter has a range 0 to 10 amp, and a resistance of 0.0025 ohm. The resistance of the coil itself is 2 ohms. It is desired to convert this instrument into a voltmeter of range 0 to 60 v. Explain what must be done, show diagrams of connections before and after the change, and make all necessary calculations.

(45-V) A voltmeter has a 0 to 75 range and a resistance of 6000 ohms. What should be the resistance of a series multiplier to extend the range to 0 to 300? By what factor would the readings be multiplied?

(**46-V**) A D'Arsonval ammeter has a 0 to 5 range and a resistance of 0.0125 ohm. What should be the resistance of a shunt to extend the range to 0 to 25? By what factor would the readings be multiplied?

(**47-V**) Show that, when a millivoltmeter is used with a shunt as an ammeter as explained in Problem 8-V,

$$I = R\frac{A}{S},\tag{5.52}$$

where I is the current in amperes.

    R is reading in scale divisions.

    A is the ampere rating of the shunt.

    S is the number of scale divisions on the meter.

(**48-V**) Prove that for a galvanometer of resistance G, paralleled by a shunt of resistance S as in Fig. 5.3,

$$I_G = I_0\frac{S}{S + G}.\tag{5.53}$$

(**49-V**) In order to find the resistance G of a galvanometer, it is connected in series with a resistance r and a battery having an emf of E volts, so as to obtain a deflection of d scale divisions. The resistance is then changed to a value R such that the deflection is reduced to $\frac{1}{2}d$. Show that

$$G = R - 2r.\tag{5.54}$$

(**50-V**) In order to find the resistance G of a galvanometer, it is connected in series with a large resistance R to a battery of emf E and the deflection d observed. It is then shunted by a resistance S of such value that the deflection is reduced to $d/2$. Show that, if $R >> G$, then

$$G = S.\tag{5.55}$$

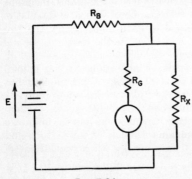

Fig. 5.21.

(**51-V**) Ohmmeters are sometimes designed to have the unknown resistance act as a shunt, as in Fig. 5.21. When R_X is zero, the voltmeter is shortcircuited and reads zero. As R_X is increased, the reading of the voltmeter increases, reaching a maximum when R_X is infinity. Assuming $E = 4.5$ v, $R_B = 150$ ohms, and the voltmeter is 0 to 3 range with resistance $R_G = 300$ ohms, calculate the ohm scale for the meter.

(**52-V**) In a certain Wheatstone bridge, A is 100 ohms, B is 1000 ohms, and R is 400 ohms for balance. The resistances in each arm of the bridge are guaranteed by the manufacturer to be accurate to within 0.2 of 1 per cent. Between what limits is X certain to be? Within what percentage is X certainly determined?

(**53-V**) It is often impossible to say exactly what setting of R balances the bridge. Owing to lack of sensitivity, the galvanometer may show no deflection when R is varied appreciably. Assume that in Problem 52-V, the setting of R to give a barely perceptible plus deflection is 399 ohms and the setting to give a barely perceptible minus deflection is 401 ohms. Between what limits is X certain to be? Within what percentage is X certainly determined?

(**54-V**) Derive the equation of the Wheatstone bridge shown in Fig. 5.17 if the battery and galvanometer are interchanged.

(**55-V**) In a certain Wheatstone bridge arrangement, as in Fig. 5.17, $A = 10$ ohms, $B = 1000$ ohms, $R = 2000$ ohms, $X = 20.2$ ohms, $G = 250$ ohms, M is negligible, and the battery emf is 3 v. Calculate the galvanometer current.

(**56-V**) By what percentage is the bridge in Problem 55-V unbalanced? How sensitive must the galvanometer be to detect this amount of unbalance? Assume that the operator can detect a movement of the galvanometer pointer of 0.1 scale division

(**57-V**) Show that, for the Kelvin bridge as shown in Fig. 5.18, if $A \neq B$ and $C \neq D$, the equation of the bridge becomes

$$X = \frac{RD}{B} + \frac{M(DA - BC)}{(A + C + M)B}$$

(**58-V**) A Kelvin bridge as shown in Fig. 5.18 is balanced for $A = 100$, $B = 100$, $C = 200$, $D = 200$, $M = 0.1$ and $R = 0.005$. (a) What is the value of X? (b) If B is actually 101 ohms instead of 100 as marked, what is the value of X? By what per cent would the value calculated in (a) be in error? Use the expression developed in Problem 57-V.

(**59-V**) An instructor gives a student a resistance to measure by the volt-meter-ammeter method. The instructor knows the resistance to be exactly 0.01 ohm. The voltmeter to be used has a resistance of 2.25 ohms, including leads, and a range of 0–100 millivolts. The ammeter has a resistance of 0.0075 ohm, including one lead, and a range of 0–10 amp. Show the two possible connections the student may use, and calculate the resistance he will find in each case if he makes no corrections.

(**60-V**) A volt box used in connection with a potentiometer has a total resistance of 100,000 ohms and is tapped at 2000 ohms. With the volt box connected to the potentiometer in the normal way, an unknown voltage V_X is measured and a reading of 1.055 v is obtained on the potentiometer. Calculate V_X. (b) Suppose an error had been made in connecting and the unknown voltage had been applied to the potentiometer terminals of the voltbox and the V_X terminals to the potentiometer. Calculate V_X for a potentiometer reading of 1.055 v.

(**61-V**) For calibrating a wattmeter, connections are made as in Fig. 5.22, and it is proposed to compare the readings P_X of the wattmeter under test with the readings P_S of the standard wattmeter. The voltmeter and ammeter are added for convenience but are known to read correctly. The wattmeter potential coils each have a resistance of 2750 ohms, the current coils 0.035 ohm. The voltmeter resistance is 3100 ohms and the ammeter 0.02 ohm. If the voltmeter reads 119 v and the ammeter 9.0 amp, and assuming there are no errors in the meters themselves, calculate: (a) reading P_S of standard watt-meter, (b) reading P_X of the wattmeter under test, (c) power taken by the load. Is this a satisfactory connection for calibrating a wattmeter? Can you suggest a better connection?

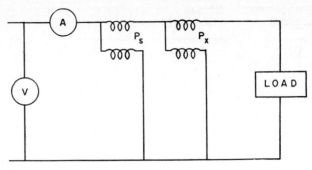

Fig. 5.22.

(**62-V**) To improve the accuracy of a wattmeter it may be provided with a compensating coil (cc) having a number of turns equal to the number of turns in the current-coil and wound on the same form as the current-coil, but connected in series with the potential coil as shown in Fig. 5.23. The magnetic field set up by the current coil, which would otherwise be too strong because of the coil carrying the potential-coil current in addition to the load current, is opposed by the magnetic field of the compensating coil which carries the potential coil current only. Thus the current coil and compensating coil together produce a magnetic field of just the correct strength. Suppose a certain wattmeter has resistances as follows: potential coil 2500

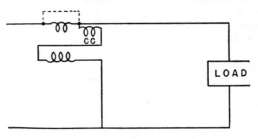

Fig. 5.23.

ohms, current coil 0.05 ohm, and compensating coil 0.5 ohm. If the current and potential difference at the load are 5 amp and 100 v, respectively, what will the wattmeter read (a) without the compensating coil, (b) with the compensating coil, (c) with the compensating coil, but with the connection to the potential circuit on the line side of the current coil, as indicated by the dotted line?

(**63-V**) A compensated wattmeter (see Problem 62-V) is used to measure the power taken by a device. Four connections are made as shown in Fig. 5.24a, b, c, and d. In the connections shown in Fig. 5.24b and c, the compensating feature is not used. Connected as in Fig. 5.24a, the wattmeter reads 175 w. Connected as in Fig. 5.24b, it reads 179 w. Connected as in Fig. 5.24c, it reads 186 w. Find (a) power taken by the device, (b) loss in the potential coil of the wattmeter, (c) loss in the current coil of the wattmeter, (d) reading of the wattmeter connected as in Fig. 5.24d.

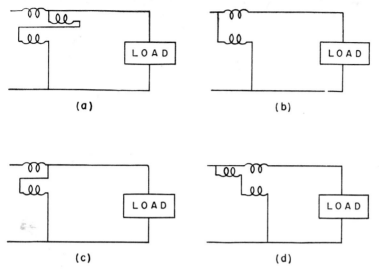

(a)

(b)

(c)

(d)

Fig. 5.24.

Study Questions

1. What would happen if an alternating current measurement was attempted with a D'Arsonval instrument? What would happen if a direct current measurement was attempted with an iron-vane instrument? Assume the range of the instrument to be correct in each case.

2. In order to prevent the pointer from oscillating too long about the equilibrium position, most indicating meters are fitted with some sort of damping device. One commonly used on iron-vane meters is an air vane attached to the shaft and moving in a nearly air-tight enclosure. Would this affect the equilibrium position? Why?

3. What is the relative magnitude of the deflecting torque and the restoring torque of a D'Arsonval meter (a) at the instant the meter is connected, (b) when a reading is being taken, (c) at the instant the meter is disconnected, (d) when the meter is on the shelf?

4. Is the cylindrical iron core in a D'Arsonval meter stationary or part of the moving system? Why?

5. How can a D'Arsonval ammeter of one range most readily be converted to a different range? How can an iron-vane ammeter of one range be converted to a different range? Which would be the more complicated procedure?

6. How can D'Arsonval voltmeters of one range be converted to a different range? How can an iron-vane voltmeter of one range be converted to a different range? Which would be the more complicated procedure?

7. The resistance of a voltmeter divided by its range gives "ohms per volt," which is an indication of whether the instrument is suitable for a certain use. D'Arsonval voltmeters are often "100 ohms per volt" or "1000 ohms per volt." Which would be the better instrument from the standpoint of disturbing least the circuit to which it is connected? Why?

8. Why are simultaneous measurements of current and potential difference necessary? Why not, using connection as shown in Fig. 5.7a, take a current reading with the voltmeter disconnected, then connect the voltmeter and read potential difference?

9. Ohmmeters usually are provided with a zero adjustment (in addition to the zero adjustment on the moving element itself). With the terminals short-circuited, a rheostat is adjusted until the pointer indicates zero on the ohm scale. Why is such an adjustment necessary? How does it work?

10. Two identical boxes are known to contain, one a source of electromotive force, the other, a resistance. The boxes are connected by two wires to form a circuit. The circuit must not be opened, even momentarily. A voltmeter and an ammeter of suitable range and with polarity marks are provided. Explain how you would proceed to find out which box contains the source of electromotive force.

11. A pair of wires enter a room through holes in the ceiling and leave it through holes in the floor. A wattmeter is connected into this (supposed) circuit and indicates energy flowing from floor to ceiling at the rate of 100 w. To verify that the source of electromotive force is below and not above, the wires are cut and a voltmeter is connected to the ends projecting from the floor. A voltage of 200 is measured. The voltmeter is then connected to the ends projecting from the ceiling and again a voltage of 200 is measured. Prepare the simplest wiring diagram that would be consistent with these measurements. Show the wattmeter with polarities marked and show numerical values of circuit quantities.

12. Formulate a general rule for making the connections when resistance is to be measured by the voltmeter-ammeter method, so that the results will be subject to as little error as possible. Assume no corrections are to be made.

13. In using a Wheatstone bridge what would be the first remedy to try if these difficulties arose: (a) R cannot be set high enough to balance the bridge, (b) R cannot be set low enough to balance the bridge, (c) R can vary over a wide range without disturbing the balance, (d) unbalance (as indicated by galvanometer deflection) changes from $+$ to $-$ with the slightest change that can be made in R.

14. It is desired to use a Kelvin bridge set-up in the laboratory to measure the resistance of a steel rail outside in the yard. Would this be practical? How many wires would have to be run? Draw a diagram.

15. (a) How could a potentiometer be used to check the correctness of a voltmeter at various readings? Draw a diagram, using a three-point rheostat to vary the voltage. (b) How could a potentiometer be used in connection with a standard resistance to check the correctness of an ammeter at various readings. Draw a diagram.

CHAPTER VI

CHARACTERISTICS OF METALLIC CONDUCTORS

1. Variation of resistance with dimensions of conductor. The resistance of a cylindrical conductor varies directly as its length.

$$R \text{ is proportional to } L. \tag{6.1}$$

This is readily demonstrated experimentally, and it appears logical inasmuch as increasing the length of a conductor is equivalent to joining in series pieces of the conductor material, and we have seen that the resistance of a series circuit is the sum of the resistances of its parts.

The resistance of a conductor varies inversely as its cross-sectional area. Increasing the cross-sectional area is equivalent to connecting pieces of the conductor material in parallel, which results in the reciprocal of the total resistance being equal to the sum of the reciprocals of the individual resistances.

$$R \text{ is proportional to } \frac{1}{A}. \tag{6.2}$$

Combining the proportionalities (6.1) and (6.2), we have

$$R \text{ is proportional to } \frac{L}{A}, \tag{6.3}$$

and introducing a proportionality constant ρ (rho),

$$R = \frac{\rho L}{A}. \tag{6.4}$$

The constant ρ depends upon the material used and upon the units chosen for R, L, and A. It is called **resistivity** or **specific resistance**. Since it is a quantity which, when multiplied by a length and divided by an area, gives resistance, it must have the dimensions of resistance times length. The MKS unit of resistivity would be the **ohm-meter**. This unit, however, is of such inconvenient size that it is seldom used, and resistivity is measured in (a) microhm-centimeters or (b) ohm-circular mils per foot. The microhm-centimeter is used almost exclusively for laboratory or purely scientific investigations, and it is also well-suited for calculations which involve conductors of square or rectangular cross section. The ohm-circular mil per foot is particularly convenient for calculations involving round conductors, and is, therefore, much used in industry. In any event, the resistivity is found by test. The resistance of a specimen of known length and known cross-sectional area is measured, and the value of ρ is found by substituting in (6.4). The following examples illustrate the use of the ohm-meter.

EXAMPLE 1: The resistance of a copper bar, 50 cm long and having a constant cross-sectional area of 2 sq cm, is measured and found to be 4.31×10^{-5} ohm. What is the resistivity in ohm-meters?

SOLUTION: Expressing length in meters and cross-sectional area in square meters, we have

$$L = 50 \text{ cm} = 0.5 \text{ m}.$$
$$A = 2 \text{ sq cm} = 2 \times 10^{-4} \text{ sq m}.$$

Substituting in (6.4),

$$4.31 \times 10^{-5} = \frac{\rho(0.5)}{2 \times 10^{-4}}$$
$$\rho = 1.724 \times 10^{-8} \text{ ohm-m}.$$

EXAMPLE 2: What is the resistivity in microhm-centimeters of the copper bar described in Example 1? What would be the resistance of a bar of the same material 62.5 in. long and having a cross-sectional area of 0.5 sq in.?

SOLUTION: Resistance of the bar is

$$4.31 \times 10^{-5} \text{ ohm} = 43.1 \text{ microhms}.$$
$$L = 50 \text{ cm}.$$
$$A = 2 \text{ sq cm}.$$

Substituting in (6.4),

$$43.1 = \frac{\rho(50)}{2}$$
$$\rho = 1.724 \text{ microhm-cm}.$$

Expressing the length and cross section of the second bar in centimeters and square centimeters, respectively,

$$L = 62.5 \text{ in.} = 159 \text{ cm}.$$
$$A = 0.5 \text{ sq in.} = 3.225 \text{ sq cm}.$$

Substituting in (6.4),

$$R = \frac{(1.724)(159)}{3.225} = 84.9 \text{ microhm}$$
$$= 8.49 \times 10^{-5} \text{ ohm.}$$

2. Resistance calculations for round conductors.   The calculation of the resistances of round conductors is simplified by measuring the cross-sectional area in **circular mils.**   The circular mil is a unit of area, and is a circle one mil ($\frac{1}{1000}$ of an inch) in diameter.   The principle of measuring with this unit is the same as always—we simply find how many times the unit is contained in the thing to be

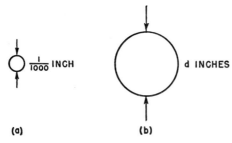

(a)   (b)

Fig. 6.1.   Measurement of area in circular units.   The small circle $\frac{1}{1000}$ inch in diameter is a unit of area, a **CIRCULAR MIL.**

measured.   Let us apply it to the measurement of the area of a circle d inches in diameter.   The area of our unit is

$$A_1 = \frac{\pi(0.001)^2}{4} \text{ sq in.}$$

The area of the circle to be measured is

$$A_2 = \frac{\pi d^2}{4} \text{ sq in.}$$

To find how many times the unit is contained in the area to be measured, we take

$$\frac{A_2}{A_1} = \frac{\pi \dfrac{d^2}{4}}{\pi \dfrac{(0.001)^2}{4}} = \frac{d^2}{(0.001)^2} = (1000d)^2.$$

Thus, to find the area of a circle in circular mils, we simply take its diameter in inches, multiply it by 1000, and square the product.   This eliminates the use of the factor π, thereby saving a step in calculating such areas.

EXAMPLE: The resistance of a round copper wire, 100 ft long and 0.1 in. in diameter is 0.1042 ohm.   What is the resistivity of the copper in ohm-circular mils per foot?   What would be the resistance of a piece of the same wire 0.08 in. in diameter and 1 mile long?

SOLUTION:

$$\text{Area} = (0.1 \times 1000)^2 = 10{,}000 \text{ cir mils}$$

$$0.1042 = \frac{\rho(100)}{10{,}000}$$

$$\rho = 10.42 \text{ ohm-cir mils per ft.}$$

$$\text{Area of second piece} = (0.08 \times 1000)^2 = 6400 \text{ cir mils}$$

$$R = \frac{10.42(5280)}{6400} = 8.6 \text{ ohms.}$$

Resistivity may be thought of as being numerically equal to the resistance of a piece of material of unit length and unit cross-sectional area.   Resistivity in microhm-centimeters, for example, is numerically equal to the resistance of a piece of material 1 cm in length and 1 sq cm in cross-sectional area, or in other words, to the resistance of a centimeter cube of the material.   For this reason, we sometimes see the expression "microhms per centimeter cube," instead of the correct "microhm-centimeters."   Similarly, the resistivity in ohm-circular mils per foot is numerically equal to the resistance of a piece of material 1 cir mil in cross-sectional area and 1 ft long, and the expression "ohms per circular mil-foot" is sometimes used in place of "ohm-circular mils per foot."   These substitute expressions are dimensionally incorrect and, furthermore, they imply that resistance is a function of volume, which is not the case.   It is, therefore, recommended that the correct expressions, microhm-centimeters and ohm-circular mils per foot be used, though thinking of resistivity as being numerically equal to the resistance of a certain piece of material is often useful.

The resistivities of some materials commonly used in the electrical industries are given in Table IV.

3. Conductivity.   As stated in Section 10 Chapter III, conductance G is the reciprocal of resistance.   Any factor that tends to make resistance large would, therefore, make conductance small, and vice versa.   Thus, we can see that the conductance would decrease with length,

$$G \text{ is proportional to } \frac{1}{L}, \tag{6.5}$$

and that it would increase with cross-sectional area,

$$G \text{ is proportional to } A; \tag{6.6}$$

combining (6.5) and (6.6), we have

$$G \text{ is proportional to } \frac{A}{L}. \tag{6.7}$$

Introducing a proportionality constant σ (sigma),

$$G = \frac{\sigma A}{L}. \tag{6.8}$$

The constant σ is called **conductivity**. Since it is a quantity which, when multiplied by an area and divided by a length, gives conductance, it must have the dimensions of conductance divided by length. From (6.4) and (6.8), and sincee

$$G = \frac{1}{R},$$

it can be seen that

$$\sigma = \frac{1}{\rho}. \tag{6.9}$$

Conductivity is the reciprocal of resistivity. The MKS unit of conductivity is the **mho per meter.**

Conductivity is most often expressed as a percentage, the conductivity of standard annealed copper being taken as 100 per cent.

$$\text{Percentage of conductivity} = \frac{\sigma \text{ of material}}{\sigma \text{ of standard annealed copper}} \times 100, \tag{6.10}$$

or, replacing σ by ρ according to (~~6.5~~)(6.9),

$$\text{Percentage of conductivity} = \frac{\rho \text{ of standard annealed copper}}{\rho \text{ of material}} \times 100. \tag{6.11}$$

EXAMPLE: What is the percentage of conductivity of a material having a resistivity of 2 microhm-cm?

SOLUTION: The resistivity of standard annealed copper from Table IV is 1.724 microhm-cm. By (6.11),

$$\text{Percentage of conductivity} = \frac{1.724}{2} \times 100 = 86.2.$$

Copper of greater purity than standard annealed copper and, hence, having more than 100 per cent conductivity is obtainable. Aluminum has about 60 per cent conductivity, steel wire about 10 per cent.

In general the combining of pure metals to form alloys, or even the presence of a small percentage of impurity, results in a material of greatly lowered conductivity.   Nichrome, which is an alloy of copper, iron, and nickel, all of which are good conductors, has a conductivity of only about 1.5 per cent.   Such alloys are of considerable practical importance, because it is often desirable, as in rheostats and heating elements, to obtain considerable resistance in a relatively short length of conductor.

The ratio of the heat conductivity of a metal to its electrical conductivity at the same temperature is approximately the same for all metals.   This is the Wiedemann-Franz relation, and it implies that the medium of heat conduction must be the same as the medium of electrical conduction, the electron.

TABLE IV

RESISTIVITY   AND   RESISTANCE—TEMPERATURE   COEFFICIENTS

Material	Resistivity (microhm-cm at 20° C)	Resistivity (ohms-cir mils per ft at 20° C)	Resistance— temperature coefficient at 20° C
Advance (alloy)..........	. . . . .	298	.00002
Aluminum	2.828	. . . . .	.0039
Brass...................	. . . . .	40	.0017
Carbon.................	3000		
Copper (std annealed).....	1.724	10.37	.00393
Copper (hard drawn)......	. . . . .	10.78	.00382
Graphite................	800		
Manganin...............	44	. . . . .	.000006
Nichrome...............	100	. . . . .	.0004
Silver..................	1.63	. . . . .	.0038
Steel (Siemens-Martin)....	. . . . .	98.1	
Steel (4% silicon)........	50		
Steel (rails)..............	21.55	. . . . .	.0059
Tungsten	. . . . .	33.2	.0045

Problems

(1-VI) What is the area in circular mils of a circle 1 in. in diam?   What is the diameter of a conductor having a cross-sectional area of 500,000 cir mils?

(2-VI) What is the diameter of a conductor having a cross-sectional area of 1021 cir mils?   What is the area in circular mils of a conductor 0.005 in. in diam?

(3-VI) What is the resistance of 1 mile of No. 4 hard-drawn copper wire (diam 0.204 in.)?

(4-VI) What is the resistance of a two-wire line, 20 miles in length, built of No. 8 Siemens-Martin steel wire (diam 0.129 in.)?

(5-VI) What is the resistance of a steel rail, 8.83 sq in. in cross section and 30 ft long?

(6-VI) What is the resistance of a bus bar, 82 ft long, ¼ by 4 in. cross section, of standard annealed copper?

(7-VI) What is the resistivity in microhm-meters of a material the resistivity of which is 3 microhm-cm? What is the resistivity in microhm-centimeters of a material that has a resistivity of 3 microhm-in.?

(8-VI) What is the resistivity in ohm-circular mils per foot of a material that has a resistivity of 3 microhm-cm?

(9-VI) What is the resistivity in microhm-meters of a material that has a resistivity of 40 ohm-cir mils per ft?

(10-VI) What is the percentage of conductivity of silver? of brass? of nichrome?

(11-VI) What is the resistance of a piece of copper wire of 101.8 per cent conductivity 1 mm in diam and 100 m long?

(12-VI) What is the resistance per mile of ASCR (aluminum steel core reinforced) made up of 1 steel strand 0.102 in. diam and 6 aluminum strands 0.102 in. diam? Assume the resistance of each aluminum strand to be increased by 2 per cent owing to spiral effect.

(13-VI) A copper wire bar, 0.875 in. diam and 60 ft long, is hard-drawn into No. 14 copper wire (diam 0.064 in.) What is the resistance of the wire?

(14-VI) What should be the diameter of the steel core of a No. 0 (0.325 in. diam) copper-clad steel conductor in order for the conductivity to be 40 per cent?

(15-VI) What would be the percentage of conductivity of a copper-clad steel conductor of which the over-all diameter is 0.46 in. and the diameter of the steel core is 0.411 in?

(16-VI) Show that the percentage of conductivity of a copper-clad steel conductor is given by

$$\% \, \sigma_0 = \frac{\% \, \sigma_s \, \% \, S}{100} + \frac{\% \, \sigma_c \, \% \, C}{100}, \tag{6.12}$$

where $\% \, \sigma_s$ = percentage of conductivity of steel.

$\% \, S$ = percentage of steel in make-up of conductor.

$\% \, \sigma_c$ = percentage of conductivity of copper.

$\% \, C$ = percentage of copper in make-up of conductor.

4. Variation of resistance with temperature. The resistance of any metal conductor increases with temperature. In the temperature interval from $-50°$ to $+200°$ C, the temperature-resistance graph is found to be so nearly a straight line that we may regard it as such with negligible error. This embraces the range of temperature at which electrical conductors (except heating elements) are required to operate, and in practical problems, we may conveniently make use of the straight-line graph in calculating changes of resistances with temperature. Let D and E (Fig. 6.2) be points on the straight portion of the graph. If this line be projected back until it intersects the temperature axis at T_0, and perpendiculars be erected at T_1 and T_2, similar triangles ABD and ACE will be formed. From geometry, we may set up the proportionality.

$$\frac{AB}{BD} = \frac{AC}{CE},\tag{6.13}$$

$$\frac{T_0 + T_1}{T_0 + T_2} = \frac{R_1}{R_2}.\tag{6.14}$$

From this relation, it can be seen that if the resistance of a conductor is known at one temperature, it can be found at any other temperature, provided that T_0 is known and that both temperatures lie within the interval for which the graph is a straight line. The T intercept, T_0, may be found experimentally by measuring the resistance of a specimen of the conductor material at two different temperatures and plotting the graph, or substituting in (6.14). It need be

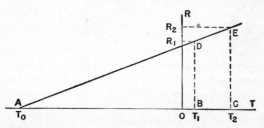

Fig. 6.2. Graph showing the resistance of a metal conductor as a function of temperature.

determined but once for a given material; all T-R graphs for conductors of that material have the same T intercept regardless of their dimensions.

Problems

(17-VI) A specimen of standard annealed copper wire is found to have a resistance of 1 ohm at 20° C and 1.276 ohms at 90° C. Plot the graph and determine the T intercept.

(18-VI) A piece of standard annealed copper wire has a resistance of 12.5 ohms at 15° C. What will be its resistance at 31° C?

(19-VI) A coil of standard annealed copper wire having a resistance of 10 ohms at 20° C is imbedded in the core of a large transformer. After the transformer has been in operation several hours, the resistance of the temperature coil has become 11.08 ohms. What is its temperature?

It must be made plain that the T-R graph is not a straight line except within reasonable limits of temperature. One of the most interesting parts of the graph from the standpoint of theoretical physics is the interval just above absolute zero ($-273°$ C). As the specimen is cooled down, its resistance decreases consistently, until at a temperature a few degrees above absolute zero, there is a sharp break in the graph, and the resistance drops abruptly to zero. This phenomenon, known as **superconductivity,** is found in some metals, such as lead (at 7° C above absolute zero); not in others, such as gold.

5. Temperature coefficient of resistance.   The slope of the T-R graph (Fig. 6.2) by analytic geometry is

$$m = \frac{R_2 - R_1}{T_2 - T_1}.$$ (6.15)

This slope has a physical significance, it being the change in resistance per degree change in temperature for a particular piece of wire.   If the slope be divided by the resistance of the specimen at any particular temperature, we have the change of resistance per degree change in temperature per ohm.

$$\alpha_1 = \frac{\dfrac{R_2 - R_1}{T_2 - T_1}}{R_1}.$$ (6.16)

This quantity is called the **temperature coefficient of resistance** and is designated by the symbol α (alpha).   It is obvious that the value obtained for alpha will depend upon the resistance by which the slope is divided, which in turn depends upon the temperature.   In other words, the temperature coefficient is different for every temperature.

Problems

(**20-VI**) Calculate the temperature coefficient of resistance for standard annealed copper at 20° C, using the data from Problem 17-VI.

(**21-VI**) Calculate the value of α_{90} for standard annealed copper, using data from Problem 17-VI.   Calculate α_0, α_{55}, and α_{100}.   *Suggestion:* First use Equation (6.14) to find the resistance at each temperature.

Equation (6.16) may be put into the form

$$R_2 = R_1[1 + \alpha_1(T_2 - T_1)],$$ (6.17)

which is more convenient for solving problems.   It can be seen that if the resistance of a conductor is known to be R_1 at temperature T_1, its resistance at any other temperature, T_2, may be found, provided α_1 is known.   Or, more generally, if any three of the quantities, R_1, R_2, T_1, and T_2 are known, the other can be found provided α_1 is known. It is important that all the quantities subscripted 1 must correspond. That is, if α_1 is the temperature coefficient at 20° C, then T_1 must be 20° C, and R_1 must be the resistance at 20° C.

EXAMPLE: A brass conductor has a resistance of 50 ohms at 20° C. What would be its resistance at 0° C?

From Table IV, the temperature coefficient of brass is 0.0017 at 20° C.   Substituting in (6.17),

$$R_0 = R_{20}[1 + \alpha_{20}(0 - 20)]$$
$$= 50[1 + 0.0017(0 - 20)] = 48.3 \text{ ohms.}$$

It is sometimes necessary to start with the resistance of a conductor at a given temperature, and find resistance at some new temperature when the only temperature coefficient available corresponds to a third temperature. In such cases, we may calculate a new value for temperature coefficient, using the relation

$$\alpha_2 = \frac{\alpha_1}{1 + \alpha_1(T_2 - T_1)}, \tag{6.18}$$

and then proceed to use Equation (6.17). An alternate method would be to make use of the relation

$$\alpha_1 = \frac{1}{T_0 + T_1} \tag{6.19}$$

to find the T intercept of the temperature-resistance graph, and then use Equation (6.14).

EXAMPLE: A brass conductor has a resistance of 50 ohms at 0° C. What would be its resistance at 50° C?

SOLUTION 1: The resistance-temperature coefficient corresponding to 0° C may be found from Equation 6.18, using the value 0.0017 at 20° C taken from Table IV,

$$\alpha_0 = \frac{0.0017}{1 + 0.0017(0 - 20)} = 0.00176.$$

Then, from (6.17),

$$R_{50} = R_0[1 + \alpha_0(50 - 0)]$$
$$= 50[1 + 0.00176(50 - 0)]$$
$$= 54.4 \text{ ohms.}$$

SOLUTION 2: The T intercept for brass may be found from Equation 6.19,

$$0.0017 = \frac{1}{T_0 + 20},$$
$$T_0 = 568.$$

Then, from (6.14),

$$\frac{568 + 0}{568 + 50} = \frac{50}{R_{50}},$$
$$R_{50} = 54.4 \text{ ohms.}$$

Most pure metals have positive temperature coefficients ranging from 0.003 to 0.006 at 20° C. Alloys in general show much smaller values, and carbon has a negative temperature coefficient (its resistance decreases with increasing temperature). The temperature coefficients for several materials are to be found in Table IV.

Problems

(22-VI) The resistance of an aluminum conductor is 150 ohms at 20° C. What will its resistance be at 75° C?

(23-VI) The resistance of a steel cable is 80 ohms at 50° C. What will its resistance be at 20° C?

(24-VI) The resistance of a hard-drawn copper conductor is 1.48 ohms at 70° C. What will be its resistance at 40° C?

(25-VI) The resistance of a railroad track is 0.031 ohm per mile at 80° F. What will be its resistance at 0° F?

(26-VI) The resistance of a silver conductor is 3.5 ohms at 130° F. What will be its resistance at 150° F?

(27-VI) Show that

$$\alpha_2 = \frac{\alpha_1}{1 + \alpha_1(T_2 - T_1)}. \qquad (6.18)$$

(28-VI) Show that

$$\alpha_1 = \frac{1}{T_0 + T_1}. \qquad (6.19)$$

6. Other factors affecting resistance. It is found that the resistance of a metal conductor varies slightly with pressure, some metals showing an increase in resistance with increasing pressure, others a decrease in resistance. One element, selenium, shows a change in resistance with illumination, the resistivity being quite large in the dark and decreasing as the intensity of the light is increased. This property of selenium was at one time regarded as possibly having some important practical applications, as for light-sensitive relays, and for measuring light intensity. Photoelectric cells have proved superior for these purposes, however, and selenium is little used.

The boundary surface formed between a layer of selenium and a layer of iron, or between a layer of copper and a layer of copper oxide, has the property of offering much greater resistance to current in one direction than in the other. This is an example of the class of conductors known as *unilateral*, as distinguished from *bilateral* conductors which offer the same resistance in either direction. This property is the basis of the selenium-iron and the copper-oxide rectifiers which are being employed in a wide variety of applications.

7. Commercial wire sizes. The most commonly used conductor material in the electrical industry is copper. Copper conductors may be obtained in sizes running from less than 10 cir mils up to 2,000,000 cir mils cross-sectional area. Certain standard sizes are most often used, though conductors not of standard size are produced for special jobs, such as the winding of armatures. Some standard sizes are designated by gage numbers, the system used in the United States being known as AWG (American Wire Gage) or B&S (Brown & Sharpe). This system originally included forty sizes, numbered from 0000 (the largest) with a diameter of 0.46 in., to 36 (the smallest) with a diameter of 0.005 in. The diameters of the intermediate gage numbers were to form a geometrical progression, and since there were 39 intervals, this fixed the ratio of the diameter of one size to the diameter of the next as

$$\sqrt[39]{\frac{0.46}{0.005}} = \sqrt[39]{92} = 1.123.$$

The system has since been extended to take in gage numbers 37 to 40, the diameters of these sizes being determined according to the ratio indicated above. If the resistivity of the copper is known, we may calculate the resistance per unit length for wire of any specified gage number, but for convenience, the results of such calculations for

TABLE V
COPPER-WIRE DATA

AWG Number	Area (cir mils)	Resistance[1] (ohms/1000 ft)	Weight[2] (lb/1000 ft)	Allowable Current[3]
0000	212,000	.0490	640	358
000	168,000	.0618	508	310
00	133,000	.0779	402	267
0	106,000	.0983	319	230
1	83,700	.124	253	196
2	66,400	.156	201	170
3	52,600	.197	159	146
4	41,700	.248	126	125
5	33,100	.313	100	110
6	26,300	.395	79.5	94
8	16,500	.628	50	69
10	10,400	.999	31.4	50
12	6,530	1.59	19.8	37
14	4,110	2.52	12.4	29
16	2,580	4.01	7.82	
18	1,620	6.38	4.92	
20	1,020	10.1	3.09	
24	404	25.7	1.22	
28	160	64.9	0.484	
32	63.2	164	0.191	
36	25	415	0.0759	
40	9.89	1049	0.0299	

[1] Std annealed copper at 20° C.
[2] Bare copper.
[3] National Electric Code figures for Type RH insulation in open air.

standard annealed copper wire are made available in **wire tables.** Table V gives data on a few commonly used sizes. Complete tables may be found in any electrical handbook.

Larger conductors than No. 0000 are specified by area, certain sizes such as 250,000 cir mil, 300,000 cir mil, and so forth being standard. The larger sizes are usually stranded for convenience in handling, the number of strands and the cross section of the strands being selected to give the required total cross-sectional area.

Electrical conductors other than copper are also made in AWG sizes, with the exception of iron and steel wires, which are measured by Birmingham wire-gage numbers. Tables for other materials may be found in handbooks and in manufacturers' literature.

8. Heating of conductors. In any conductor that carries current, we have seen that electrical energy is being converted into heat energy at a rate equal to I^2R watts. The effect of this conversion is a tendency to raise the temperature of the conductor, and any increase in the temperature of the conductor results in the increased transfer of heat from the conductor to its surroundings. Sometimes, as in electrical heating appliances, this transfer of heat from the conductor to its surroundings is exactly the purpose of the installation. In most instances, however, such as electric wiring and the windings of electrical machinery, heating is an undesirable but unavoidable consequence of having the current. In any case, the size of the conductor must be so selected that the rate of heat production will not cause an excessive rise in its temperature.

What constitutes an excessive temperature rise naturally depends on the purpose for which the conductor is used and on what its surroundings are. Bare wire mounted in open air on mica insulators might safely be operated at a temperature of 600° C, or at any temperature at which the rate of oxidation of the wire does not proceed too rapidly. Insulated wire in the windings of a machine or in a building, however, could never be operated at any such temperature because the material used as insulation would be destroyed. Good practice requires that the temperature of such conductors never exceed 90° to 130° C, depending on the material used as insulation.

Let us consider further what happens when heat is produced in a current-carrying conductor. Assuming that the conductor is at room temperature to begin with, it is not able to transfer any heat to its surroundings either by conduction, convection, or radiation, and, consequently, heat is stored in the conductor at the same rate as it is being produced (I^2R). Temperature rise is an inevitable consequence of heat storage, and the temperature of the conductor begins to go up.

Now, as soon as the temperature of the conductor exceeds the temperature of its surroundings, heat transfer begins. At first the rate of transfer is small because it is a function of temperature difference. Small temperature difference means small rate of heat transfer. Most of the heat produced continues to be stored and the temperature continues to rise. But the greater becomes the temperature difference between the conductor and its surroundings, the greater becomes the rate of heat transfer. The greater the rate of heat transfer, the smaller is the rate of heat storage (assuming the rate of heat production is constant), and the less rapid is the temperature rise. Finally a temperature will be reached where the conductor will be able to transfer heat at the same rate at which heat is produced, and heat storage and temperature rise cease. This is called **steady-state temperature.** As we have seen, one of the most important problems before the designer of electrical apparatus or wiring is to be sure the steady-state temperature does not exceed the safe temperature for the grade of insulation used.

The determination of steady-state temperature by theoretical calculations is not a simple matter. In fact, it is so difficult that it is seldom undertaken in practice, except in the simplest cases. In a multilayer coil, for example, heat has to be conducted to the surface through successive layers of copper and insulation, and dissipated from the surface to the surrounding air by conduction, convection, and radiation. The inner layer of the coil will reach a higher equilibrium temperature than the second layer, which will reach a higher temperature than the third layer, and so forth. Obviously, the temperature of the inner layer will be the determining factor in the design of the coil, and this temperature is not readily calculated from theory. Designers make considerable use of accumulated test data, and new designs are constructed and tested to find out whether the steady-state temperature is within the safe limits.

Assuming that a given design gives too high a steady-state temperature, there are several things that may be done. First, we may substitute a grade of insulation that will stand higher temperature—that is, enameled wire in place of cotton-covered wire in a coil, or asbestos-insulated wire for rubber-covered wire in a building. Second, we may seek some means of increasing the rate of heat transfer away from the conductor, such as redesigning a coil so as to have more surface area exposed to the air, or using a blower to force air over the coil at a greater rate. Third, we may select a conductor of larger cross section and, therefore, of less resistance, so that the I^2R loss will be less.

In designing wiring for a building, the National Electric Code must be consulted. This Code, which has the force of law in most localities, specifies the allowable current in conductors of all sizes permitted in wiring installations, for various methods of installation, and for the different grades of insulation available. The Code is based on test data, and aims to limit the heating of conductors so that in no case will the steady-state temperature exceed the value at which deterioration of the insulation begins. Some data on allowable currents are given in Table V.

EXAMPLE: A circuit in a certain wiring installation must carry a current of 65 amp. What wire size is required by the National Electric Code?

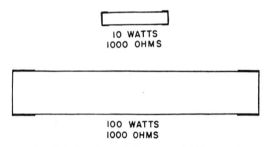

Fig. 6.3.   Relative sizes of 10 watt and 100 watt resistors.

SOLUTION: Assuming that the circuit is not in conduit, and that Type RH insulation is used, Table V shows the allowable current for No. 8 is 69 amp, and it would, therefore, be suitable. If the wiring is to be installed in conduit or if another type of insulation is to be used, reference must be had to the complete tables given in electrical handbooks, or in the Code itself.

For rheostats, resistors, and so forth, it is common practice to give the device a watt rating according to the rate (determined by test) at which it can dissipate heat without exceeding a safe temperature. The user must then assure himself that the device is never installed in a circuit where the I^2R loss will exceed the watt rating.

EXAMPLE: A 500-ohm resistor is required in a circuit where it will carry a current of 15 ma. What should be the watt rating of the resistor?

SOLUTION:
$$P = I^2R = (0.015)^2 \times 500 = 1.125 \text{ w.}$$

A 2-w resistor is the nearest commercial size which will answer the purpose.

Problems

(**29-VI**) What wire size is required in a wiring installation (open wiring Type RH insulation) for a current of 25 amp? 90 amp? 200 amp?

(**30-VI**) Consult the tables in an electrical handbook to determine the effect on allowable current of placing wires in conduit. By what percentage is the allowable current decreased? Explain.

(**31-VI**) Consult the tables in an electrical handbook to determine the allowable currents for various types of insulation for a given size of wire, say No. 4. Explain.

(**32-VI**) Consult an electrical handbook, catalogue, or display board for information on standard watt ratings of resistors. List the standard ratings. How does a 1-w, 1000-ohm resistor differ from a 100-w, 1000-ohm resistor as regards size? As regards cost? Explain.

(**33-VI**) It is desired to insert 1000 ohms resistance in a circuit which is to carry a current of 0.2 amp. There are available a number of 10-w, 1000-ohm resistors. What combination of these resistors would serve the purpose?

(**34-VI**) A D'Arsonval type instrument having a resistance of 5 ohms and requiring 10 ma for full-scale deflection is to be adapted for use as a 0 to 500-range voltmeter. What must be the watt rating of the series resistor used?

(**35-VI**) A D'Arsonval type instrument having a resistance of 5 ohms and requiring 10 ma for full-scale deflection is to be adapted for use as a 0 to 500-range ammeter. What must be the watt rating of the resistor used as a shunt?

(**36-VI**) The tubular-type rheostats used in the electrical engineering laboratories are 10 in. long and 2 in. in diam. Assume these rheostats can dissipate 7 w per sq in. of winding surface and still remain at safe temperature, and that they are wound with bare Advance alloy wire with the turns in contact. What would be the resistance and ampere rating of a rheostat wound with No. 28 AWG?

(**37-VI**) Using the data furnished in Problem 36-VI, find the proper size of wire for a 50-ohm rheostat. What would its ampere rating be?

9. Current density. For some purposes, the current per unit cross-sectional area has more significance than the current itself. This quantity, called **current density,** is defined by the equation

$$J = \frac{I}{A}, \tag{6.20}$$

where J is average current density, I is current, and A is cross-sectional area of the conductor. In the MKS system, I is measured in amperes and A in square meters, making the unit of current density the **ampere per square meter.** Since practical conductors are never as large as 1 sq m in cross section, the MKS unit is not convenient in size, and current density is more often expressed in amperes per square centimeter or amperes per square inch.

The maximum current density which may be used in a given conductor depends, of course, on the purpose for which the conductor is used, on whether it is insulated, and, if so, upon the material used for insulation. In coils and in the windings of electrical machinery, such as motors, generators, and transformers, current densities are usually from 1000 to 2500 amp per sq in. In electric wiring, current densities range from less than 1000 amp per sq in. in large conductors to as high as 10,000 amp per sq in. in No. 14, the smallest size permitted. In electric heating elements and in the filaments of incandescent lamps, current densities may sometimes be as great as 2×10^5 amp per sq in.

In conductors which carry alternating current, the current density is not uniform over the cross-sectional area of the conductor, but is greatest in the elements nearest the surface, and least in an element at the center. This phenomenon is known as **skin effect.** It is negligible at power frequencies, except in large conductors. At radio frequencies and ultra high frequencies, it becomes such an important factor that the resistance of a hollow tube may be not much greater than that of a solid conductor of the same diameter. This is the basis for the statement often heard that current flows along the surface of the conductor. As seen from the foregoing, the statement is not generally correct.

Problem

(**38-VI**) Determine the maximum current density allowed by the National Electric Code for each wire size listed in Table V. How does the maximum allowable current density vary with cross-sectional area? Explain.

10. Design of wiring installations. In any wiring installation, the power company usually brings its wires to a certain point known as the **service entrance.** At this point is installed the main switch and protective devices (fuses or circuit breakers) and metering equipment. From the service entrance, heavy conductors are run to the central distributing point, where the **main panel board** is installed. This panel board provides a switch and protective device for each of a number of circuits known as **feeders** which run to **subpanel boards** in various parts of the building. From each subpanel board, **branch circuits** run to the various **outlets,** at which lamps or appliances are connected. In smaller installations, such as residences, feeders and subpanel boards are dispensed with, and the branch circuits run directly from the main panel board.

In choosing the proper wire size for any feeder or branch circuit, two questions have to be considered:

1. What is the smallest size that will carry the required current without getting hot enough to damage the insulation?

2. What is the smallest size that will not cause excessive voltage drop?

The first question has already been discussed in Section 8, and it has to be answered by reference to the National Electric Code. The answer to the other question, that of voltage drop, often means the installation of a larger conductor than would be necessary to satisfy the Code requirements. Lamps and appliances are designed to operate at a specified constant voltage, and satisfactory operation cannot be expected unless they are supplied with a voltage very close to that for which they were designed. In no case should the voltage differ by more than 5 per cent. Assuming that the power company maintains correct voltage at the service entrance, the voltage drop between that point and the most remote outlet should, therefore, never be more than 5 per cent, and preferably less. This voltage drop could be prorated, say 3 per cent to the feeders, and 2 per cent to the branches, or 1 per

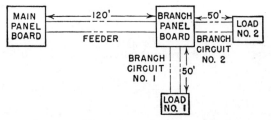

Fig. 6.4. Wiring layout for light and power.

cent to the feeders and 4 per cent to the branches, or in any one of a number of other ways. One way usually results in the use of less pounds of wire than any of the others, and is, therefore, preferable.

EXAMPLE: Determine wire sizes for the installation shown in Fig. 6.4 so that the voltage drop from the main panel board to the outlets will in no case exceed 3 per cent. For simplicity, the outlets on branch circuit No. 1 are shown as load No. 1, which requires 3000 w, and the outlets on branch circuit No. 2 are shown as load No. 2, which requires 1800 w. The voltage at the main panel board is 120.

SOLUTION: Let the voltage drop in the feeder be 1 per cent, permitting in each branch a voltage drop of 2 per cent.

For branch No. 1,

$$\text{Allowable voltage drop} = 0.02 \times 120 = 2.4,$$
$$\text{Current} = {}^{3000}\!/_{120} = 25 \text{ amp},$$
$$\text{Resistance} = \frac{2.4}{25} = 0.096,$$
$$\text{Resistance per 1000 ft} = \frac{0.096}{2 \times 50} \times 1000 = 0.96 \text{ ohm}.$$

From Table V, No. 10 wire is found to have a resistance of 0.99 ohm per 1000 ft, and the allowable current is 50 amp.

For branch No. 2,

$$\text{Allowable voltage drop} = 0.02 \times 120 = 2.4,$$
$$\text{Current} = {}^{1800}\!/_{120} = 15 \text{ amp,}$$
$$\text{Resistance} = \frac{2.4}{15} = 0.16,$$
$$\text{Resistance per 1000 ft} = \frac{0.16}{2 \times 50} \times 1000 = 1.6 \text{ ohms.}$$

From Table V, No. 12 wire is found to have a resistance of 1.59 ohms per 1000 ft, and the allowable current is 37 amp.

For the feeder,

$$\text{Allowable voltage drop} = 0.01 \times 120 = 1.2 \text{ v,}$$
$$\text{Current} = 25 + 15 = 40 \text{ amp,}$$
$$\text{Resistance} = \frac{1.2}{40} = 0.03 \text{ ohm,}$$
$$\text{Resistance per 1000 ft} = \frac{0.03}{2 \times 120} \times 1000 = 0.125 \text{ ohm.}$$

From Table V, No. 1 wire is found to have a resistance of 0.124 ohm per 1000 ft, and the allowable current is 196 amp.

Copper required is:

$$\frac{2 \times 50}{1000} \times 31.4 = 3.14 \text{ lb of No. 10,}$$
$$\frac{2 \times 50}{1000} \times 19.8 = 1.98 \text{ lb of No. 12,}$$
$$\frac{2 \times 120}{1000} \times 253 = 60.7 \text{ lb of No. 1,}$$

or 65.8 lb total.

Problems

(**39-VI**) What is the proper wire size for a feeder 150 ft long to handle 50 amp with a voltage drop not to exceed 5 v?

(**40-VI**) What is the proper wire size for a branch circuit 90 ft long to handle 20 amp with a voltage drop not to exceed 2.4 v?

(**41-VI**) What is the proper size for a feeder 105 ft long to handle 500 amp with a voltage drop not to exceed 12.5 v?

(**42-VI**) Determine the wire sizes for the installation shown in Fig. 6.4 on the basis of 2 per cent drop in the feeder and 1 per cent in the branches. Calculate the total number of pounds of copper required, and compare with that calculated in the example.

(**43-VI**) The installation shown in Fig. 6.4 is redesigned with a three-wire feeder, branch circuit No. 1 being connected from one line to neutral, and branch circuit No. 2 from the other line to neutral. The voltage at the main panel board is 120 from each line to neutral. Determine the wire sizes required on the basis of 2 per cent drop in the feeder and 1 per cent in the branches. The line wires of the feeder must be the same size, but the neutral may be a smaller size if desirable. Calculate the total copper required and compare with that calculated in Problem 42-VI.

(**44-VI**) A heating element is to be made up of nichrome ribbon 0.0625 in. wide by 0.012 in. thick and is to take 500 w from 110-v mains when operated at a temperature of 400° F. How many feet of ribbon should be used? What power will the element take when first switched on?

(**45-VI**) A line 35 miles long is constructed of No. 8 hard-drawn copper wire. The temperatures in the locality range from −20° F in the winter to +100° F in the summer. What is the resistance of the line on the coldest day of the year? On the hottest day in summer? By what percentage does the line resistance change?

(**46-VI**) A load that takes 10 amp at 220 v is placed at the receiving end of a line 600 ft long and built of No. 8 copper wire. Find (a) resistance of the line, (b) voltage drop in the line, (c) sending-end voltage, (d) I^2R loss in lines, and (e) efficiency of line.

(**47-VI**) A line is required to transmit power to a load requiring 5000 w at a distance of ¼ mile. The sending-end voltage is 500 and the drop in the line must not exceed 5 per cent of sending-end voltage. Select the proper wire size to meet this requirement. Will it also meet the Code requirement?

(**48-VI**) A line 2½ miles long is built of No. 4 copper wire. The sending-end voltage is 500 and the power at the receiving end is to be 5 kw. What two values might the voltage at the receiving end have? What load resistance corresponds to each of the above values? Which value would be the most practical one to use?

(**49-VI**) The feeders from the generator to the main panel board in a certain building are 150 ft long (total). The power to be supplied is 20 kw, the voltage at the generator is 230, and the voltage drop must not exceed 2 per cent of this. What is the smallest wire size that will meet the Code requirements? Will it also meet the voltage-drop requirements?

Study Questions

1. Of what would each of the following be a unit: (a) mho-ft per circular mil; (b) feet per ohm-circular mil; (c) ohm-inches; (d) (feet)² per mho-circular mil?

2. What would be the T intercept of the extended straight part of the T-R graph for Advance alloy? (See Table IV.) What does this imply as to the shape of the lower part of the graph?

3. From the data given in Table IV, select the material that would be best suited for making shunts for ammeters and series resistances for voltmeters. State the reasons for your choice.

4. Aluminum conductors are extensively used for transmission lines, but practically not at all for wiring installations and windings. By comparing the physical properties of copper and aluminum and their current market prices, can you justify the practice?

5. Does it seem likely that the efficiency of electrical apparatus and wiring installations may be improved by the discovery of a new low-resistivity conductor material? Why?

6. Since the ratio of the diameter of a copper wire to the diameter of the next gage number is 1.123, the ratio of the cross-section areas (and therefore of the weights and resistances) will be $(1.123)^2 = 1.26$. The ratio of the areas, weights, and resistances will be $(1.26)^2 = 1.59$ for the next gage number but one, and it will be $(1.26)^3 = 2$ for the third gage number. If these numbers be memorized, together with the data on one particular wire size, say No. 10, as a starting point, the entire wire table, or any portion of it can readily be constructed. For instance No. 13, the third gage number from No. 10 would have half the cross-sectional area, half the weight, and twice the resistance of No. 10 (5200 circular mils, 15.7 lb. per 1000 ft., and 2 ohms, approximately). Without consulting the wire table, compute the approximate: (a) cross section of No. 16; (b) weight of No. 11; (c) resistance of No. 8; (d) cross section of No. 4; (e) weight of No. 27; (f) resistance of No. 0.

7. The cross-section area of No. 4 copper wire is about 10 times that of No. 14, but the allowable current (for Type *R-H* insulation) is only about four times as much. Why is this?

8. Which would be the larger (as regards space occupied) a 1000-ohm 10-w resistor or a 1-ohm 50-w resistor? Why?

9. The average temperature rise of a coil is determined by measuring the increase in its resistance after several hours of operation, and is found to be within the limits regarded as safe for the type of insulation used. Is this sufficient assurance that the coil will not be damaged by over-heating? Explain.

10. In making a "heat-run" on an electrical machine it is operated, usually at rated output, until its temperature becomes steady. The temperature rises fairly rapidly during the first hour or two, then less rapidly until at the last the machine may have to be operated several hours during which the rise is almost imperceptible. Explain.

11. The power loss in a certain conductor carrying 10 amp direct current is measured and found to be 100 w. The loss in the same conductor when carrying 10 amp alternating current is measured as 115 w. What is one factor that might account for the difference? (Several factors may actually be involved.)

12. For which feeders and branches in a wiring installation would it be the heating rather than the voltage drop which determined the minimum wire size?

CHAPTER VII

MAGNETIC CONCEPTS AND UNITS

1. Magnetic fields. Any region in space in which a current-carrying conductor is acted upon by a force is said to be a **magnetic field.** The most extensive magnetic field of which we have any knowledge is that surrounding the earth itself. It is not a particularly strong field by comparison with some that have been produced by man, but it has strength enough to cause a measurable force on a delicately suspended current-carrying coil, or to line up the magnetic needle of a pocket compass. The magnetic fields with which we are concerned in electrical engineering are usually produced by (a) a current-carrying conductor, or coil, or (b) a permanent magnet. Both these means of producing fields have already been mentioned in describing electrical measuring instruments, the permanent magnet being an essential part of the D'Arsonval type, and the current-carrying coil, of the soft-iron and electrodynamometer types.

The action of a force on a current-carrying conductor in a magnetic field is in reality the same phenomenon that was described in Chapter II, and which served as our basis for defining unit current. Then we spoke of the force as acting between the two conductors directly. Now we regard one of the conductors as producing a magnetic field and the force as being caused by the interaction of this field and the second conductor. The magnetic field has been made an intermediate agency.

The magnetic field is of the general type referred to as **vector fields.** A vector field differs from a scalar field in that it has direction as well as magnitude. Any scalar field, such as temperature, can be completely described by giving a numerical value for each point in space throughout the region occupied by the field, but to describe completely a particular magnetic field it is necessary to specify for every point a numerical value (either field intensity or flux density), and a direction as well. The direction of a magnetic field at any point may be defined in terms of the orientation of a small current-carrying coil, so suspended that it is free to turn. Such a coil, known as an **exploring coil,** is shown in Fig. 7.1a, where it is being used to determine the direction of the field at various points in the vicinity of a straight vertical

conductor that carries current.   If we send current through the suspended coil, one of its sides will be attracted and the other repelled by
the conductor, and the coil will take up a position such that the conductor lies in the plane of the coil.   *The positive direction of the field is
conventionally taken as perpendicular to the plane of the coil, and away
from the observer when he faces the coil, so that the positive direction of the
current in it appears clockwise to him.*

If we suspend the coil in a new position, it again aligns itself so
that the conductor lies in its plane, and we may continue this procedure
to investigate the direction of the field at any number of points

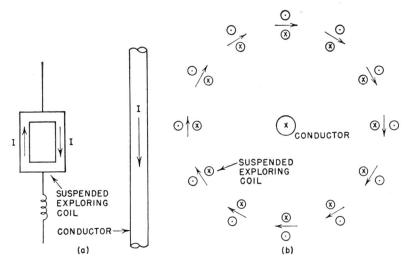

Fig. 7.1. Mapping the magnetic field around a long straight conductor by means of an
exploring coil (a) side view (b) top view.

required.   For each point investigated, we may show the direction of
the field on a plot or map by means of a small arrow, or **vector,** placed
according to the definition above.   A number of coil positions and the
corresponding arrows are shown in Fig. 7.1*b*.   It must be made clear,
however, that the field is not confined to any one plane or to any
finite distance from the conductor.   As we investigate points at
greater and greater distances, we find that our exploring coil is aligned
with less and less force, until it becomes too insensitive to give any
indication.

The suspended coil presents some difficulties in use.   For one
thing, it is difficult to conduct any considerable current into the coil
and out, and still have it perfectly free to turn.   Another objection
is that it cannot be used if the direction of the field is not horizontal,

or more precisely, it indicates only the horizontal component of the field. In practical field mapping, it is much more convenient to use magnetic needles mounted so that they can be used in either horizontal or vertical positions. It is readily demonstrated that the north-seeking end of the needle points in the direction of the field as defined above, and thus the needle may take the place of the coil.

Fundamentally, the suspended-coil method and the magnetic-needle method are the same. The needle may be regarded as containing concealed currents which account for its behavior in exactly the same way as the basic principle of forces of attraction and repulsion between current-carrying conductors accounts for the way in which the suspended coil orients itself.

2. The right-hand rule. The exploring coil and the compass needle enable us, by the rules laid down in the preceding section, to determine the direction of a magnetic field, irrespective of how the field is produced. If the field is produced by a conductor or coil in which the direction of the current is known, the direction of the field can be readily found by the following rule: *Grasp the conductor with the right hand so that the thumb points in the positive direction of the current. The fingers then encircle the wire in the positive direction of the magnetic field.*

This rule can readily be verified by applying it to the conductor shown in Fig. 7.1*b*. The rule works both ways—that is, we may use it to determine which direction current must flow in the conductor to produce a field in a given direction. In applying the rule to a coil, it is easier to let the fingers of the right hand encircle the turns in the direction of current. The thumb then points in the direction of the field inside the coil.

3. The simplest magnetic field—The toroid. The magnetic field in the vicinity of a long, straight conductor is found upon investigation to have at every point a direction which is tangent to a circle drawn in a plane perpendicular to the conductor, the circle having the conductor as its center. That the field becomes weaker as we move away from the wire is demonstrated by the behavior of the exploring coil, but just how far the field extends cannot be definitely stated. In studying the properties of magnetic fields, it would be useful if we could begin with a field the geometry of which was as simple as in the case of the straight conductor, and which, at the same time, was confined to a definite region in space. The magnetic field set up by toroidal winding which carries current (Fig. 7.2) is just such a field.

The form on which the winding is made is a wooden ring, or a paper tube bent into a circle, or if fairly stiff wire is used, the form may be removed and dispensed with altogether.   Tests with the exploring coil or compass needle show that within the turns, the field is everywhere parallel to the axis of the toroid, as indicated by the vectors in Fig. 7.2.

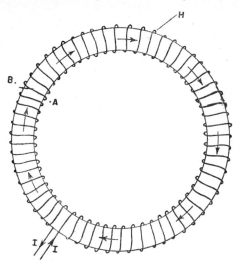

Fig. 7.2.   The simplest magnetic field—produced by a toroidal coil.

Immediately outside the turns, as at points A and B, the field is found to be very feeble as compared with the field inside, and at a small distance away from the turns, no field at all can be detected.   We can

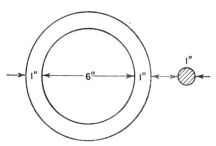

Fig. 7.3.

say with little error that the field is limited to the space inside the turns.[1]

The field of a toroidal coil, since it is practically confined to a definite region, may be thought of as having definite dimensions.   Its

[1] The error becomes smaller as the turns are more closely spaced.   If the winding consists of many turns of small wire with insulation of negligible thickness, it approximates a sheet of current over the surface of the toroid, and the field outside the toroid becomes extremely weak.

cross-sectional area is the cross-sectional area of the toroid itself, measured in a plane perpendicular to its axis. Its mean length is the circumference of the toroid, measured along its axis. The possibility of assigning a definite cross-sectional area and a definite length to the region occupied by the field makes the toroidal coil very satisfactory for framing our definitions of magnetic units.

EXAMPLE: What are the dimensions of the magnetic field set up by a toroidal coil having an inside diameter of 6 in. and an outside diameter of 8 in., as shown in Fig. 7.3?

SOLUTION:

$$\text{Radius of the cross section} = \frac{8 \text{ in.} - 6 \text{ in.}}{4} = 0.5 \text{ in.}$$

$$\text{Cross-sectional area} = \pi r^2 = 0.785 \text{ sq in.} = 0.000507 \text{ sq m.}$$

$$\text{Mean diameter of toroid} = \frac{6 \text{ in.} + 8 \text{ in.}}{2} = 7 \text{ in.}$$

$$\text{Mean length} = \pi d = 21.99 \text{ in.} = 0.559 \text{ m.}$$

4. Magnetic field strength. The torque which orients the exploring coil or the magnetic needle at a given point gives an indication of the strength of the magnetic field at that point. In the case of the field produced by the straight wire, this torque is found to decrease steadily as we move away from the wire. For the toroidal coil, the torque is found to be substantially the same for all points within the turns of the coil and to be extremely small for all points outside.

Now, let us suppose that we place the exploring coil at some certain point within the toroid, and leave it there while we try the effect of changing the current in the winding of the toroid. It is found that the torque acting to align the exploring coil is proportional to the current in the winding, as might have been expected, since this is simply a case of parallel conductors which carry current. The torque which the exploring coil experiences is found to be twice as much for a current of 2 amp in the coil as for a current of 1 amp, so we may conclude the strength of the field is proportional to the current in the toroidal winding.

In a similar way it may be shown that the strength of the field depends upon the number of turns wound upon the toroid. Doubling the number of turns will double the strength of the magnetic field, other things being equal.

5. Magnetomotive force. The effectiveness of a coil or circuit as a means of producing a magnetic field is thus measured by the product of the number of turns and the current. Any conductor, if it is to carry current, must have a return path somewhere, and is thus equivalent to one turn. When we speak of a long, straight conductor, we mean merely that the return path is so far away as to have a negligible effect on the pattern of the field in the locality. The product of turns and current is called **magnetomotive force.** The MKS unit is the **ampere-turn,** defined as follows: *One ampere-turn is the magnetomotive force produced by a current of* 1 *amp flowing in a coil of* 1 *turn.* Magnetomotive force is often abbreviated to mmf and is represented by the symbol F. The defining equation is

$$F = NI, \tag{7.1}$$

where F is the mmf in ampere-turns.

    N is number of turns.

    I is current in amperes.

The only other unit of mmf in common use is the **gilbert,** defined by the following identity:

$$1 \text{ gilbert} \equiv \frac{1}{0.4\pi} \text{ ampere-turns.} \tag{7.2}$$

6. Magnetic field intensity. In general, magnetic field intensity is a vector quantity which varies from point to point, both in direction and in magnitude. Consider a path *a-b-c-d* (Fig. 7.4) arbitrarily drawn in a magnetic field. At every point on the path, there will be a magnetic field intensity which can be represented by a vector such as H_1 in the figure. Now suppose the path to be divided up into short segments Δl so short that, for the accuracy desired, H may be considered the same in magnitude and direction all along a segment. Let us then form products by multiplying the length of each segment by the component of H that lies along the segment. One such product, for example, would be $H_1 \cos \theta_1 \Delta l$, where θ_1 is the angle made by H_1 with the segment Δl. There would be a similar product for each segment. Now let us sum up all of the products around the path and equate this to the number of ampere turns which happen to be linked by the path.

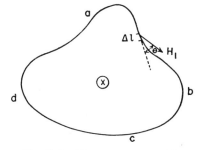

Fig. 7.4. The summation of H cos $\theta \Delta l$ around the closed path a-b-c-d is equal to the number of ampere-turns linked by the path.

$$\sum_{0}^{L} H \cos \theta \, \Delta l = NI \tag{7.3[1]}$$

This equation is to serve as our defining equation of **magnetic field intensity.** *Magnetic field intensity is that quantity which, if its products with elements of length be taken as described above, and summed up around any closed path, the summation is equal to the number of ampere turns linked by the path.*

It is obvious that any number of paths could be drawn in a magnetic field and not link the conductors or turns which were producing the field. Furthermore, the magnetic field might be produced by a permanent magnet, with no current-carrying conductors or turns involved. In such cases the right-hand side of Equation (7.3) is zero, and the summation $H \cos \theta \, \Delta l$ around the path must also be zero. This does not mean that H must be zero at any point; it simply means that H must have such values at the various points along the path that the summation will be zero.

Now let us consider the axis of a toroidal coil as a closed path in the magnetic field produced by a current in the coil. The direction of the magnetic field is everywhere parallel to the axis, making the angle θ equal to zero. Every point on the axis is situated with regard to the turns exactly as every other point, making H the same at every point. Thus, the summation becomes simply the product of H by the length of the path, and for the case of the toroid, Equation (7.3) becomes

$$HL = NI \tag{7.4}$$

or

$$H = \frac{NI}{L} \tag{7.5}$$

Magnetic field intensity at any point on the axis of the toroid is, therefore, simply magnetomotive force per unit length, measured in the direction of the field. The MKS unit of magnetic field intensity is the **ampere-turn per meter.**

EXAMPLE: What is the magnetic field intensity at a point on the axis of a toroidal coil having an inside diameter of 6 in. and an outside diameter of 8 in. and consisting of 1200 turns of wire carrying a current of 1.5 amp?

SOLUTION: The mmf by Equation (7.1) is

$$F = NI = 1200 \times 1.5 = 1800 \text{ ampere-turns.}$$

[1] More rigorously, $\int_{0}^{L} H \cos \theta \, dl = NI$, the definite integral replacing the summation, as Δl approaches zero.

The axial length of this toroid, calculated in a previous example, is 0.559 m.

The magnetic field intensity by Equation (7.5) is

$$H = \frac{NI}{L} = \frac{1800}{0.559} = 3220 \text{ ampere-turns per m.}$$

Other units of magnetic field intensity in common use are the ampere-turn per inch, and the gilbert per centimeter, or **oersted**. These units may be defined by the following identities:

$$1 \text{ ampere-turn per in.} \equiv 39.37 \text{ ampere-turns per m.} \quad (7.6)$$
$$1 \text{ oersted} \equiv 1 \text{ gilbert per cm} \equiv 79.6 \text{ ampere-turns per m.} \quad (7.7)$$

Problems

(**1-VII**) What mmf is produced by (a) A current of 1000 amp flowing in a coil of 10 turns? (b) A current of 10 amp flowing in a coil of 1000 turns? (c) A current of 53.75 amp flowing in a coil of 186 turns?

(**2-VII**) (a) Express a mmf of 1000 gilberts in ampere-turns. (b) Express a mmf of 1000 ampere-turns in gilberts.

(**3-VII**) What is the magnetic field intensity at any point on the axis of a toroid having an inside diameter of 50 cm, a diameter of cross section of 5 cm, and a winding of 1500 turns carrying a current of 0.25 amp?

(**4-VII**) For the toroid described in Problem 3-VII, what would be the greatest and the smallest magnetic field intensities at points within the turns? By what percentage do these field intensities differ from those on the axis?

(**5-VII**) What current in an 800-turn toroidal coil having an inside diameter of 15 cm and an outside diameter of 20 cm would set up a magnetic field intensity of 50 oersteds on the axis of the coil?

7. Ampere's law. Magnetic field intensity in the MKS system is always measured in ampere-turns per meter, but it cannot in general be found by simply dividing a number of ampere-turns by a number of meters. This is valid only in simple problems like that of the toroid, where it is obvious that the magnetic field intensity is the same at every point along the selected path. The student will naturally want to know how it is to be found in other problems.

A general method that is applicable whenever the field is produced by an arrangement of current-carrying conductors, and when the field lies entirely in one medium (for example, in free space) depends upon the use of

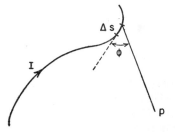

Fig. 7.5. The magnetic field intensity at the point p is found by summing up the effect of every segment ΔS of the current-carrying conductor.

certain assumptions made by Ampere and proved by him to be valid. We begin by dividing the conductor into short segments each of length ΔS (Fig. 7.5). Then we may assume that at any specified point p there will be a magnetic field intensity ΔH due to the current in a particular segment, and further that

ΔH is proportional to the current I in the segment;

ΔH is proportional to ΔS, the length of the segment;

ΔH is inversely proportional to the square of X, the distance from the segment to the point;

ΔH is proportional to the sine of the angle ϕ made with the segment by a line joining the segment to the point.

Combining these proportionalities we obtain

$$\Delta H \quad \text{is proportional to} \quad \frac{I \, \Delta S \sin \phi}{X^2}, \tag{7.8}$$

or, introducing a proportionality constant,

$$\Delta H = \frac{KI \, \Delta S \sin \phi}{X^2}. \tag{7.9}$$

Equation (7.9) is known as **Ampere's law.** In order to find the magnetic field intensity at the specified point, it is then necessary to sum up the ΔH's for every segment of the conductor which contributes to the field.

$$H = \sum_0^S \frac{KI \, \Delta S \sin \phi}{X^2}. \tag{7.10}[1]$$

As described above the computation of magnetic field intensity might seem to be a formidable undertaking and, generally speaking, this is correct. Certain symmetrical conductor arrangements, such as circular coils and solenoids, lend themselves to the ready calculation of magnetic field intensity by the methods of calculus. The magnetic field intensity produced at a given point by a straight wire, or by a conductor arrangement that can be broken down into a number of straight-wire components, may also be handled with facility.

The validity of the assumptions made is proved by the results obtained when Equation (7.10) is used to compute the magnetic field intensity at points, say on the axis of a toroidal coil, which can be

---

[1] As ΔS is allowed to approach zero, the summation becomes the definite integral

$$H = \int_0^S \frac{KI \sin \phi \, ds}{X^2}. \tag{7.11}$$

computed also by Equation (7.5). If the value assigned to K in Equation (7.10) is $1/4\pi$, the two computations give the same result. This is found to be true for any field intensity calculation that can be made by both methods.

Problems

(**6-VII**) Use Equation (7.5) to show that the magnetic field intensity at a distance of R meters from the middle of a very long straight wire carrying a current I is given by

$$H = \frac{I}{2\pi R} \text{ ampere-turns per meter.}$$

(*Hint:* Consider a circular path of radius R meters having the wire as its center and lying in a plane perpendicular to the wire. Note that the field intensity is the same at every point on the path, and its direction at any point is a tangent to the path.)

✓ (**7-VII**) The magnetic field intensity is to be found at a point 1 meter distant from the middle of a very long straight wire carrying a current of 100 amp by using Ampere's law. As a first approximation, consider the conductor to be divided up into 1-meter segments, and compute ΔH for each of the four segments nearest the point. Then take the summation and compare with the magnetic field intensity calculated by using the expression derived in Problem 6-VII. Is the difference about what you might expect? Why?

✓ (**8-VII**) Compute the magnetic field intensity at a point 1 meter distant from the middle of a very long straight wire carrying a current of 100 amp by the procedure explained in Problem 7-VII, but taking into consideration the eight 1-meter segments of wire nearest the point. Is this a better approximation than that in Problem 7-VII?

✓ (**9-VII**) Compute the magnetic field intensity at a point 1 meter distant from the middle of a very long straight wire carrying a current of 100 amp by the procedure explained in Problem 7-VII, but considering the wire divided into ½-meter segments and taking the summation of the 16 segments nearest the point. Is this a better approximation than that in Problem 7-VII?

(**10-VII**) (*This problem requires calculus.*) Compute the magnetic field intensity, at a point R meters distant from the middle, of a long straight conductor carrying a current of I amp by use of Ampere's law. Set up the expression for the differential field intensity at the point due to an element of length ΔS and, by integration, find the total field intensity due to all the elements of an infinite length of wire. Compare with the expression obtained in Problem 6-VII.

8. Faraday's law of electromagnetic induction—Magnetic flux lines.

In seeking for a relation between electricity and magnetism, Faraday, in 1831, wound two coils of insulated wire upon an iron ring. One of these coils he connected to a battery, including in the circuit a key for opening and closing it, as shown in Fig. 7.6. The other coil he connected to a galvanometer. When he closed the battery key, he noted a momentary deflection of the galvanometer, which proved that current flowed in that circuit.   Upon opening the key, a deflection in the opposite direction resulted.   To explain this phenomenon, Faraday made use of what are called **magnetic lines of flux.**   When any conductor or coil carries current, we may consider to exist in and around it and interlinked with it, a number of these magnetic lines of flux.   They may also interlink with any other coil or conductor in the region.   So long as the current in the first coil remains unchanged, the number of lines is constant, and no effect is produced.   But any change in the current in the first coil results in a change in the number of lines, and an emf is set up in the second coil.

This phenomena, which was discovered independently at about the same time by Joseph Henry, an American, is called **electromagnetic induction.**   From a theoretical viewpoint it is one of the most important of physical phenomena in that it establishes the relationship

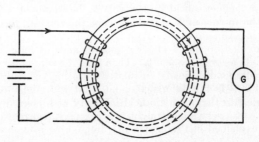

Fig. 7.6.   Induction of electromotive force by changing current in a neighboring circuit.

between electricity and magnetism; and it also has an important practical application as the principle of the transformer.   Faraday's discovery led to the formulation of the law of electromagnetic induction as follows: *Whenever the number of magnetic lines which link a coil undergoes a change, an electromotive force is induced in the coil proportional to the number of turns and to the time rate of change of lines.* Although the law was actually stated by Neumann several years after Faraday's discovery, it is usually referred to as Faraday's law of electromagnetic induction.

Obviously, what we are dealing with here is another aspect of the magnetic field.   We first described the field in terms of the forces which act upon current-carrying conductors introduced into it.   These forces (in the case of the toroid) were seen to depend upon the current in the coil and the number of turns.   We are now describing the field in terms of something we call *magnetic lines of flux*, which, when they change in number, are able to induce an emf in a coil or conductor with which they are interlinked.

The direction of the lines of flux is at any point the same as the direction of the field as defined in Section 1.   Thus, if we use the exploring coil or magnetic needle to determine field direction at a large number of points, *being careful always to move the coil or needle in the indicated direction of the field,* and marking down an arrow to represent the field direction at each point, we may draw in the lines of flux as smooth lines which coincide at each point with the direction arrows. In the case of the toroidal coil, this procedure would yield circles parallel to the axis of the toroid, as indicated by the dotted lines in Fig. 7.6.   In general, magnetic flux lines are closed lines, having no beginning and no end.

The lines, of course, are purely imaginary; they do not exist in the sense that a line on the blackboard exists.   Yet there are few, if any, concepts that are more useful.   In working with the problems of magnetism, we soon fall into the habit of referring to the lines as though they were real and as if they were the true underlying cause of forces on current-carrying conductors and emf's induced in coils. No harm is likely to come of this habit, and the concept greatly helps in clarifying our thinking, speaking, and writing about magnetic fields.

9. Magnetic flux—The weber.   Collectively, the lines are spoken of as **magnetic flux,** and are to be thought of as increasing, or decreasing, in number with the mmf of the coil that produces them.   Faraday's law of electromagnetic induction furnishes the basis for defining and measuring magnetic flux.   The MKS unit is the **weber,** defined as follows: *One weber is that flux, which if brought to zero in one second, will cause an average electromotive force of one volt to be induced in a one-turn coil which is interlinked with the flux.*

The defining equation is a mathematical statement of Faraday's law, using average rate of change of flux:

$$E = N \frac{\Delta\phi}{\Delta T},\tag{7.12}[1]$$

where E is average emf in volts.

N is number of turns on the coil.[2]

$\Delta\phi$ is change in flux in webers.

ΔT is time in seconds for the change in flux to take place.

---

[1] The student of calculus will see that the limit of $\Delta\phi / \Delta T$ as ΔT approaches zero is the derivative $d\phi/dt$.   The emf found in Equation (7.12) would be the average emf during the time ΔT, whereas the emf found by the derivative is instantaneous. The instantaneous emf would be the same as the average emf only if the rate of change of flux were uniform.

[2] An emf is induced in *any* coil with which the changing flux is interlinked.   In measuring flux a *secondary* coil, or *search* coil, is usually provided in addition to the coil which establishes the flux.

It would seem that this is a definition of change of flux, rather than of flux itself, and that is the case. An unchanging flux does not manifest itself: it is only when a change occurs that an emf will be induced in an interlinked coil   Thus, in measuring a flux we cannot establish the flux, and then determine its magnitude: we must start with the flux at some known value (usually zero), and measure the change which takes place as the flux is established.

EXAMPLE: A magnetic flux is established in a carefully demagnetized iron ring, and induces an emf of 5 v in a 20-turn coil which links the ring. The rate of establishing the flux is uniform and requires 0.01 sec. What is the final value of the flux?

SOLUTION:

$$5 = 20 \frac{\Delta\phi}{0.01}$$

$$\Delta\phi = 0.0025 \text{ weber.}$$

Assuming $\phi = 0$ to begin with, the final value of the flux is

$$0 + 0.0025 = 0.0025 \text{ weber.}$$

The only other units of magnetic flux in common use are the **maxwell** or **line,** and the **kiloline.** These units are related to the weber as follows:

$$1 \text{ maxwell} \equiv 1 \text{ line} \equiv 10^{-8} \text{ weber.} \tag{7.13}$$
$$1 \text{ kiloline} \equiv 10^{-5} \text{ weber.} \tag{7.14}$$

In this book, the weber will be consistently used in all theoretical derivations. The line and kiloline will be used in problems and calculations whenever it is more convenient.

10. Practical measurement of magnetic flux. The method of measuring flux just described is not practicable because (a) it is difficult to cause the flux to change at a uniform rate, (b) it is difficult to measure accurately the time occupied by the change, and (c) it is difficult to measure the emf induced in the search coil. In practice, we avoid these difficulties by use of a **ballistic galvanometer** or a **fluxmeter.** A ballistic galvanometer differs from an ordinary wall-type D'Arsonval galvanometer principally in the manner of its use. Instead of obtaining a steady deflection, due to a constant current passing through its coil, we obtain the maximum swing which takes place due to a momentary current. The instrument is purposely made sluggish in action, so that by the time the current ceases to flow, the movable coil will not have moved appreciably. The movement takes place after the current has ceased and may be aptly compared to the movement of a pendulum that has been struck a blow with a hammer. For such a galvanometer, it can be shown that

$$d = K_1 Q, \qquad (7.15)$$

where d is the maximum swing in scale divisions.

Q is the quantity of electricity in coulombs that passed through the galvanometer coil.

K_1 is a constant.

Now,
$$Q = I\Delta T = \frac{E}{R}\Delta T, \qquad (7.16)$$

where I is current in amperes that flows through the galvanometer coil.

ΔT is time in seconds during which current flows.

E is emf in volts developed in the coil interlinked by the changing flux.

R is the resistance of the circuit containing the search coil and the galvanometer.

From Faraday's law,

$$E\Delta T = N\Delta\phi, \qquad (7.17)$$

where N is number of turns on coil interlinked by the changing flux.

$\Delta\phi$ is change in flux in webers.

Substituting in (7.15),

$$d = \frac{K_1 N \Delta\phi}{R} = K_2 \Delta\phi, \qquad (7.18)$$

or
$$\Delta\phi = K_3 d, \qquad (7.19)$$

where
$$K_3 = \frac{R}{K_1 N}. \qquad (7.20)[1]$$

The ballistic galvanometer thus becomes, in effect, an instrument for measuring changes in magnetic flux. The constant K_3 may be calculated by Equation (7.20) provided K_1 is known, or it may be

---

[1] The mathematical development given above assumes that a steady current I flows for a time ΔT. Actually, in a flux measurement, the current would not be steady and a rigorous development would have to begin with instantaneous current i and proceed as follows:

$$Q = \int_0^I i\, dt = \int_0^I \frac{e}{R}\, dt, \qquad (7.21)$$

$$e\, dt = N\, d\phi, \qquad (7.22)$$

$$d = \frac{K_1 N}{R}\int_{\phi_1}^{\phi_2} d\phi = \frac{K_1 N}{R}[\phi_2 - \phi_1] = \frac{K_1 N \Delta\phi}{R} \qquad (7.23)$$

determined experimentally by observing the deflection which occurs when a known change of flux is brought about. An arrangement for determining the galvanometer constant experimentally and for measuring an unknown flux in an iron ring is shown in Fig. 7.7.

The flux which will be established when a certain current flows in the winding of an air-cored toroid may be calculated from the dimensions of the toroid, the number of turns, and the current. In order to determine the galvanometer constant, therefore, the dpdt switch is thrown to the left, and the current through N_1 is adjusted

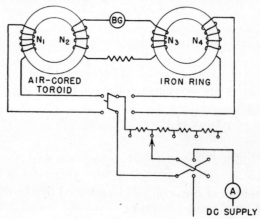

Fig. 7.7. Laboratory set-up for measuring the magnetic flux in an iron ring.

to any convenient value I_1. The flux established in the toroid may be shown to be

$$\phi = \frac{\mu_0 N_1 I_1 A}{L}, \qquad (7.24)$$

where ϕ is the flux in webers.

μ_0 is the permeability of free space $(4\pi \times 10^{-7})$.

A is the cross-sectional area of the toroid in square meters.

L is the mean length of the flux path in the toroid in meters.

The reversing switch is then operated, causing a change in flux from ϕ to $-\phi$—that is, a change $\Delta\phi = 2\phi$. This change in flux induces an emf in N_2, which sends current through the galvanometer circuit, resulting in a maximum deflection of d scale divisions. The constant of the galvanometer is then found by

$$K_3 = \frac{\Delta\phi}{d}. \qquad (7.25)$$

The dpdt switch is then thrown to the right, and the current through N_4 is adjusted to the desired value.   The reversing switch is again operated, causing a change in flux, which induces an emf in N_3 and causes the galvanometer to be deflected.   The observer reads the maximum swing, and having already determined the galvanometer constant, he is able to calculate the change in flux by Equation (7.19). If the flux in the iron ring has been put through several reversals before the reading is taken, it may usually be assumed to change from a certain value in one direction to an equal value in the opposite direction, and, on this assumption, may be taken as half the measured change.

Attention must be called to the fact that the galvanometer constant is determined for a search coil of a certain number of turns (N_2), and for a certain circuit resistance R.   A change in either of these quantities changes the constant.   By connecting the secondary coils N_2 and N_3 permanently in series with the galvanometer, as in Fig. 7.7, constant circuit resistance is assured.   Unless $N_3 = N_2$, however, the constant must be corrected for the difference in number of turns, using Equation (7.20).

EXAMPLE 1: An air-cored toroid and an iron ring are connected as shown in Fig. 7.7.   The toroid has a mean perimeter of 25 cm and a cross-sectional area of 5 sq cm. N_1 consists of 398 turns, N_2 and N_3 consist of 600 turns each.   When a current of 5 amp is reversed in N_1, a deflection of 10 scale divisions is observed.   When a current of 2 amp is reversed in N_4, a deflection of 140 scale divisions is observed.   What is the galvanometer constant?   What is the flux in the iron ring?

SOLUTION: From (7.24) the flux set up in the air-cored toroid is

$$\phi = \frac{\mu_0 N_1 I_1 A}{L} = \frac{(4\pi \times 10^{-7})(398)(5)(5 \times 10^{-4})}{(25 \times 10^{-2})} = 50 \times 10^{-7} \text{ weber.}$$

The change of flux, upon reversing the current, is

$$\Delta\phi = 2\phi = 100 \times 10^{-7} \text{ weber.}$$

The galvanometer constant is

$$K_3 = \frac{\Delta\phi}{d} = \frac{100 \times 10^{-7}}{10} = 10 \times 10^{-7} \text{ weber per scale division.}$$

Since $N_3 = N_2$, the constant is the same when the change in flux occurs in the iron ring, and

$$\Delta\phi = K_3 d = (10 \times 10^{-7})(140) = 1400 \times 10^{-7} \text{ weber.}$$

Assuming that this change is from a certain value in one direction to an equal value in the other direction,

$$\phi = \frac{\Delta\phi}{2} = \frac{1400 \times 10^{-7}}{2} = 700 \times 10^{-7} \text{ weber} = 7000 \text{ maxwells}.$$

EXAMPLE 2: What would have been the galvanometer constant in Example 1 if N_3 had been 300 turns? What deflection would have been observed when the current in N_4 was reversed?

SOLUTION: From (7.20),

$$K_3 = \frac{R}{K_1 N}.$$

Since R and K_1 remain unchanged, reducing N to half as much would make K_3 twice as much. The new K_3 would, therefore, be

$$2 \times (10 \times 10^{-7}) = 20 \times 10^{-7}.$$

Since the change of flux in the iron ring is the same as before, the new deflection, from (7.25), will be

$$d = \frac{\Delta\phi}{K_3} = \frac{1400 \times 10^{-7}}{20 \times 10^{-7}} = 70 \text{ scale divisions}.$$

A fluxmeter is essentially a ballistic galvanometer in which the restoring torque has been made as nearly zero as possible by suitably designing the leads by which connection to the moving coil is made. The moving coil will thus remain at rest in any position, and some means is usually provided for setting the indicator on zero before a reading is to be taken. The instrument is calibrated with a suitable search coil, and the scale is marked to read in webers or kilolines directly. The calibration is valid so long as the same search coil is used. Since there is no restoring torque it is not necessary to watch for a maximum deflection as with a ballistic galvanometer. The pointer comes to rest to indicate the change of flux linking the search coil. These features, and the portability of the fluxmeter make it considerably more convenient to use than a ballistic galvanometer.

11. Magnetic flux density. Magnetic flux density, like magnetic field intensity, is a vector quantity which may vary from point to point, both in direction and in magnitude. Consider a surface a-b-c-d, Fig. 7.8, which lies in a magnetic field and which is penetrated by the lines of magnetic flux. At every point there will be a magnetic flux density which can be represented by a vector such as B. The direction of the vector is the direction of the field at that point, and its length is proportional to the flux density. Now suppose the surface to be divided into small areas ΔA, so small that the flux density may be considered as being uniform over ΔA.   Then suppose we form products such as $B \cos \theta \, \Delta A$ by multiplying the area by the component of flux density perpendicular to the area, and finally that we sum up all the products over the specified surface and equate this to the flux ϕ which penetrates the surface.

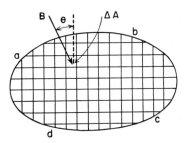

$$\sum_{0}^{A} B \cos \theta \, \Delta A \; = \; \phi. \qquad (7.26)^1$$

This equation is to serve as our definition of **magnetic flux density**.   *Magnetic flux density is that quantity which, if its products with elements of area be taken as described above, and summed up over any given surface, the summation is equal to the amount of magnetic flux penetrating the surface.*

Fig. 7.8. The summation of B cos $\theta \Delta$A over the surface is equal to the total flux penetrating the surface.

   In a case where the flux density is the same at every point over a specified surface and is perpendicular to the surface, Equation (7.26) would become simply

$$BA \; = \; \phi, \qquad (7.27)$$

or

$$B \; = \; \frac{\phi}{A}. \qquad (7.28)$$

Magnetic flux density in this case is seen to be the magnetic flux per unit area, and this is true in general, but it must be remembered that it is not possible, in general, to find the flux density at a point by simply dividing a flux by an area.   This is valid only if the flux density is uniform over the area.

   The MKS unit of magnetic flux density is the **weber per sq. meter.**

   EXAMPLE: The toroid shown in Fig. 7.3 has a flux of 10^{-4} weber established in it by current in a magnetizing winding.   What is the mean flux density?

   SOLUTION: The magnetic lines in a toroidal coil are all parallel to the axis.   The area of the flux path perpendicular to the lines is, therefore, simply the cross-sectional area of the toroid.   This was

---

[1] To be rigorously correct we must reduce ΔA to a point.   As the elemental areas are made smaller and smaller and ΔA approaches zero the summation of equation 7.26 becomes the definite integral

$$\int_{0}^{A} B \cos \theta \, dA \; = \; \phi.$$

calculated in a previous example to be 0.000507 sq m. The flux density from Equation (7.28) is, therefore,

$$B = \frac{10^{-4}}{5.07 \times 10^{-4}} = 0.1975 \text{ weber per sq m.}$$

The flux density is not the same at every point in a given cross section of the toroid, but varies from a maximum value at a point on the shortest magnetic line just inside the turns to a minimum value at a point on the longest magnetic line which lies within the turns. The flux density calculated in the foregoing example is an average, or mean value, and does not prevail at every point. If the diameter of the toroid is great as compared with the diameter of its cross section, however, the difference in minimum and maximum flux densities will be small, and there is not much error in assuming the flux density to be uniform.

Other units of flux density in common use are the **gauss,** which is one line per square centimeter, and the kiloline per square inch. These units are related to the MKS unit as follows:

$$1 \text{ gauss} \equiv 10^{-4} \text{ weber per sq m.} \tag{7.29}$$
$$1 \text{ kiloline per sq in.} \equiv .0155 \text{ weber per sq m.} \tag{7.30}$$

Problems

(**11-VII**) The flux through a 500-turn search coil is changed at a uniform rate from $+\phi$ to $-\phi$ in 0.05 sec. The emf induced in the search coil is 0.0015 v. What is the value of ϕ?

(**12-VII**) Flux changing at a uniform rate induces an emf of 0.004 v in a 1000-turn coil which is linked by the flux. What is the rate of change of flux? What is the final value of the flux if the initial value was zero and the change continues at the same rate for 0.075 sec?

(**13-VII**) A ballistic galvanometer used with a certain coil has a constant of 0.001 weber per scale division. A certain change in the amount of flux linking the coil results in a deflection of 35 scale divisions. If the flux was 2.5 webers before the change and is known to have decreased, what is the new value of the flux after the change?

(**14-VII**) A ballistic galvanometer used in connection with a 200-turn coil gives a deflection of 120 scale divisions when the flux linking the coil is changed from 1.10×10^{-4} weber to -1.10×10^{-4} weber. What is the constant of the galvanometer used with this coil? What would be the constant of the galvanometer used with a 15-turn coil?

(**15-VII**) A ballistic galvanometer used in connection with a 25-turn coil gives a deflection of 30 scale divisions when the flux linking the coil is doubled, the initial value being 2×10^{-4} weber. The resistance of the galvanometer circuit is 15,000 ohms. What is the constant of the galvanometer with this coil? What would be the galvanometer constant if a 100-turn coil were used?

(16-VII) Write the equations relating the various units of flux.

(17-VII) (a) Express a flux of 1.5 webers in kilolines. (b) Express a flux of 1,600,000 maxwells in webers. (c) Express a flux of 0.0005 weber in lines. (d) Express a flux of 200 kilolines in webers.

(18-VII) What is the flux density in a surface where (a) A flux of 1 weber is uniformly distributed over an area of 100 sq cm? (b) A flux of 6000 maxwells is uniformly distributed over an area of 1 sq m?

(19-VII) What is the total flux through a plane surface 20 cm $\times$ 20 cm if the flux density is (a) 10^{-4} weber per sq m, (b) 100 kilolines per sq in., (c) 15,000 gausses? The flux density may be considered to be uniform over the entire area.

(20-VII) Write the equations relating the various units of flux density.

(21-VII) The flux density in the magnetic field of the earth at a certain locality is 0.6 gauss. The magnetic lines make an angle of 65° with the horizontal. What total flux in webers penetrates a horizontal surface of 10 sq. in. area?

(22-VII) For studying the earth's magnetic field a concentrated circular coil of many turns of fine wire, and rotatable about a diameter, is sometimes used in connection with a ballistic galvanometer or flux meter. Using a coil of 30 cm mean diameter and flux meter calibrated to give a deflection of 1 scale division for a change of flux of 10 lines, the following data is taken:

1. Beginning with the plane of the coil horizontal and the turning axis in a N-S line, the coil is rotated through 180° and a deflection of 79.4 scale divisions is obtained.

2. Beginning with the turning axis vertical and the plane of the coil in an E-W line, the coil is rotated through 180° and a deflection of 45.8 scale divisions is observed.

Calculate the flux density of the magnetic field and the angle which the flux lines make with the horizontal.

12. Relation of flux density to magnetic field intensity.

We have now two ways of describing a magnetic field (a) we may state the magnetic field intensity at every point or (b) we may state the magnetic flux density at every point. The statement in either case may take the form of an equation, for simple fields like that of the toroidal coil, or it may take the form of a graphical representation or field map. The later form may be the only one possible if the field is at all complicated. In either case, the statement must tell the direction of the field, as well as the magnitude, at every point.

Magnetic field intensity is a function of the current in the magnetizing coil or conductor which sets up the field, of the number of turns, and of the location of the point relative to the coil or conductor. Magnetic field intensity does not depend upon the medium, or substance, in which the field is set up. For the simple case of the toroidal coil, the magnetic field intensity is readily calculated by Equation (7.5). The value obtained is the same regardless of whether the toroid itself is empty or filled with some substance, such as iron.

Magnetic flux density, however, depends upon the substance in which the field exists. If arrangements are made to measure the flux which is established in a toroid, using a ballistic galvanometer as outlined in Section 10, it will be found that the flux (and, consequently, the flux density) will be enormously increased by substituting an iron core for the air within the toroid.

Our next task is to show that flux density is related to field intensity through permeability, which, it will be remembered, is one of the four fundamental concepts upon which our MKS system of units is based. In order to do this, we shall make use of dimensional analysis, and of the various defining equations which have been given for the electric and magnetic quantities we have studied. In dimensional analysis, we deal with symbols rather than numbers. Any length is dimensionally the equivalent of any other length, and an area is dimensionally a length squared. We shall not concern ourselves about what length or what area or what current is meant, but solely with the dimensions of these quantities. Factors that are merely numbers without dimensions are neglected.

Dimensionally, flux density is

$$B = \frac{\phi}{A}. \tag{7.28}$$

The defining equation of flux is

$$E = N \frac{\Delta \phi}{\Delta T}, \tag{7.12}$$

from which, dimensionally,

$$\phi = ET. \tag{7.31}$$

Substituting (7.31) in (7.28) and putting L^2 for A, we get

$$B = \frac{ET}{L^2}. \tag{7.32}$$

The defining equation for potential difference is

$$E = \frac{W}{Q}. \tag{2.16}$$

Substituting (2.16) in (7.32), we get

$$B = \frac{WT}{QL^2}. \tag{7.33}$$

The defining equation for work is

$$W = FL. \tag{1.4}$$

The defining equation for quantity of electricity is

$$Q = IT. \tag{2.13}$$

Substituting (1.4) and (2.13) in (7.33),

$$B = \frac{FLT}{ITL^2} = \frac{F}{IL}. \tag{7.34}$$

Dimensionally, magnetic field intensity is

$$H = \frac{I}{L}. \tag{7.35}$$

Dividing (7.34) by (7.35),

$$\frac{B}{H} = \frac{FL}{I^2L} = \frac{F}{I^2}. \tag{7.36}$$

The defining equation for current is

$$F = \frac{\mu L I_1 I_2}{2\pi S}, \tag{2.8}$$

from which dimensionally

$$F = \mu I^2. \tag{7.37}$$

Substituting (7.37) in (7.36),

$$\frac{B}{H} = \frac{\mu I^2}{I^2} = \mu. \tag{7.38}$$

We have thus shown that, dimensionally, magnetic flux density divided by magnetic field intensity is permeability. It is not evident from the above analysis, however, that the correct numerical value of permeability would be obtained. It would seem that disregarding constants and considering one length the equivalent of another would make Equation (7.38) useless for calculations. That this is not the case may be demonstrated by measuring the flux set up within the turns of an air-cored toroid when they carry a known current. By the method outlined on p. 163, the flux constant of a ballistic galvanometer may be obtained independently, and the instrument may then be used to measure the flux in the toroid. If the measured flux density in webers per sq. m. be divided by the magnetic field intensity in ampere-turns per meter, the result will be found to have a numerical value of $4\pi \times 10^{-7}$. This is the value assigned to the permeability of space.

The earlier statement that a numerical value was arbitrarily assigned to the permeability of space is not quite correct. A value *could have been* arbitrarily assigned, had the MKS system been set up without regard to any earlier system. It was necessary, however, if the system was to become generally used that the units of current, potential difference, resistance etc. be identical with the practical units of those quantities already in general use. This made necessary the factor 10^{-7} in the numerical value selected for the permeability of space. The decision to set up a rationalized system (one in which magneto-motive force would be calculated as amperes $\times$ turns rather than $4\pi \times$ amperes $\times$ turns) was responsible for the factor 4π in the value selected.

As was pointed out in Chapter II, the permeabilities of most substances are almost exactly equal to the permeability of space. The only substances having permeabilities greatly different from this value are those such as iron, nickel, cobalt, and certain ferromagnetic alloys. For such substances, permeability is a function of magnetic flux density and has to be determined experimentally.

The ratio of the flux density over the magnetic field intensity will be the absolute permeability of the substance within the toroid, according to Equation (7.38).

The **relative permeability** μ_R of a substance is the ratio of its absolute permeability over the permeability of free space

$$\mu_R = \frac{\mu}{\mu_0} = \frac{\mu}{4\pi \times 10^{-7}}. \tag{7.39}$$

Relative permeability is useful when it is desired to compare the magnetic properties of a given substance with those of space. In all calculations involving permeability, however, it is the absolute value that must be used.

Problems

(**23-VII**) What is the permeability in MKS units of a material in which (a) A magnetic flux density of 1 weber per sq m corresponds to a magnetic field intensity of 400 ampere-turns per m? (b) A magnetic flux density of 0.5 weber per sq m corresponds to a magnetic field intensity of 5000 ampere-turns per m? (c) A magnetic flux density of 0.875 weber per sq m corresponds to a magnetic field intensity of 35 ampere-turns per in? (d) A magnetic flux density of 12,500 gausses corresponds to a magnetic field intensity of 2550 ampere-turns per m? What is the relative permeability?

(**24-VII**) Show that for an air-cored toroid $\phi = \mu_0 N_1 I_1 A / L$.

(**25-VII**) By means of dimensional analysis, show that

$$H = M^{1/2}L^{-1/2}T^{-1}\mu^{-1/2},$$

where H is magnetic field intensity, M is mass, L is length, T is time, and μ is permeability.

(**26-VII**) By means of dimensional analysis, show that

$$B = M^{1/2}L^{-1/2}T^{-1}\mu^{1/2},$$

where B is magnetic flux density, M is mass, L is length, T is time, and μ is permeability.

13. Energy of the magnetic field. The establishing of any magnetic field involves the storage of a definite amount of energy. This energy must necessarily come from the circuit containing the coil, or conductor, which establishes the field. If the field is in free space, all of the energy stored is recoverable, and is returned to the circuit when current ceases to flow and the field collapses. In general, however, some part of the energy is lost in the medium, or substance, in

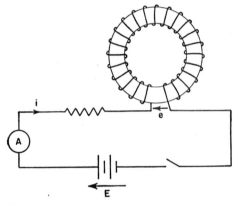

Fig. 7.9. Storage of energy in a magnetic field.

which the field is established, and is not recoverable. The amount of energy stored in any magnetic field may be expressed in terms of the magnetic field intensity, the magnetic flux density, and the volume of the space occupied by the field. In working out this expression, we shall again take advantage of the simplicity offered by the magnetic field of the toroid. If we close the switch in the circuit shown in Fig. 7.9, current will begin to flow, and the establishment of the magnetic field within the turns of the toroid will commence. As a result of the increasing number of magnetic lines, an emf,

$$E = N \frac{\Delta\phi}{\Delta T}, \tag{7.12}$$

will be induced in the coil, according to Faraday's law. Now, it must be understood that this emf is induced only so long as the flux is increasing—which is to say, only so long as the current is increasing. It is a well-established fact that the current does not assume its steady-state value instantly upon closing the switch, but requires a definite length of time to increase from zero to the value finally indicated by the ammeter. How long a time is required depends upon the coil itself and upon the resistance included in the circuit; it may be only a few microseconds in the case of an air-cored coil with only a few turns, or several seconds for an iron-cored coil with many turns. But in any case, the emf persists as long as the current and the number of magnetic lines continue to increase. While this is going on, energy is being supplied to the coil at a rate

$$P = EI = N \frac{\Delta \phi}{\Delta T} I. \tag{7.40}^1$$

But
$$\phi = BA \tag{7.27}$$

and
$$H = \frac{NI}{L}, \tag{7.5}$$

from which
$$I = \frac{HL}{N}.$$

Substituting in (7.40),

$$P = N \frac{\Delta BA}{\Delta T} \left(\frac{HL}{N} \right)$$
$$= \frac{H \Delta B}{\Delta T} (AL). \tag{7.41}$$

The incremental amount of energy supplied during a time ΔT is

$$\Delta W = P \Delta T = H \Delta B (AL), \tag{7.42}$$

and the total energy that has to be supplied to establish a magnetic field of flux density B is the summation of all the incremental amounts of energy, beginning with B equal to zero, and continuing until B becomes equal to the desired value.

$$W = \Sigma H \Delta B (AL). \tag{7.43}$$

But it can be seen that AL is simply the volume of the toroid; therefore, the energy per unit volume is

$$W = \Sigma H \Delta B. \tag{7.44}^2$$

[1] To be more rigorous, we would use the methods of calculus and deal with instantaneous values of e, i, ϕ, B and H. In the approximate derivation above E and I are the average values of emf and current during the interval of time ΔT.

[2] The student of calculus can see that as ΔB approaches zero, this expression becomes the definite integral $\int H dB$. This expression is not particularly useful, however, since if permeability is constant, energy of the field can be calculated by (7.46) or (7.47) as shown, whereas if permeability is not constant, it is easier to use the summation than to try to evaluate the integral.

The meaning of this expression can be made clear by referring to the graphical representation in Fig. 7.10.   Here the flux density B is plotted against the magnetic field intensity H for a substance of constant permeability, such as air.   It can be seen that $H\Delta B$ is approximately the area of one of the strips of length H and width ΔB, and that the approximation becomes closer as ΔB is made smaller. $\Sigma H \Delta B$ is the total area of all such strips from $B = 0$ to $B = B$.   Therefore, the stored energy can be found by determining the area oab in Fig. 7.10, taking into account the scale of H and the scale of B.   Since this area

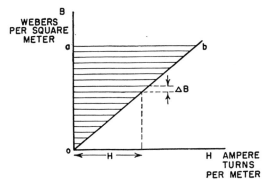

Fig. 7.10.   Graphical representation of energy storage in a magnetic field.

is a triangle when the field is in air, its area is $\frac{1}{2}BH$, and the energy per unit volume is

$$W = \frac{1}{2}\, BH, \tag{7.45}$$

or since
$$B = \mu_0 H, \tag{7.38}$$

$$W = \frac{1}{2}\frac{B^2}{\mu_0} \tag{7.46}$$

$$= \frac{1}{2}\, \mu_0 H^2, \tag{7.47}$$

where B is the final value of the flux density in webers per square
   meter.

   H is magnetic field intensity in ampere-turns per meter.

   W is energy in joules per cubic meter.

   It is important to point out that Equation (7.44) is general and holds regardless of whether permeability is constant or not, whereas Equations (7.46) and (7.47) are useful only if the field was established in a medium of constant permeability.

Problems

(**27-VII**) Calculate the energy stored in the magnetic field of an air-cored toroid which has a mean diameter of 25 cm and a cross-sectional area of 5 sq cm when the winding of 800 turns carries a current of 2.5 amp. Assume that the field is confined to the space within the turns.

(**28-VII**) The air gaps of a six-pole dynamo are 0.275 in. long (in the direction of the magnetic lines) and the cross-sectional area under each pole is 100 sq in. Calculate the energy stored in the magnetic field in the air gaps when the flux density is 1.5 webers per sq m.

14. Reluctance and the magnetic circuit. When a magnetic field is practically confined to a definite region (as in the toroidal coil or in any instance where the path of the magnetic flux lines lies entirely in iron, or nearly so), we have what is called a **magnetic circuit.** This

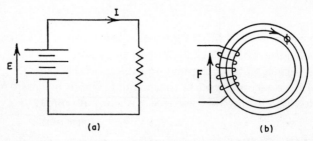

Fig. 7.11. Comparison of simple electric and magnetic circuits.

name was applied because of certain similarities between the establishment of magnetic flux lines in iron paths and the flow of current in electric circuits. These similarities are brought out in Fig. 7.11. In Fig. 7.11a, a battery having an emf E causes a current I to flow around a circuit made up of conductors having a total resistance R. In Fig. 7.11b, a coil having an mmf F causes a magnetic flux ϕ to be established throughout a circuit consisting of an iron ring having a total **reluctance** $\Re$. Reluctance is thus introduced as the magnetic equivalent of electrical resistance. No name has yet been assigned to the MKS unit of reluctance, but the definition can be stated as follows: *A magnetic flux path has a reluctance of one MKS unit if a magnetomotive force of one ampere-turn causes a flux of one weber.*

The defining equation is

$$\Re = \frac{F}{\phi}, \tag{7.48}$$

where $\Re$ is reluctance in MKS units.

F is mmf in ampere-turns.

ϕ is magnetic flux in webers.

We may calculate the reluctance of a magnetic circuit from its dimensions and the permeability of the material, as will now be shown. From the definition of magnetic field intensity,

$$F = HL,$$

and from Equation (7.27),

$$\phi = BA.$$

Substituting in (7.48),

$$\mathfrak{R} = \frac{HL}{BA}. \tag{7.49}$$

From Equation (7.38),

$$B = \mu H.$$

Substituting in (7.49),

$$\mathfrak{R} = \frac{HL}{\mu H A} = \frac{L}{\mu A}, \tag{7.50}$$

where $\mathfrak{R}$ is reluctance in MKS units.

L is length of the magnetic circuit in meters.

μ is permeability of the material used, in MKS units.

A is cross-sectional area of the magnetic circuit in square meters.

Equation (7.50) may be compared with Equation 6.4:

$$R = \frac{\rho L}{A},$$

which enables us to calculate the resistance of a conductor from its dimensions. Equation (7.48) is often called Ohm's law for magnetic circuits, from its similarity to the expression

$$R = \frac{V}{I}. \tag{3.6}$$

This method of dealing with the magnetic field in certain instances as though it were a kind of circuit makes it possible for the student to understand and solve some of the most important magnetic problems. In general, the calculation of magnetic field intensities, even for simple conductor arrangements, is a formidable mathematical task, involving vectors in three-dimensional space. By making certain assumptions, which are not too far from true, we are often able to treat the field as though it were in one dimension only.

In some respects, however, the magnetic circuit is quite different from the electric circuit, and these differences should be understood. First, the magnetic circuit is not a circuit at all, in the sense that anything circulates around it. There is no magnetic particle comparable to the electron. The name magnetic flux implies *flow of something*, yet the magnetic lines, as has been pointed out, are purely imaginary.

The second difference to be pointed out lies in the available materials for constructing circuits. If it is desired to confine electric current to a certain path, it is readily done, because we have insulating materials that, as compared with the metals used for conductors, have practically zero conductivity. For low-voltage circuits, such as used in the laboratory, insulation presents so little difficulty that the student may well be unaware of the problem altogether. The task of confining magnetic lines to a certain path is not so easy. The permeability of most materials as compared with that of the best iron is by no means zero. As it is sometimes stated, there is no "magnetic insulator." Consequently, we must expect to find magnetic flux existing in paths other than the one which we wish it to take. It is this **leakage flux** about which assumptions must usually be made when setting up a magnetic-circuit problem.

A third difference is also attributable to the nature of magnetic materials as compared with those used for electric circuits. Metal wires, so long as their temperatures remain reasonably constant, have constant resistances. Since most circuits are constructed of metal wires, Ohm's law is applicable, and many calculations are made by use of it. Some circuits contain elements having variable resistances, and requiring special treatment, but these nonlinear circuits are the exception rather than the rule. Magnetic circuits, on the other hand, are built of iron or other ferromagnetic material of which the permeability is a function of flux density. The reluctance, in turn, depends upon permeability, and consequently can seldom be treated as a constant. The so-called "Ohm's law for the magnetic circuit," therefore, is by no means as useful as Ohm's law for the electric circuit. Magnetic circuits are nonlinear almost without exception, and require graphical or semigraphical treatment.

Problems

(**29-VII**) What is the reluctance of a magnetic circuit in which a mmf of 1525 ampere-turns establishes a flux of 0.083 weber?

(**30-VII**) What is the reluctance of an air gap in a magnetic circuit that is 0.1665 cm long and 5 sq cm in cross-sectional area?

(**31-VII**) An iron ring of rectangular cross section has an inside diameter of 6 in., an outside diameter of 8 in., and a thickness of 0.75 in. It is uniformly wound with a coil of 750 turns. When a current of 1.5 amp flows in the coil, a flux of 0.0002 weber is established. Calculate the mmf, the magnetic field intensity, the magnetic flux density, the reluctance, the permeability, and the relative permeability.

(**32-VII**) A toroidal coil of circular cross section is wound on a paper form and has an inside diameter of 12 in., an outside diameter of 15 in., and is wound with 1050 turns of wire. What flux will be set up in this coil by a current of 2 amp?

(**33-VII**) A 50-turn secondary coil is wound over the toroidal coil described in Problem 32-VII and connected in series with a 20,000-ohm resistance to a ballistic galvanometer. It is then found that reversing a current of 2 amp in the primary coil gives a deflection of 42 scale divisions. What is the galvanometer constant in webers per scale division? What precautions must be taken in using the galvanometer constant found by this procedure?

(**34-VII**) An air-cored toroid and an iron ring are connected as in Fig. 7.7 for taking magnetic data on the iron ring. The air-cored toroid has a mean diameter of 10 in. and a diameter of cross section of 1 in. The iron ring is rectangular in cross section, has an inside diameter of 6 in., an outside diameter of 8 in., and a thickness of ¾ in. The number of turns N_1 is 850, N_2 is 550, N_3 is 50, and N_4 is 1500. The resistance R is 20,000 ohms. Data are taken by the method of reversing the current and reading the deflection of the galvanometer, as described in Section 10. When a current of 4.5 amp is reversed in coil N_1, a deflection of 30 scale divisions is observed. When a current of 1.25 amp is reversed in coil N_4, a deflection of 210 scale divisions is observed. Calculate the magnetic field intensity in the ring in ampere-turns per in. Calculate the magnetic flux density in the ring in kilolines per sq in. By what number must the galvanometer deflection be multiplied to obtain flux density directly? Could this number be treated as a constant?

Study Questions

1. How would you obtain data for plotting a temperature field? Why is this a scalar and not a vector field?

2. How would you obtain data for plotting a gravitational field? Is it a scalar field or a vector field? Why?

3. Instead of the right-hand rule as stated in Art. 2, many books state a "right-hand screw" relationship between current direction and direction of the magnetic field. What would the relationship be?

4. A toroidal coil is to be built for demonstrating the simplicity of the field as described in Art. 3. A small magnetic needle is to be used to indicate field direction and strength What suggestions can you offer on how to design the coil (number of turns, spacing of turns, etc.)?

5. At Station A in an electrical laboratory a magnetic needle behaves in the normal manner, its north-seeking end pointing to the magnetic north. As the needle is moved toward station B, it begins to point east of the magnetic north and at Station B is violently deflected to point east. Make a sketch of the floor plan of the lab, showing the stations A and B and a hypothetical current-carrying conductor that would cause the needle to behave as outlined above.

6. Under what circumstances would magnetomotive force be numerically equal to the current producing it?

7. In a plane perpendicular to a long straight vertical wire carrying a current of $+I$ amp upward, a circle of radius R meters is drawn with the wire as the center. Sketch this arrangement as seen from above, and place a vector to indicate the magnetic field intensity at one point on the circle. Would you expect the magnetic field intensity at any other point on the circle to be the same in magnitude? In direction? If the summation of magnetic field intensity around the circle is taken according to Equation (7.5), what value must it have?

8. In a plane perpendicular to a long straight vertical wire carrying a current of $+I$ amp upward, a circle of radius R meters is drawn with its center $2R$ meters from the point where the wire intersects the plane. Sketch this arrangement as seen from above, and place a vector to indicate the magnetic field intensity at one point on the circle. Would you expect the magnetic field intensity at any other point on the circle to be the same in magnitude? In direction? If the summation of magnetic field intensity around the circle is taken according to Equation (7.3), what value must it have? How is this possible?

9. The magnetic field intensity at a point opposite the middle of a long straight current-carrying conductor is to be found by Ampere's law. Which segment of wire contributes the most? If the contribution of this segment is taken as 1.0, what would be the contribution of a segment 1 m further along the wire? Assume the point is 10 cm distant from the wire.

10. Could a ballistic galvanometer or a fluxmeter be correctly called a "volt-second meter"? What basis exists for this usage?

11. Interference with telephone and telegraph lines often results from alternating current power lines running parallel to them and close by. Explain. Would there be interference from direct current power lines carrying steady currents? Why?

12. Make sketches showing the flux lines in the vicinity of a long straight current-carrying conductor, both end-view and side-view. Indicate relative flux density by spacing of the flux lines. Indicate positive directions of flux lines and current. How far from the conductor do the flux lines extend?

13. Is it possible to have a flux density of 1 weber per sq m without having a total flux of 1 weber? Explain.

14. Permeability was introduced in Chapter II as that property of a substance which influences the force acting between current-carrying conductors placed in it. In this chapter we find that permeability may also be regarded as that property of a substance . . . . Complete the statement.

15. Is any energy required to *maintain* a steady magnetic field after it is established? Explain.

16. A paramount principle in designing electrical machinery is to produce a given magnetic flux with as few ampere-turns as possible. What does this imply as to reluctance? How can this be brought about?

CHAPTER VIII

CHARACTERISTICS OF FERROMAGNETIC MATERIALS

1. Magnetic properties of matter. The magnetic properties of most substances differ so little from the magnetic properties of free space that they are of no practical use in the construction of magnetic circuits. Substances generally may be classified as **diamagnetic,** having permeabilities slightly less than the permeability of free space, and **paramagnetic,** having permeabilities slightly greater than that of free space. Bismuth, silver, copper, and hydrogen, for example, are diamagnetic, but platinum, aluminum, and oxygen are paramagnetic. A few substances have permeabilities so much greater than free space that they are treated as a separate class, called **ferromagnetic.** The principal ferromagnetic element is iron. Iron and the various steels are used almost altogether in electrical machinery, though cobalt and nickel are also ferromagnetic, and various alloys containing these elements are used for special purposes.

The magnetic properties of substances are explained by supposing that there exist within the atoms themselves the equivalent of minute circuits in which currents flow. This theory was suggested by Ampere, long before anything was known of atomic structure, and it was necessarily vague as to the details until recent years. The present-day theory of atomic structure lends support to Ampere's theory of a hundred years ago. In addition to the magnetic effects of the electrons moving in their orbits about the nucleus of the atom (which would obviously be the equivalent of currents), the electrons themselves are believed to spin about their own axes, and thereby also to produce magnetic effects. The magnetic behavior of an atom of any particular element is then determined by the combined effects of all the orbital motions and all the electron spins within the atom. Since there is the possibility of the orbital motions or the spins having such senses and such orientations as to partially or wholly neutralize one another's effects, it is not surprising that atoms of various elements possess widely different magnetic properties. An atom in which the neutralization of all magnetic effects is complete would possess no **magnetic moment**—that is, no torque would act on such an atom to orient it in any particular way in a magnetic field.   Magnetic moment is thus a measure of the extent to which atoms of any particular substance are magnetic.

In a paramagnetic substance, the atoms or molecules have small magnetic moments.   If a paramagnetic substance is placed in a magnetic field, the atoms (or molecules in the case of a gas) are oriented just as small current-carrying loops would be.   They then contribute their bit to the effect of the current that sets up the field, and thus increase the flux density without any increase in magnetic field intensity.   The permeability of the substance is, therefore, slightly greater

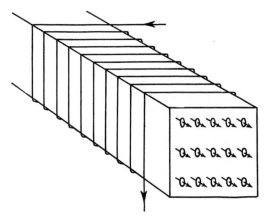

Fig. 8.1.   Orientation of the atoms of a paramagnetic substance in a magnetic field.

than the permeability of space.   It is not necessary that the entire atom change its angular position in the process of being oriented. Orientation can be accomplished by certain electron spins, or orbits, within the atom realigning themselves so that their magnetic effects coincide with the applied field.

If a diamagnetic substance is placed in a magnetic field, instead of the atoms being oriented so as to aid the field, the magnetic axis of each atom apparently takes up a precessional motion about the direction of the applied field, as the axis of a spinning top precesses about the vertical.   Precession can be shown to have the same effect as would the realignment of the atoms in such a way as to oppose the applied field.   There is, therefore, a decrease in flux density without any change in magnetic field intensity, and the permeability of the substance is slightly less than the permeability of space.

2. Theory of ferromagnetism. In ferromagnetic substances, the atoms, instead of acting independently, appear to be grouped magnetically into what are called **domains.** A domain may contain as many as 10^{15} atoms, and all of the atoms in a domain are believed to be so aligned that their magnetic effects are all in the same direction. The atoms are so interlocked within the domain that the realignment of any must mean the realignment of all. A single, large magnetic moment is thus substituted for a larger number of small independent ones. At some temperature between 400° and 700° C, any specimen of iron or steel loses its ferromagnetic properties. This is evidently due to the thermal agitation becoming so great that the regimentation of individual atomic magnetic moments into domains no longer exists. The temperature at which this occurs is called the **Curie point.**

Iron, like all metals, is crystalline in structure, the crystals being made up of atoms arranged geo-metrically in the space lattice. The arrangement in iron is cubic, with atoms at the corners of the cubes and at the centers, as shown in Fig. 8.2. This type of space lattice is known as **body-centered.** The normal direction of alignment of any particular domain is parallel to the edges of the cubes which make up the space lattice, in what is called, in crystallography, a **100** direction. Any diagonal of the

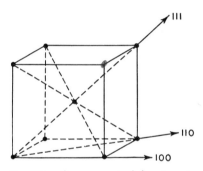

Fig. 8.2. Arrangement of the atoms in the space-lattice of iron.

faces of the cubes is a **110 direction,** and any diagonal of the cubes themselves is a **111 direction.** The iron crystals are made up, in turn, of large numbers of domains. About one sixth of all the domains in a crystal have their magnetic axes aligned in each of the six possible 100 directions, so that the crystal as a whole has zero magnetic moment. Any ordinary specimen of iron consists of a large number of crystals, with no particular orientation of the space lattice of one relative to the space lattice of the next. It is possible, however, to produce single crystals large enough to be tested magnetically, and much has been learned from the study of these crystals.

If a specimen of iron consisting of a single crystal is placed in a magnetic field so that the direction of the field coincides with one of the 100 directions of the crystal, part of the domains are already in alignment with the field, as shown in Fig. 8.3a. As the magnetic field intensity is increased, the remainder of the domains readily realign their magnetic axes to coincide with the particular 100 direction in which the field acts, as shown in Fig. 8.3*b*. The alignment of these domains gives rise to what is known as the **Barkhausen effect.** If a second coil is wound on the specimen of iron and connected to a suitable amplifier, which in turn operates a loud-speaker, magnetization of the specimen is attended by a rapid succession of clicks, corresponding to the sudden orientation of domains from one of the 100 directions to another. It is believed, furthermore, that the domains which happen to be already in alignment gain slightly in size at the expense of neighboring domains when the field is applied. This is thought to be the explanation of the phenomenon known as **magnetostriction**—an actual change in the dimensions of a specimen of iron when it is magnetized.

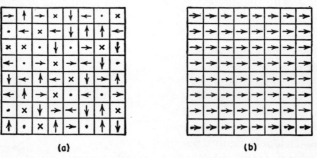

(a)　　　　　　　　　(b)

Fig. 8.3. Orientation of the domains in an iron crystal: (a) unmagnetized (b) in a magnetic field.

Any 100 direction is referred to as an **easy axis** of magnetization. Domains will change readily from one 100 direction to another, but they are very reluctant to take up any in-between orientation. If magnetization of a single-crystal specimen is attempted in a 110 or a 111 direction, it is thus necessary for all the domains to realign themselves to directions that are not natural. They begin by changing to the 100 direction that is nearest to the direction of the field. Then gradually they allow themselves to be oriented closer and closer to the field direction. Complete alignment of all the domains necessitates the use of much greater magnetic field intensities than did the alignment in the easy direction. The 110 and 111 directions are, therefore, referred to as **difficult axes** of magnetization.

We are now in a better position to understand what happens when we undertake to magnetize an ordinary specimen of iron. The direction of magnetization makes little difference now because we are dealing with large aggregations of crystals the space lattices of which are oriented in every conceivable direction.[1]   It is evident that, in any case, the flux density will be substantially increased by the contributions of the domains of the ferromagnetic material above what it would be in free space for the same field intensity.   The rate at which flux density increases with magnetic field intensity will vary widely with the material and with the field intensity itself, and we may now proceed to see how this relationship can best be expressed.

3. *B-H* curves.   The relation of the magnetic flux density to the magnetic field intensity for any ferromagnetic material is nonlinear and is usually expressed graphically.[2]   Such a graph, commonly called a *B-H* curve, is shown in Fig. 8.4.   The curve rises rapidly at first owing to the alignment by relatively small magnetic field intensities

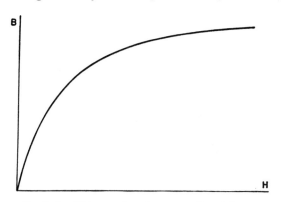

Fig. 8.4.   B-H curve for a ferromagnetic substance.

of the domains in the more favorably oriented crystals.   The gradual decrease in the slope of the curve is explained by the increasingly larger values of *H* required to orient the domains of crystals of which 110 or 111 axes lie in the direction of the field.   The curve never becomes horizontal because *B* will always increase with increasing *H*, even in free space.   When all the domains are oriented, the slope of

---

[1] There is, however, some difference in the magnetic properties of rolled steel, depending on whether magnetization is along the direction of rolling or across it. This is explained by differences in crystal orientation caused by the rolling.

[2] It is also possible to express the relation by an equation of the form

$$B = \frac{aH}{b + H},$$

where a and b are constants which have to be determined from data.   This is known as Froelich's equation.   Although it is of some interest to the student, it does not offer any saving in labor as compared with the graphical method when it comes to solving problems.

the curve becomes constant at a value equal to μ_0, the permeability of free space. The condition known as **saturation** then prevails.

Flux density may thus be regarded in two different ways: (a) Consisting of two components, one due to the coil which sets up the magnetic field and equal to $\mu_0 H$; the other, called **intrinsic flux density,** owing to the domains of the magnetic material itself. (b) Equal simply to μH, where the permeability μ is a function of flux density. The second way is the simpler for engineering purposes and is more generally used. Unless stated to the contrary, the total flux density and not the intrinsic flux density is meant.

In using B-H curves for solving practical problems, the MKS units for flux density and for field intensity are not particularly convenient. This is partly because, in the United States, we commonly express dimensions of apparatus in inches rather than meters. Accordingly, for the curves in this book, we shall take the units most commonly used in industry (H in ampere-turns per inch, B in kilolines per square inch). Curves for some commonly used materials appear on page 204.

4. Cyclic magnetization and hysteresis. If a specimen of any ferromagnetic material be carried step by step through a complete cycle of magnetization and the flux density calculated for each step and plotted against the magnetic field intensity, a closed figure like that shown in Fig. 8.5 will result. The data for such a curve can readily be obtained by using an experimental setup like that shown in Fig. 7.7. Beginning with the specimen carefully demagnetized, the current is started at zero and increased step by step, noting the deflection of the ballistic galvanometer caused by each increase, and calculating the corresponding change in flux density, which is plotted against magnetic field intensity. When maximum current is reached, the flux density and field intensity are those corresponding to point a, Fig. 8.5. The current is then reduced step by step and the resulting data plotted. It is seen that, instead of retracing the ascending curve, the points fall above it, and when H has been reduced to zero, B instead of being zero, as at the beginning, now has a value ob. This value is called the **residual flux density.**

The reversing switch is now thrown over, and the current again increased but in the opposite direction. The magnetic field intensity is, therefore, negative, and the value oc that will bring the flux density to zero is called **coercive force.** The increase of H in the negative direction is continued until a value equal to the previous maximum positive value is attained. This is point d. H is next reduced step by step to zero, corresponding to point e, at which point the reversing switch is again thrown to restore the current to its original direction

Increasing H step by step then brings us through point f back to close the loop at point a.   It may be that, owing to the fact that the magnetization has only been carried through one cycle, the loop will not be quite symmetrical and may fail to close at the point a.   This difficulty may be avoided by carrying the magnetization through one or more complete cycles before any data are taken.

Cyclic magnetization occurs in electrical apparatus whenever a coil or conductor carries alternating current.   The core of a transformer in

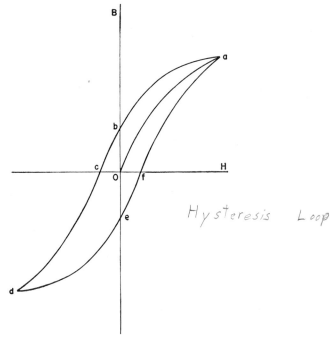

Fig. 8.5.   Curve showing variation of B with H for cyclic magnetization.

service is being continually carried through the cycle of events just described, as is the iron adjacent to the windings of any a-c motor or generator.   Cyclic magnetization also occurs in d-c motors and generators, owing to the rotation of the armature in the magnetic field set up by the stationary poles.   A particle of iron in any given part of the armature is being magnetized, first in one direction, then in the opposite direction, as the armature rotates.

Residual flux density and coercive forces are peculiar to ferromagnetic materials.   In all other substances, the descending B-H curve coincides with the ascending, zero flux density always corresponding to zero magnetic field intensity.   The closed figure obtained when the magnetization of a ferromagnetic substance is carried through a complete cycle of magnetization is called a **hysteresis loop,** and the characteristic of a ferromagnetic material that gives rise to the loop is called **hysteresis.**   Hysteresis is sometimes defined as the lag of flux density behind magnetic field intensity, but this definition must be qualified by stating that it is not a time lag.   The residual flux density does not become zero after the passage of time, but only upon the application of a suitable coercive force.

5. Hysteresis loss.   It was pointed out in Chapter VII that, in order to establish a magnetic field, a certain amount of energy has to be

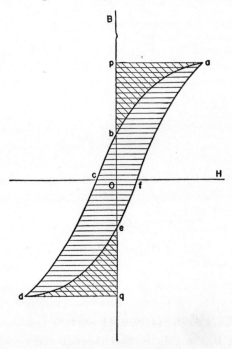

Fig. 8.6.   Hysteresis loop.

supplied.   If the field is in free space, this energy is stored, and it is returned to the circuit when the field collapses.   If the field is wholly or partly in a ferromagnetic material, not all of the energy supplied can be returned, part of it having been converted into heat in the process of aligning the domains in the ferromagnetic substance.   If the magnetization is carried through a complete cycle, the energy lost can be shown to be proportional to the area of the hysteresis loop. As the flux density is being changed from B_1, corresponding to the point e in Fig. 8.6, to B_2, corresponding to point a, the amount of energy supplied, according to Equation (7.44), is

$$W_1 = \sum_{B_1}^{B_2} H \Delta B, \tag{8.1}$$

which is represented (to scale) by the area *efapbo* in Fig. 8.6. If H is ampere-turns per meter and B is webers per square meter, W will be in joules per cubic meter. As the flux density is changed from B_2, corresponding to point a, to B_3, corresponding to point b, the amount of energy returned to the circuit is

$$W_2 = \sum_{B_3}^{B_2} H \Delta B, \tag{8.2}$$

which is represented by the area *apb*. A net amount of energy $W_1 - W_2$, represented by the area *efabo*, has, therefore, been lost. In like manner, it can be shown that when the flux density is changed from B_3, corresponding to point b, to B_4, corresponding to point d, the energy supplied is

$$W_3 = \sum_{B_4}^{B_3} H \Delta B, \tag{8.3}$$

which is represented by the area *bcdqeo*, and that when the flux density is changed from B_4, corresponding to point d, to B_1, corresponding to point e, the energy returned is

$$W_4 = \sum_{B_4}^{B_1} H \Delta B, \tag{8.4}$$

which is represented by area *dqe*. A net amount of energy $W_3 - W_4$, represented by area *bcdeo*, has, therefore, been lost during this half cycle. Therefore, the energy lost per cycle is

$$W_T = (W_1 - W_2) + (W_3 - W_4) \text{ joules per cu m per cycle,} \tag{8.5}$$

which is represented to scale by the area *efabcd*, which is the area of the hysteresis loop. In determining the loss from area of the loop, the scales to which H and B are plotted must, of course, be taken into account.

EXAMPLE: In order to determine the energy loss due to hysteresis in an iron ring, data are taken through a complete cycle of magnetization and plotted according to the following scales:

H: 1 in. = 25 ampere-turns per in.
B: 1 in. = 10 kilolines per sq in.

The area of the resulting loop is determined by means of a planimeter to be 5.6 sq in., and the volume of the ring is 50 cu in.   What is the loss in joules per cycle?

SOLUTION: Changing to MKS units, each inch represents

$$H = 25 \times 39.37 = 985 \text{ ampere-turns per m.}$$
$$B = 10 \times 10^{-5} \times (39.37)^2 = 0.155 \text{ weber per sq m.}$$
$$\text{Volume} = \frac{50}{(39.37)^3} = 0.00082 \text{ cu m.}$$
$$W = 5.6 \times 985 \times 0.155 \times 0.00082 = 0.7 \text{ joule per cycle.}$$

When placed in an alternating magnetic field, any specimen of iron or other ferromagnetic material will be carried repeatedly through the cycle of magnetization, and energy will be lost owing to hysteresis. Since the loss per cycle is a definite quantity at any particular maximum flux density, the power, which is the energy per unit time, will depend on the number of cycles per second through which the magnetization is carried.   The power, or rate at which energy is lost, is called **hysteresis loss.**

The variation of hysteresis loss with flux density was studied by Steinmetz, who developed the empirical equation

$$P_h = K_h f B_m{}^x V, \tag{8.6}$$

where P_h is hysteresis loss in watts.

K_h is a constant which depends on the chemical analysis of the material and the heat treatment and mechanical treatment to which it has been subjected.

f is frequency in cycles per second.

B_m is maximum flux density in kilolines per square inch.

x is an exponent which depends on the material.

V is the volume of the material in cubic inches.

The constant K_h may be as low as 5×10^{-7} for permalloy and as large as 6×10^{-5} for cast iron.   A typical value for electrical sheet steel is 4×10^{-6}.

The exponent x was determined by Steinmetz to be 1.6, and this value is found to hold fairly well for most materials at flux densities not exceeding 1 weber per sq m.   For higher flux densities, however, the value of the exponent is not constant and may be as great at 2.5.

Problems

(1-VIII) A hysteresis loop is plotted according to the scales 1 cm = 5 ampere-turns per in. and 1 cm = 10 kilolines per sq in.   The area of the resulting loop is found to be 25 sq cm, and the volume of the test specimen is 500 cu cm.   Calculate the hysteresis loss for the specimen in joules per cycle.

(2-VIII) In order to determine the exponent in the empirical equation for hysteresis loss for a certain material, data for a loop are taken carrying the flux density to a maximum value of 50 kilolines per sq in. The resulting loop has an area of 3.21 sq in. Data for a second loop are then taken, carrying the flux density to a maximum value of 75 kilolines per sq in. The resulting loop has an area of 6.27 sq in. Calculate the exponent.

(3-VIII) The hysteresis loops in Problem 2-VIII were plotted to an H scale of 1 in. = 20 ampere-turns per in. and a B scale of 1 in. = 10 kilolines per sq in. Calculate K_h in the empirical equation for hysteresis loss.

(4-VIII) The hysteresis loss in the core of a certain transformer is known to be 37.5 w at a frequency of 60 cycles per sec and a flux density of 1 weber per sq m. If the frequency is decreased to 50 cycles per sec, and the flux density increased to 1.25 webers per sq m, find the new value of hysteresis loss. Assume a Steinmetz exponent of 1.9.

(5-VIII) The hysteresis loss in the core of a certain transformer is 7.17 w at a frequency of 400 cycles per sec and a flux density of 90 kilolines per sq in. To what value would the flux density have to be reduced to keep the loss the same when the frequency is increased to 500 cycles per sec? Assume the Steinmetz exponent to be 1.6.

6. Eddy currents and eddy-current loss.

Whenever there is a change in the magnetic flux linking a coil, or a turn of wire, an emf is induced according to Faraday's law,

$$E = N \frac{\Delta \phi}{\Delta T}. \tag{7.12}$$

Electromotive forces are likewise induced in various paths in any piece of metal whenever there is a change in the flux that links them. As a consequence, currents known as **eddy currents** are caused to circulate in the metal. Eddy currents are not peculiar to ferromagnetic materials: they may occur in any conducting substance. Our present interest, however, is in the eddy currents that are set up in iron or other material used for magnetic circuits which are subjected to cyclic magnetization. In Fig. 8.7 is shown a cross section of a piece of iron so used.

The magnetization is caused by the alternating current i flowing in the coil. The magnetic flux is indicated by the small x marks, the positive direction selected for the flux being related to the positive direction of the current by Ampere's right-hand rule. The flux will increase and decrease with the current, being in the direction selected as positive when the current is positive, and reversing when the current reverses.

Now, consider a path a-b-c-d in the plane of the cross section shown in Fig. 8.7. When the flux is increasing in the positive direction, an emf will be induced in this path (and in any other path linked by the changing flux), in such a direction as to cause a counterclockwise current around the path. As a consequence of this current, energy will be converted into heat in the resistance of the path. There would be in the specimen a total loss that could be found by summing up the i^2R losses in all such elemental paths as *abcd*, beginning with a very small path near the center of the cross section and ending with a path

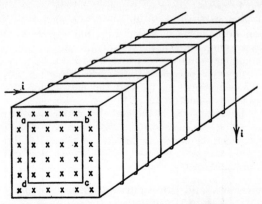

Fig. 8.7. Eddy-current path in a magnetic core.

lying just under the surface. This totalized i^2R loss is called **eddy-current loss**. In solid iron flux paths in which the flux varies with time eddy-current losses may be so large as to create a serious problem as to how to dissipate the resulting heat.

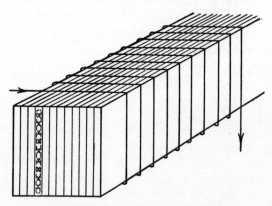

Fig. 8.8. Laminated magnetic core.

It has been found that this loss may be materially reduced by building up the required cross section for the flux path by stacking thin pieces known as **laminations,** as shown in Fig. 8.8.[1] Since the

[1] The loss may also be reduced by grinding the ferromagnetic material to a

emf's set up in the material by the varying flux are usually of small magnitude, the natural oxide on the surface of the sheet iron or steel from which the laminations are punched will effectively insulate the laminations from one another, and thus limit each eddy-current path to a single lamination.

We shall now proceed to study mathematically the effect of the several variables, such as lamination thickness, frequency, and flux density, upon eddy-current loss.   Fig. 8.9 shows a magnified cross section of one of the laminations of the magnetic circuit shown in

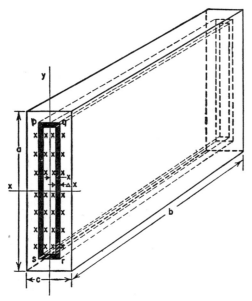

Fig. 8.9. Magnified view of a single lamination showing dimensions of eddy-current path.

Fig. 8.8.   The magnetic lines are again represented by x marks, and we shall assume the eddy-current paths to be represented in the cross section by long, narrow rectangles, such as the one marked $pqrs$.   All paths are assumed to extend in the y direction for the full distance a, but to vary from zero to c in the x direction.

Let us take the value of the flux density as B and assume it to vary sinusoidally according to the equation

$$B = B_{max} \sin \omega t \text{ webers per sq m.} \tag{8.7}$$

powder and mixing it with a binder that effectively insulates the particles one from another.   This mixture is then formed under pressure into the desired shape and heat-treated.   Magnetic cores for use in communication equipment are frequently made by this process.

The flux linking the eddy-current path $pqrs$ will then be

$$\phi = AB = 2xaB_{max} \sin \omega t \text{ webers.} \qquad (8.8)$$

The eddy-current path is equivalent to a single turn, and the emf induced in the path is, therefore,

$$e = \lim_{\Delta t \to 0} N \frac{\Delta\phi}{\Delta t} = N \frac{d\phi}{dt} = \frac{d[2xaB_{max} \sin \omega t]}{dt}$$

$$= 2\omega xaB_{max} \cos \omega t \text{ v.} \qquad (8.9)^1$$

The resistance of the eddy-current path, neglecting the ends, is

$$R = \frac{\rho L}{A} = \frac{\rho(2a)}{b\Delta x} \text{ ohms.} \qquad (8.10)$$

The current flowing in the path is then given by

$$i = \frac{e}{R} = \frac{\omega x B_{max} \cos \omega t \, b\Delta x}{\rho}, \qquad (8.11)$$

and power loss can be calculated as

$$p = i^2 R = \frac{2\omega^2 B^2_{max} \cos^2 \omega t \, abx^2\Delta x}{\rho} \text{ w.} \qquad (8.12)$$

To find the total eddy-current loss, it is now necessary to take the summation of the losses in all possible paths, from the one of zero thickness to the one of thickness c, just under the surface of the lamination.

$$p_{total} = \sum_0^{\frac{c}{2}} \frac{2\omega^2 B^2_{max} \cos^2 \omega t \, abx^2\Delta x}{\rho}$$

$$= \left[\frac{2\omega^2 B^2_{max} \cos^2 \omega t \, abx^3}{3\rho} \right]_0^{\frac{c}{2}} \text{ w.} \qquad (8.13)^2$$

Substituting the limits and putting $\omega = 2\pi f$, we get

$$p_{total} = \frac{\pi^2 f^2 B^2_{max} \cos^2 \omega t \, abc^3}{3\rho} \text{ w,} \qquad (8.14)$$

[1] To find the instantaneous emf induced in the path, it is necessary to take the limit of $N \frac{\Delta\phi}{\Delta T}$ as ΔT approaches zero. This is known as the **derivative** and will be familiar to the student of calculus.

[2] The actual evaluation of this summation must be carried out as a definite integral. The student of calculus will be able to check (8.13), but others will have to accept this equation on authority.

and since abc is the volume of the iron, we may write

$$p_{total} = \frac{\pi^2 f^2 c^2 B^2_{max} \cos^2 \omega t}{3\rho} \text{ w per cu m.} \qquad (8.15)$$

The quantities B, e, and p are plotted against time in Fig. 8.10. It is seen that the power varies between zero and a maximum value

$$P_{max} = \frac{\pi^2 f^2 c^2 B^2_{max}}{3\rho}, \qquad (8.16)$$

corresponding to a value of t that makes $\cos^2 \omega t = 1$. It can be shown

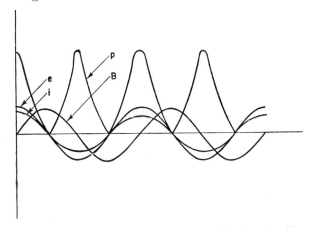

Fig. 8.10. Curves showing variation of flux density, induced emf, eddy-current, and eddy-current loss in a magnetic core subjected to cyclic magnetization.

by integrating (8.15) over a complete cycle and dividing by the corresponding time that

$$P_{average} = \frac{1}{2} P_{max} = \frac{\pi^2 f^2 c^2 B^2_{max}}{6\rho} \text{ w per cu m,} \qquad (8.17)$$

where f is frequency in cycles per second.

c is lamination thickness in meters.

B_{max} is maximum flux density in webers per square meter.

ρ is resistivity of material in ohm-meters.

Equation (8.17) may be used to calculate eddy-current loss in any magnetic circuit built of laminated material, or in general to calculate the eddy-current loss in thin metal strips, or sheets, placed in a magnetic field parallel to the direction of the lines of flux. It is not adapted to calculating the losses in very thick sheets, or in solid masses of metal of any kind.

It is interesting to note that the power loss decreases with increasing resistivity. Thus, everything else being equal, the loss in copper would be several times as much as in iron. It would not be practicable, however, to establish in copper the high flux densities that are commonly used in iron. Adding alloying materials, silicon in particular, to steel increases its resistivity, and thus decreases the eddy-current loss.

For practical calculations, Equation (8.17) may be rewritten

$$P_{average} = K_e f^2 c^2 B^2_{max} V, \tag{8.18}$$

where P is eddy-current loss in watts.

K_e is a constant which depends on the resistivity of the material.

f is frequency in cycles per second.

c is lamination thickness in inches.

B_{max} is maximum flux density in kilolines per square inch.

V is volume of the material in cubic inches.

The constant K_e varies from 1.5×10^{-5} to 6×10^{-5} for the steel sheets used in electrical apparatus, the smaller value corresponding to the greater resistivity.

Problems

(**6-VIII**) The eddy-current constant for a certain grade of 29-gage sheet steel (thickness 0.014 in.) is 2×10^{-5}. Calculate the eddy-current loss in a magnetic core made of this steel for a frequency of 500 cycles per sec and a flux density of 100 kilolines per sq in. The volume of the core is 107 cu in.

(**7-VIII**) The eddy-current loss in a sample of sheet steel is 12 w at a frequency of 100 cycles per sec and a flux density of 65 kilolines per sq in. What eddy-current loss might be expected in this sample at 120 cycles per sec and a flux density of 80 kilolines per sq in.?

(**8-VIII**) What would be the effect on eddy-current loss of redesigning a magnetic core to use laminations of 29-gage steel (thickness 0.014 in.) in place of 26-gage (thickness 0.0185 in.) steel of the same grade? Express your answer as a percentage.

(**9-VIII**) What would be the effect on eddy-current loss of doubling the cross-sectional area of a magnetic core, thus reducing the flux density to half and keeping the same total flux?

(**10-VIII**) The effective value of the emf induced in a winding on a core in which the magnetic flux varies sinusoidally is independent of changes in flux density, or in frequency, so long as the product of flux density and frequency remains constant. What would be the effect on the eddy-current loss in the core if the frequency were increased by 50 per cent, and the flux density reduced to keep the same induced emf in the winding?

7. Total core loss.

In any ferromagnetic material that is subjected to cyclic magnetization there are losses due to (a) hysteresis and (b) eddy currents. These losses make themselves evident by converting energy to the heat form and raising the temperature of the material. The energy has to be supplied electrically, and the rate at which it is supplied can be measured by a wattmeter connected into the circuit, as shown in Fig. 8.11. The measurement may be made on a sample taken from a certain batch of steel especially for test purposes, or it may be made on a piece of apparatus already built, as a transformer. The wattmeter as here connected would read (a) the I^2R loss in the wattmeter current coil, ammeter, connecting wire, and winding of the test specimen; and (b) the sum of the hysteresis and eddy-current losses in the test specimen. If the resistances of the various elements of the circuit are known and the current is measured, all of the items listed under (a) may be calculated. These items subtracted from

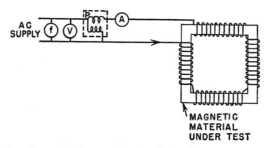

AC SUPPLY

MAGNETIC MATERIAL UNDER TEST

Fig. 8.11. Apparatus for measuring total core loss in a magnetic core.

the reading of the wattmeter give the combined hysteresis and eddy-current loss, or **core loss**:

$$P_c = K_h f B^x_{max} V + K_e f^2 B^2_{max} c^2 V. \tag{8.19}$$

For some purposes, it is sufficient to know the combined loss, but it is occasionally desirable to be able to separate the losses and find what part of the total is due to hysteresis and what part to eddy currents. This may be done by measuring the total core loss at two different frequencies (or two different maximum flux densities, or both). We then have two equations which we may solve simultaneously to determine P_h and P_e.

EXAMPLE: The core loss in a given specimen is found to be 65 w at a frequency of 30 cycles per sec and a flux density of 100 kilolines per sq in., and 190 w at 60 cycles per sec and the same flux density. What are the hysteresis loss and the eddy-current loss at each frequency?

SOLUTION: Since the flux density, the volume of the specimen, and the thickness of the laminations remain constant in this problem. Equation (8.19) may be rewritten as

$$P_c = K_h' f + K_e' f^2, \tag{8.20}$$

where $K_h' = K_h B_m{}^x V$ and $K_e' = K_e B_m{}^2 c^2 V$.

Substituting the data gives

$$65 = K_h'(30) + K_e'(30)^2$$
$$190 = K_h'(60) + K_e'(60)^2.$$

Solving these equations gives

$$K_h' = 1.167, \quad K_e' = 0.0333.$$

At 30 cycles per sec, the losses would be

$$P_h = K_h'(30) = 35 \text{ w}, P_e = K_e'(30)^2 = 30 \text{ w}.$$

At 60 cycles per sec,

$$P_h = K_h'(60) = 70 \text{ w}, P_e = K_e'(60)^2 = 120 \text{ w}.$$

Problems

(**11-VIII**) The measured loss in a magnetic circuit built of sheet-steel laminations is 42 w at a frequency of 60 cycles and a flux density of 1 weber per sq m. It is 28.5 w at the same frequency and a flux density of 0.8 weber per sq m. Determine the hysteresis loss and the eddy-current loss at each flux density.

(**12-VIII**) The measured loss in a magnetic circuit built of sheet-steel laminations is 80 w at a frequency of 600 cycles per sec and a flux density of 8000 gausses. It is 85 w at a frequency of 400 cycles per sec and a flux density of 12,000 gausses. Find the hysteresis loss and the eddy-current loss at each flux density.

(**13-VIII**) The measured loss in a magnetic circuit is 50 w at a frequency of 400 cycles per sec and flux density of 2000 gausses. Assuming that 75 per cent of this is hysteresis loss, what will be the measured total loss at 500 cycles per sec, 3000 gausses?

8. Application of ferromagnetic materials.   In selecting a material for a particular magnetic circuit we must consider (a) permeability, (b) losses, and (c) mechanical properties. Permeability must be high enough so that the desired flux density can be secured with a reasonable magnetic field intensity. High magnetic field intensities can be attained only by using a large number of turns in the winding, or by using a large current in a normal number of turns. Either solution would result in abnormally large I^2R losses in the magnetizing winding, which implies reduced efficiency and excess heating. In case the material is subject to cyclic magnetization, the hysteresis and eddy-current losses must be kept low enough to avoid excess heating, and serious reduction in efficiency. In magnetic circuits, where the magnetization is always in one direction and essentially constant, losses, of course, do not have to be considered. The material must generally be workable—that is, it must be capable of being punched or machined to get it into the desired form.   In the rotating parts of motors and generators, considerable mechanical strength is required.   In a material for permanent magnets, high **retentivity,** or high ratio of residual flux density to maximum flux density is essential, as is high **coercivity,** or high ratio of coercive force to magnetic field intensity required for saturation.

These properties are all affected by (a) the chemical composition of the material and (b) the mechanical and heat treatment it received in production.   The presence of carbon, oxygen, sulphur, and phosphorus in iron or steel tend to lower the permeability and increase the hysteresis loss; hence they are undesirable.   The effect of silicon in reducing the hysteresis loss and increasing the electrical resistivity has already been mentioned, and since it does not affect permeability seriously, it is used in certain grades of sheet steel.   The permeability of steel is increased, and its hysteresis loss decreased, by proper annealing.   To secure the maximum advantage, annealing is done subsequently to punching and shearing operations, serving to relieve the abnormal stresses and the magnetic defects they cause. In general, soft materials have lower hysteresis losses and higher permeabilities than hard materials, but lower retentivity.   Thus, suitable materials for permanent magnets are usually hard, and if subjected to varying flux, would have extremely high hysteresis losses.

Of the various forms in which iron and steel are used for magnetic circuits, rolled sheets are by far the most common.   The thickness ordinarily ranges from gage No. 22 with a thickness of 0.031 in., to gage No. 29 with a thickness of 0.014 in.   Heavier sheets or plates are used in fabricating parts not subject to cyclic magnetization, and sheets as thin as 0.005 in. are obtainable for use at higher frequencies. Several grades of steel are available in sheets, the best (lowest loss) grade containing about 4 per cent of silicon and costing the most per pound.   The cheapest grade contains a fraction of 1 per cent of silicon and has the highest loss.

Rolled sections and castings of iron and steel are used in magnetic circuits where the flux is constant in magnitude and direction.   In many instances, magnetic circuits are made up of several parts of different materials, often including one or more air gaps.

9. Magnetic materials for special purposes.   For permanent magnets, the desired characteristics of high retentivity and high coercivity are obtained in steels containing carbon, tungsten, chromium, or cobalt.   The carbon steels were the first used for this purpose, and they continue to be used in some apparatus because of their lower cost.   They have, however, the disadvantage of losing their residual magnetism, particularly if subjected to vibration or high temperatures, and they cannot be depended on where constant strength is required, as in the magnets of D'Arsonval type meters. Tungsten and chromium steels have the same defect in lesser degree; cobalt steel is the most satisfactory of those mentioned.   More recently, alloys of iron, nickel, cobalt, aluminum, and copper have been developed which are superior in retentivity and coercivity to any steel.   These alloys, known as **alnico,** make it possible to produce permanent magnets of given strength which have only a fraction of the weight of steel magnets of like strength.   Alnico has the disadvantage of being very difficult to machine, and has to be shaped mostly by grinding.

In the communications industries, currents of the order of a few milliamperes are used.   It is desirable, therefore, to build the magnetic circuits of the apparatus of some material which has a very high permeability at very small value of magnetic field intensity.   A nickel-iron alloy known as **permalloy** was especially developed for this purpose, and permits flux densities as high as 0.5 weber per sq m, to be established with very small (5 ampere-turns per m) magnetic field intensities.   The heat treatment of this alloy is as important as its chemical composition in securing the desired characteristics. Another nickel-iron alloy known as **hypernik,** and another known as **Allegheny electric metal** have similar high permeability characteristics at low field intensities, and may be produced at low enough cost to allow their use in heavier apparatus.

For certain devices, it is desirable to have a material the permeability of which changes with temperature.   Iron has this property, but its Curie point is at a rather high temperature (400° C).   Several alloys have been developed for which the Curie point is much lower and which show appreciable change in permeability for small changes in temperature.

For other purposes, a ferromagnetic material having constant permeability over a wide range of flux densities would be useful. A nickel-iron-cobalt-manganese alloy known as **perminvar** has been found which has this property.

Bismuth, although not a ferromagnetic material, has the unique property of changing its resistance when placed in a magnetic field. It is possible, therefore, to use a bismuth wire as the sensitive element of an instrument for measuring magnetic field intensity.

Study Questions

1. How is it possible for the atoms of a solid substance to be oriented by the action of a magnetic field?

2. Is a domain large enough to be seen with the aid of a microscope? (There are about 10^{23} atoms per cubic centimeter of iron.)

3. Is the Barkhausen effect evidence of the existence of domains? Would it occur if magnetization were the orientation of atoms individually?

4. Magnetization of a single-crystal specimen of iron is undertaken in one of its 100 directions. In what manner would the B-H curve differ from the one shown in Fig. 8.4?

5. After magnetic saturation is reached is it possible to increase further the flux density by increasing the magnetic field intensity? Why?

6. How can residual flux density be accounted for in terms of domain orientation?

7. In terms of domain orientation, how does the application of a coercive force bring the flux density to zero?

8. What would be the effect on the hysteresis loss in an iron core of each of the following changes: (a) doubling the frequency, (b) doubling the flux density, (c) doubling the cross section of the magnetic path, total flux and length of path to remain the same?

9. What would be the effect on the eddy current loss in a laminated iron core of each of the following changes: (a) doubling the frequency, (b) rebuilding the core using laminations half as thick, (c) rebuilding the core using lamination material of twice the resistivity?

10. What reason, other than increased efficiency, makes it essential to reduce the hysteresis and eddy current losses in the iron cores of electrical apparatus to the smallest practicable amount?

11. Why would a good permanent magnet material be a poor material for a transformer core which is subjected to cyclic magnetization?

12. What element is particularly useful in steel which is to be subjected to cyclic magnetization? Why?

13. For measurement of total core loss in sheet steel, the standard test specimen consists of four bundles of strips arranged to form a magnetic circuit in the form of a rectangle (Fig. 8.11). Depending upon how carefully the ends are abutted, the measured current and power are subject to considerable variation. Will this cause error in the core loss determination? Why?

14. Would the test specimen described above be suitable for determining points for a B-H curve? Why?

15. Is there any useful application of hysteresis and eddy current loss? Explain.

CHAPTER IX

THE MAGNETIC CIRCUIT

1. Magnetic circuits in electrical apparatus. Magnetic flux paths constructed of ferromagnetic materials constitute important parts of many pieces of electrical apparatus. Every generator, every motor, and every transformer (except those which operate at high frequency) makes use of one or more such flux paths. The flux path of a D'Arsonval type meter, consisting of a U-shaped permanent magnet, pole pieces, air gaps, and central core, is shown in Fig. 5.2. Watt-hour meters, telephone receivers, loud-speakers, relays for power, telephone, and telegraph circuits, and certain types of circuit breakers, all depend upon magnetic flux confined to paths of finite length and cross section. The variety of shapes and sizes which these magnetic circuits take is endless. Some are extremely simple, as the familiar iron ring used for formulating the magnetic concepts in Chapter VII, and which is used in practice in certain telephone apparatus. Some are rather complex, as the magnetic core of an ordinary watt-hour meter, shown in Fig. 9.1.

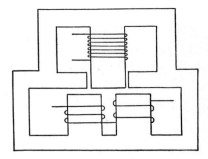

Fig. 9.1. Magnetic circuit of an a-c watt-hour meter.

A magnetic circuit is usually designed and built for the purpose of establishing, with as few ampere-turns as possible, a predetermined flux, in a certain definite space, as in the air gap between the armature and poles of a generator or motor. The utilization of the magnetic flux requires in most apparatus that one or more air gaps be included in the magnetic circuit. A notable exception is the transformer, in which the flux path may be in iron throughout its length, the operation of the transformer depending upon the variation of the flux with time.

The problems encountered in connection with magnetic circuits can usually be recognized as one of two types (a) to find the mmf required to establish a given flux and (b) to find the flux that will be established by a given mmf. The solution of a problem of the first type is usually straightforward, but problems of the second type usually have to be solved by trial and error because of the nonlinear nature of the magnetic circuit. The flux, instead of being directly proportional to the mmf, varies in a manner that can best be expressed graphically. The *B-H* curves for the various materials used are, therefore, essential for the solution of any magnetic circuit problem, and in the sections which follow the student must continually refer to the curves on page 204.

Let us now proceed to the consideration of problems relating to simple magnetic circuits and devise methods for solving them.

2. Magnetic circuits that are of same cross section and material throughout. This is the simplest problem of all. Suppose the

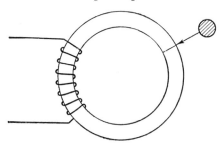

Fig. 9.2.   Iron ring—the simplest possible magnetic circuit.

magnetic circuit takes the form of an iron ring, such as the one illustrated in Fig. 9.2, and that we are required to calculate the number of ampere-turns necessary to establish a given flux. By measurements, we determine the cross-sectional area of the ring, and proceed to calculate the flux density. We then refer to the appropriate magnetization curve and find the magnetizing force that corresponds to this flux density. Then, knowing the magnetizing force and the mean length of the flux path, we calculate the mmf.

EXAMPLE: Find the mmf necessary to establish a flux of 0.0006 weber in a cast-steel ring of circular cross section. The outside diameter of the ring is 8 in. and inside diameter 6 in.

SOLUTION:

$\phi = 0.0006 \times 10^5 = 60$ kilolines.

$A = (\text{cross-sectional area}) = \pi(0.5)^2 = 0.785$ sq in.

$B = \dfrac{\phi}{A} = \dfrac{60}{0.785} = 76.4$ kilolines per sq in.

H (from curve) $= 27.5$ ampere-turns per in.

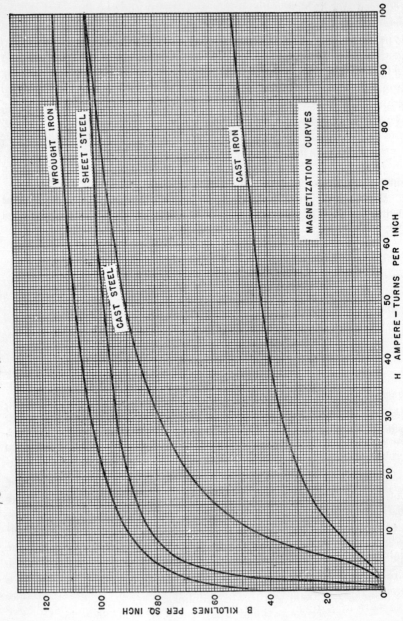

$10^5 \text{ kilolines} = 1 \text{ weber}$

$10^8 \text{ lines} = 1 \text{ weber}$
$10^3 \text{ "} = 1 \text{ kiloline}$

l (mean length of path) $= \pi \times 7 = 22$ in.

$F = Hl = 27.5 \times 22 = 605$ ampere-turns.

If we had been required to find the flux that would be established by a given mmf, our steps would have been (1) divide the given number of ampere-turns by the mean length of path to find H, (2) refer to curve to find B, and (3) multiply B by the cross-sectional area to find flux. For a magnetic circuit of this kind, it appears that one type of problem is no more difficult than the other.

Problems

(1-IX) What flux would be established in the cast steel ring described in the foregoing example by a mmf of 850 ampere-turns?.

(2-IX) What mmf will be required to establish a flux of 0.005 weber in the magnetic circuit shown in Fig. 9.3? The material is annealed sheet-steel laminations stacked to obtain the required thickness.

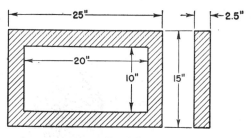

Fig. 9.3.

(3-IX) What percentage of increase in mmf will result in a 25 per cent increase in flux in the magnetic circuit described in Problem 2-IX? What percentage of decrease in mmf will result in a 25 per cent decrease in flux?

(4-IX) What flux will be established in the magnetic circuit described in Problem 2-IX by a mmf of 1000 ampere-turns??

3. **Magnetic circuits made up of two or more parts in series.** Let us now consider a magnetic circuit that consists of two or more distinct parts so arranged that the flux path is through both. These parts are said to be in **series,** from the similarity of the arrangement to a series electric circuit. Since the parts do not, in general, have the same cross-sectional area, the flux density will be different in the different parts, and they must, therefore, be considered one at a time. If we are given the flux and required to find the mmf, we take one part at a time, finding the flux density, the magnetizing force (from a curve), and the product (HL) for that part. The mmf will then be the sum of these products:

$$F = H_1L_1 + H_2L_2 + \ldots \qquad (9.1)$$

EXAMPLE 1: A magnetic circuit consists of a wrought-iron rod, 1.5 in. in diam and 30 in. long bent into a semicircle, and a cast-iron slab, 2 in. thick and 4 in. wide, as in Fig. 9.4. A perfect contact between

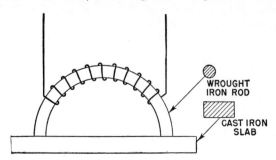

Fig. 9.4. Series magnetic circuit.

the slab and the ends of the rod is assumed. How many ampereturns will be required to establish a flux of 0.002 weber?

SOLUTION:

$\phi = 0.002 \times 10^5 = 200$ kilolines (the same throughout both parts).

For the wrought-iron rod:

Cross-sectional area $= \pi(0.75)^2 = 1.77$ sq in.

$$B = \frac{\phi}{A} = \frac{200}{1.77} = 113 \text{ kilolines per sq in.}$$

H (from curve) $= 80$ ampere-turns per in.

$HL = 80 \times 30 = 2400$ ampere-turns.

For the cast-iron slab:

Cross-sectional area $= 2 \times 4 = 8$ sq in.[1]

$$B = \frac{\phi}{A} = \frac{200}{5} = 40 \text{ kilolines per sq in.}$$

H (from curve) $= 44$ ampere-turns per in.

The length of the path in the slab is the diameter of the semicircle formed by the rod and is given by

$\pi l = 2 \times 30.$

$l = 19.1$ in.

$Hl = 44 \times 19.1 = 840$ ampere-turns.

$F = \Sigma Hl = 2400 + 840 = 3240$ ampere-turns.

[1] This neglects the crowding together of the lines in the slab as they converge toward the ends of the rod. A correct average value to take for the cross-sectional area is hard to estimate without a knowledge of field mapping, but it is obviously less than 8 sq in. and will be taken here as 5 sq in.

If our problem had been of the second type (given the mmf to find the flux) we could not make a straightforward solution, but would have to proceed by the trial-and-error method. The truth of this statement should be evident, for our straightforward procedure would be to find magnetizing force H, by dividing the mmf by the length of the path. This would be correct only if the path were of the same material and had the same cross section throughout its length. What we have to do, then, is to assume a value for the flux, and work the problem through exactly as we have done in the foregoing example to find the number of ampere-turns required. If this coincides with the number of ampere-turns available, we know our assumption must have been the correct value of flux. If the number of ampere-turns required exceeds the number available, we know that the flux assumed was too great and we must make another assumption and work through the calculations again. We continue in this way until we have reasonably close agreement (say within 2 per cent) between ampere-turns required and ampere-turns available.

The student will naturally ask how he is to know what flux to assume first. A great deal depends upon experience, but there are one or two simple rules that will be useful. First, do not assume a flux so high that the flux density in the part of smallest cross-sectional area is impossible. Second, if one part is obviously going to require more ampere-turns than all the others combined (as will be the case if air gaps occur), make a preliminary solution âs if there were no other parts in the circuit, finding the flux as though all the available ampere-turns were used up on this one part. The first assumption of flux should be somewhat less than the flux thus found. After one trial has been made and the assumed value of flux proved too great (or too small), it is well to deliberately make the next assumption on the other side of the true value. With the true value thus known to be between definite limits, a third assumption that is very nearly correct can usually be made.

EXAMPLE 2. Find the flux established by a mmf of 2100 ampere-turns acting on the magnetic circuit shown in Fig. 9.4.

SOLUTION: From Example 1, we can be sure the flux is less than 200 kilolines. We might think it would be reduced in about the same ratio as the mmf (down to about 130 kilolines). Before trying this value, however, let us note that the wrought-iron rod is the part requiring the most ampere-turns, and that in Example 1 we were reading the wrought-iron curve well out along the flat portion. We may, therefore, expect a relatively great change in mmf to cause a smaller change in flux. Let us take 180 kilolines as our first guess. Then, we have:

For the wrought-iron rod:

$$B = \frac{\phi}{A} = \frac{180}{1.77} = 101.6 \text{ kilolines per sq in.}$$

H (from curve) = 27.5 ampere-turns per in.
$F = 27.5 \times 30 = 825$ ampere-turns.

We can see there is no use to go any further with this guess, for even if the cast-iron base required as many ampere-turns as before, the total would be less than the 2100 ampere-turns available. We now have two values between which the flux must be: it is less than 200 kilolines and more than 180 kilolines. Let us next try 190 kilolines.

For the wrought-iron rod:

$$B = \frac{\phi}{A} = \frac{190}{1.77} = 107.2 \text{ kilolines per sq in.}$$

H (from curve) = 46.5 ampere-turns per in.
$F = 46.5 \times 30 = 1395$ ampere-turns.

For the cast-iron base:

$$B = \frac{190}{5} = 38 \text{ kilolines per sq in.}$$

H (from curve) = 36 ampere-turns per in.
$F = 36 \times 19.1 = 687$ ampere-turns.
$F = \Sigma Hl = 1395 + 687 = 2082$ ampere-turns required.

This is very close to our figure of 2100 ampere-turns available, and our guess of 190 kilolines is substantially correct.

Problems

(5-IX) How much flux would be established by a mmf of 3860 ampere-turns acting on the magnetic circuit of Fig. 9.4?

(6-IX) Find the mmf required to establish a flux of 150 kilolines in the magnetic circuit in Fig. 9.5.

Part	Material	Cross Section	Mean Length of Path
A	Cast steel	1.5 sq in.	5 in.
B, C	Wrought iron	1.4 sq in.	4 in.
D	Cast iron	3.0 sq in.	5 in.

(7-IX) What flux would be established in the magnetic circuit of Fig. 9.5 by a mmf of 1000 ampere-turns?

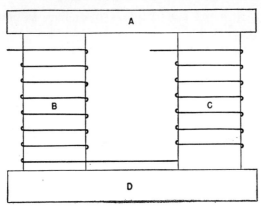

Fig. 9.5.

4. Calculations involving air gaps. The magnetic circuits of generators and motors necessarily include one or more air gaps to permit the rotating parts to move. Air gaps are also included in the magnetic circuits of reactors and other apparatus to secure the desired characteristics. Since the permeability of air is constant, B-H curves are not necessary, calculations of flux or mmf being made from the defining equations. There are two convenient methods of calculating the number of ampere-turns required to establish a given flux across an air gap (1) Calculate the reluctance of the air gap, and then find ampere-turns by taking the product of flux times reluctance or (2) Calculate the flux density in the air gap, divide it by permeability of air to obtain magnetizing force, then multiply magnetizing force by length of path to obtain ampere-turns. In making calculations by either of these methods, all quantities must be expressed MKS units.

EXAMPLE: A magnetic circuit contains an air gap 0.1 in. long and having a cross-sectional area which may be considered the same as the cross section of the steel faces between which it lies. These areas are each 4 sq in. How many ampere-turns are required to establish a flux of 400 kilolines across the gap?

SOLUTION 1:

$$\Re = \frac{L}{\mu_0 A} = \frac{\left(\dfrac{0.1}{39.37}\right)}{(4\pi \times 10^{-7})\left(\dfrac{4}{39.37^2}\right)} = 7.81 \times 10^5 \text{ MKS units.}$$

$\phi = 400 \times 10^{-5}$ weber.
$F = \phi\Re = (400 \times 10^{-5})(7.81 \times 10^5) = 3120$ ampere-turns.

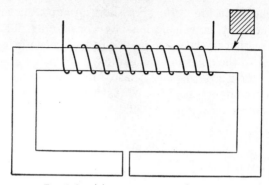

Fig. 9.6. Magnetic circuit with air gap.

SOLUTION 2:

$$B = \frac{\phi}{A} = \frac{400 \times 10^{-5}}{\dfrac{4}{(39.37)^2}} = 1.55 \text{ webers per sq m.}$$

$$H = \frac{B}{\mu_0} = \frac{1.55}{4\pi \times 10^{-7}} = 1.232 \times 10^6 \text{ ampere-turns per m.}$$

$$F = HL = (1.232 \times 10^6)\left(\frac{0.1}{39.37}\right) = 3120 \text{ ampere-turns.}$$

The ampere-turns for the air gap must, of course, be added to the ampere-turns for the other parts of the magnetic circuit to obtain the total mmf required. The methods outlined above are applicable to

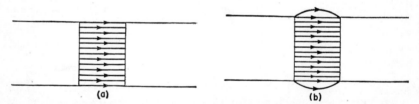

Fig. 9.7. "Fringing" of magnetic lines crossing an air gap.

parts of the magnetic circuit other than air gaps, provided the permeability of the material is known at the particular flux density used. For the ferromagnetic materials, however, that are most used, it is more convenient to use a magnetization curve than calculate reluctance or magnetizing force, as is done above.

There is always more or less "fringing" to be accounted for in problems involving air gaps. The flux lines, instead of being confined to the space defined by the metal faces of the air gap as in Fig. 9.7a, tends to bulge outward and increase the effective cross-sectional area of the gap, as in Fig. 9.7b. For short air gaps, this effect may be taken into account in calculations by considering the dimensions of the cross section of the air gap each to have been increased by an amount equal to the length of the gap.

When the air gap forms any considerable part of the total length of the magnetic circuit, the area of the path of the lines becomes so indefinite as to render a solution difficult or impossible by the methods here described.

Problems

(**8-IX**) An air gap 0.05 in. long is cut in the magnetic circuit described in Problem 2-IX.   How many ampere-turns are now required to establish a flux of 500 kilolines?

(**9-IX**) The magnetic circuit shown in Fig. 9.4 consists of a wrought-iron rod 1.6 in. in diam and 32 in. long bent into a semicircle, and a cast-iron slab 1.75 in. thick and 3.5 in. wide.   The ends of the rod are separated from the slab by air gaps 0.2 cm long.   How many ampere-turns are required to establish a flux of 200 kilolines?

(**10-IX**) What should be the length of the air gaps in Problem 9-IX in order that a mmf of 4500 ampere-turns will establish a flux of 200 kilolines?

5. Composite magnetization curves.

Where we have many problems to solve in conjunction with a particular magnetic circuit, we may often save time by plotting a **composite** or over-all magnetization curve.   For this curve we do not plot corresponding values of H and B for a certain magnetic material, but corresponding values of F and ϕ for a certain magnetic circuit, which may consist of several parts.   The points for such a curve are calculated in the usual way, simply calculating the total ampere-turns required to produce each value of flux.   We are, in fact, getting points for such a curve when we proceed by the trial-and-error method to find the flux established by a given mmf.

Problem

(**11-IX**) The magnetic circuit described in Problem 6-IX is changed by separating the parts B and C from the part D by air gaps each 0.075 in. long. Plot the composite magnetization curve, and from it determine what flux will be produced by a mmf of 3500 ampere-turns.

6. Magnetic circuits acted upon by two or more mmf's.

The magnetic circuits of most electrical machines are acted upon simultaneously by two or more mmf's.   These mmf's may aid or oppose one another, depending upon the relative directions of the currents in the several windings.   The right-hand rule gives the direction of the mmf which corresponds to the direction of current in a given winding.   The flux produced in a magnetic circuit by two or more mmf's acting simultaneously will not, in general, be the algebraic sum of the fluxes produced by the same mmf's acting separately. That is to say, if mmf F_1 produces a flux ϕ_1, and mmf F_2 produces a flux ϕ_2, both in the same direction around the circuit, then a mmf

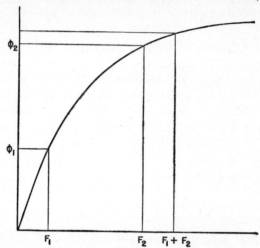

Fig. 9.8.   Effect of two magnetomotive forces acting simultaneously.

$F_1 + F_2$ will not produce a flux $\phi_1 + \phi_2$.   This may be seen from the sketch of the composite magnetization curve shown in Fig. 9.8.

Problems

(**12-IX**) The magnetic circuit shown in Fig. 9.9 is built of sheet-steel laminations.   The cross-sectional area is the same throughout, and the air

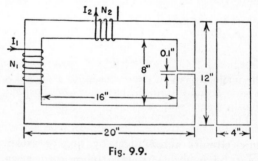

Fig. 9.9.

gap is 0.1 in. in length.   The winding N_1 has 2000 turns of small-diameter wire, and N_2 has 40 turns of larger-diameter wire.   Calculate and plot the composite magnetization curve and from it determine (a) flux established if $I_1 = 1.5$ amp and $I_2 = 0$, (b) flux established if $I_1 = 0$ and $I_2 = 25$ amp, (c) algebraic sum of the fluxes calculated in (a) and (b), and (d) flux established if $I_1 = 1.5$ amp and $I_2 = 25$ amp.

(13-IX) The magnetic circuit shown in Fig. 9.9 is built of sheet-steel laminations. The cross-sectional area is the same throughout, and the air gap is 0.05 in. long. The windings N_1 and N_2 each consist of 1000 turns. Calculate and plot the composite magnetization curve and use it to determine the limits between which the flux will vary if I_1 is a direct current of 2 amp and I_2 is an alternating current that varies according to the equation $i_2 = 0.5 \sin 377t$.

7. Magnetic potential difference. Just as we speak of potential difference between two points on an electric circuit, we may speak of difference of magnetic potential between two points on a magnetic circuit. Difference of magnetic potential, like magnetomotive force, is measured in ampere-turns. The idea may be made clearer by reference to Fig. 9.10. In the electric circuit, the potential difference between points r and s is commonly referred to as a *voltage drop*, or

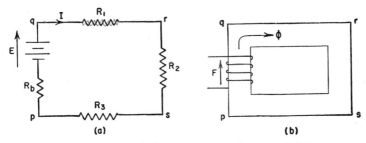

Fig. 9.10.   Comparison of electric and magnetic potential differences.

IR drop, and it is equal to the product of the current and the resistance R_2 of the part of the circuit lying between points r and s. In the magnetic circuit, the potential difference between points r and s could properly be referred to as an *ampere-turn drop*, or a $\phi\mathcal{R}$ *drop*, since it is equal to the product of the flux and the reluctance of that part of the circuit. It is more usual, however, to think of the magnetic potential difference as being an *Hl drop*, a product of magnetic field intensity by length of path. This is because it is customary to work with *B-H* curves and read values of H rather than determine the new value of $\mathcal{R}$ that corresponds to every change in flux.

Around the electric circuit, the emf of the battery equals the algebraic sum of the *IR* drops in the various resistances, according to Kirchhoff's voltage law. Around the magnetic circuit, the mmf of the coil equals the algebraic sum of the $\phi\mathcal{R}$ (or *Hl*) drops in the various sections of the core. This relation, which has already been used for series magnetic circuits, may be thought of as an adaptation of Kirchhoff's voltage law to magnetic circuits.

The electrical difference in potential between points p and q in

Fig. 9.10a is equal to the emf of the battery less the IR drop in the internal resistance of the battery itself. The magnetic difference of potential between points p and q in Fig. 9.10b is equal to the mmf of the coil less the Hl for the section of the core lying within the coil itself. From this statement, it follows that if the winding be so distributed that the ampere-turns per unit length exactly equal the Hl per unit length for each and every part of a magnetic circuit, then no magnetic potential difference will exist between points along the magnetic path, no matter how widely they are separated. This would correspond to an electric circuit in which sources of emf were inserted at small intervals around the circuit so as to exactly supply the IR drops in every section of the circuit. In a magnetic circuit, the avoidance of large differences of magnetic potential is very desirable, as will be seen shortly. Unfortunately, it is seldom practicable to distribute the ampere-turns as described above, particularly in circuits containing air gaps. The air gap, where most ampere-turns per unit length are required, must be kept clear of any windings for mechanical reasons, and the ampere-turns demanded by the air gap must be made up by increasing the number on some other part of the circuit above the number required for that part.

8. Leakage flux. Magnetic flux lines will exist along all possible paths that connect any two points between which there is a magnetic

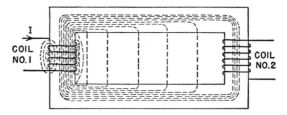

Fig. 9.11. Leakage flux paths in a magnetic circuit.

potential difference. The principal path, in the case of a coil wound upon a closed iron core is, of course, through the core, but this is not the only path. In Fig. 9.11, lines are drawn to indicate some of the other possible paths that may be taken by flux established by current in coil No. 1. If it is required that a certain definite amount of flux link coil No. 2 at the other end of the core, then any lines that fail to follow the core all the way around are useless, and are collectively called **leakage flux**. The calculation of the total amount of leakage flux is, in general, a formidable problem, and is often impossible. For magnetic circuits of simple geometry, however, we may make approximate calculations by determining the magnetic potential differences between certain points and estimating the reluctance of the paths that connect these points.

EXAMPLE: The magnetic circuit in Fig. 9.12 is built of sheet-steel laminations. The over-all dimensions are 20 in. by 8 in., and the window is 16 in. by 4 in. The thickness of the core is 4 in. A flux of 720 kilolines is to link coil No. 2. Determine the total flux that must be produced by coil No. 1, taking into account the leakage flux, and the ampere-turns required to establish this flux. Also find the ampere-turns that would have been required had there been no leakage flux.

SOLUTION: Let us begin by dividing the length of the window into four equal sections. The midpoints of these sections are designated aa', bb', cc', and dd', in Fig. 9.12. We shall assume that each of these sections forms a path for leakage flux to cross the window from top to

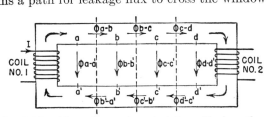

Fig. 9.12. Magnetic core for calculation of leakage flux.

bottom. The cross-sectional area of each path is 16 sq in. and the length is 4 in. The reluctance of each path will therefore be

$$\Re = \frac{l}{\mu_0 A} = \frac{\dfrac{4}{39.37}}{(4\pi \times 10^{-7})\dfrac{16}{(39.37)^2}} = 7.83 \times 10^6 \text{ MKS units.}$$

We shall now proceed to determine the magnetic potential difference that exists between the ends of each of these leakage paths, and the leakage flux which results.

The flux density in the end section of the core at the extreme right is

$$B = \frac{\phi}{A} = \frac{720}{8} = 90 \text{ kilolines per sq in.}$$

H (from curve) = 20.5 ampere-turns per in.

Assuming that the flux density is the same throughout the end section, the magnetic potential difference between points d-d' is

$$Hl_{d\text{-}d'} = 20.5 \times 12 = 246 \text{ ampere-turns.}$$

The flux over the leakage path d-d' is

$$\phi_{d\text{-}d'} = \frac{246}{7.83 \times 10^6} = 31.4 \times 10^{-6} \text{ weber} = 3.14 \text{ kilolines.}$$

The flux in the core in sections c-d and c'-d' will be greater than the flux in the end section by an amount equal to the leakage flux just calculated.

$$\phi_{c\text{-}d} = \phi_{c'\text{-}d'} = 720 + 3 = 723 \text{ kilolines.}$$

$$B_{c\text{-}d} = B_{c'\text{-}d'} = \frac{723}{8} = 90.4 \text{ kilolines sq in.}$$

$$H_{c\text{-}d} = H_{c'\text{-}d'} \text{ (from curve)} = 21 \text{ ampere-turns per inch.}$$

The magnetic potential difference between points c-c' can now be calculated as

$$Hl_{c\text{-}c'} = 246 + (21 \times 4) + (21 \times 4) = 414 \text{ ampere-turns.}$$

Repeating these calculations for each section in turn, we obtain

$$\phi_{c\text{-}c'} = \frac{414}{7.83 \times 10^6} = 52.9 \times 10^{-6} \text{ weber} = 5.29 \text{ kilolines.}$$

$$\phi_{b\text{-}c} = \phi_{b'\text{-}c'} = 723 + 5 = 728 \text{ kilolines.}$$

$$B_{b\text{-}c} = B_{b'\text{-}c'} = \frac{728}{8} = 91 \text{ kilolines per sq in.}$$

$$H_{b\text{-}c} = H_{b'\text{-}c'} \text{ (from curve)} = 22.5 \text{ ampere-turns per in.}$$

$$Hl_{b\text{-}b'} = 414 + (22.5 \times 4) + (22.5 \times 4) = 594 \text{ ampere-turns.}$$

$$\phi_{b\text{-}b'} = \frac{594}{7.83 \times 10^6} = 7.59 \text{ kilolines.}$$

$$\phi_{a\text{-}b} = \phi_{a'\text{-}b'} = 728 + 8 = 736 \text{ kilolines.}$$

$$B_{a\text{-}b} = B_{a'\text{-}b'} = \frac{736}{8} = 92 \text{ kilolines per sq in.}$$

$$H_{a\text{-}b} = H_{a'\text{-}b'} \text{ (from curve)} = 25 \text{ ampere-turns per in.}$$

$$Hl_{a\text{-}a'} = 594 + (25 \times 4) + (25 \times 4) = 794 \text{ ampere-turns.}$$

$$\phi_{a\text{-}a'} = \frac{794}{7.83 \times 10^6} = 10.1 \text{ kilolines.}$$

ϕ in extreme left-hand section of core is

$$736 + 10 = 746 \text{ kilolines.}$$

This is the total flux that must be produced by coil No. 1.

B in extreme left-hand section of core is

$$\frac{746}{8} = 93.3 \text{ kilolines per sq in.}$$

H (from curve) = 28 ampere-turns per in.

Total ampere-turns required will be

$$F = 794 + (12 \times 28) = 1130 \text{ ampere-turns.}$$

If there had been no leakage flux, the total ampere-turns required would have been

$$F = 20.5 \times 48 = 985 \text{ ampere-turns.}$$

Thus, we see that concentrating the winding on the left-hand end section of the core makes necessary the use of about 15 per cent more ampere-turns than would have been required had the winding been distributed around the core in such a manner as to avoid magnetic potential differences and leakage flux.   In some instances, the additional ampere-turns necessary in a concentrated winding may even exceed 15 per cent of the requirements for a distributed winding, though practical designs require that the windings be so placed as to keep the excess as low as possible.

Problem

(14-IX) A magnetic circuit is built of sheet-steel laminations in the form shown in Fig. 9.12.   The over-all dimensions are 20 in. by 8 in. and the window is 18 in. by 6 in.   The thickness of the core is 1.5 in.   A flux of 140 kilolines is to link coil No. 2.   Divide the length of the window into 3-in. sections, and determine (a) the magnetic potential difference between pairs of points located at the mid-sections, (b) the leakage flux over paths of cross-sectional area 3 in. by 1.5 in., corresponding to the sections for which potential differences are calculated, (c) total flux linking coil No. 1, (d) ampere-turns required to establish this flux, and (e) ampere-turns required to establish a flux of 150 kilolines had there been no leakage flux.

9. Magnetic circuits involving permanent magnets.   Any magnetic circuit, when the mmf is removed, will retain a certain residual flux density, the value of which depends upon the material and the maximum flux density to which it has been subjected.   It is thus a permanent magnet.   In order to establish saturation flux density with as few ampere-turns as possible, any air gap in the circuit is bridged during the magnetizing process.   To make the magnet useful, however, the bridge must be removed once the process is complete, and upon its removal the flux density decreases by a significant amount. The maintenance of flux across an air gap requires that there be a difference in magnetic potential between its faces, which must now be supplied by the domains remaining in alignment in the iron part of the circuit.   The iron thus becomes the seat of a mmf equal to the drop in magnetic potential across the air gap.   The supplying of this mmf by the iron has exactly the same effect as the application of a coercive force—that is, it results in a decrease in the residual flux density.   If the magnet is of the bar or U type, so that the length of path in air is a considerable part of the total length of path, the calculation of the decrease is not readily made.   In cases where the air gap is relatively short, however, the flux density in the air gap can be calculated with accuracy as high as that usually attained in magnetic-circuit calculations.

Suppose a magnetic circuit in the form of a ring, broken by a short air gap which has been temporarily bridged, is acted upon by a mmf F.

After the mmf has been discontinued and the bridge removed, the equation around the ring is

$$0 = H_i l_i + H_a l_a,\tag{9.2}$$

where H_i is the magnetic field intensity in the iron.

　　l_i is the length of the magnetic path in the iron.

　　H_a is the magnetic field intensity in the air gap.

　　l_a is the length of the air gap.

It is obvious that unless H_i and H_a are both zero (in which case there could be no flux density in the air gap), then either H_i or H_a must be negative. If H_a were negative, the direction of the magnetic field in the air gap would reverse when the bridge was removed. H_i, then, must be negative, and thus is a coercive force so far as the iron is concerned, tending to reduce the residual flux density in the iron. The relation between residual flux density and coercive force for some materials commonly used for permanent magnets is given on the curve sheet on page 219.

Since the air gap and iron part of the magnetic circuit are in series and equal in cross-sectional area (neglecting fringing), the flux density must be the same for each part:

$$B_i = B_a.\tag{9.3}$$

The determination of the flux density in the air gap, then, simply requires that we find a value which, for the particular material used, will satisfy Equation (9.2). This can readily be done by trial and error.

EXAMPLE: A ring of chrome steel, having a mean diameter of 7 in. and a cross-sectional area of $\frac{3}{4}$ sq in., contains an air gap $\frac{1}{4}$ in. long. It is magnetized to saturation with the air gap bridged. What flux density would exist in the air gap upon removal of the bridge?

SOLUTION: Let us assume a flux density of 20 kilolines per sq in. From the chrome-steel curve (page 219) H is -112 ampere-turns per in.

$$l_i = 7\pi - \frac{1}{4} = 21.75 \text{ in.}$$
$$H_i l_i = (-112)(21.75) = -2440 \text{ ampere-turns.}$$

For the air gap the flux density will be

$$B_a = 20 \times 0.0155 = 0.31 \text{ weber per sq m.}$$
$$H_a = \frac{B_a}{\mu_0} = \frac{0.31}{4\pi \times 10^{-7}} = 2.47 \times 10^5 \text{ ampere-turns per m.}$$
$$= 6270 \text{ ampere-turns per in.}$$
$$H_a l_a = 6270 \times 0.25 = 1567 \text{ ampere-turns.}$$

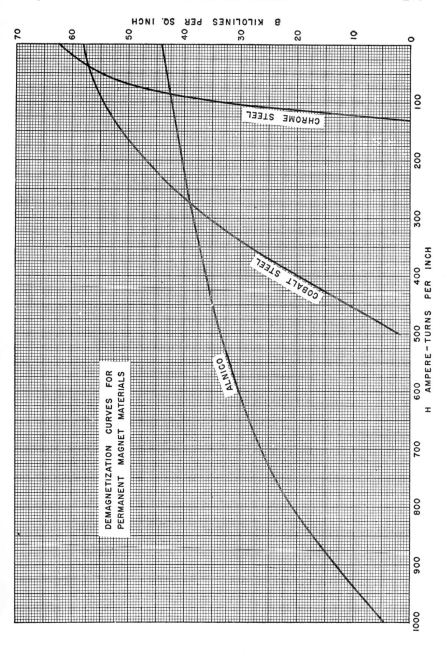

DEMAGNETIZATION CURVES FOR
PERMANENT MAGNET MATERIALS

These values obviously will not satisfy Equation (9.2), and it can be seen further that the assumed flux density must be increased. Let us try $B = 30$ kilolines per sq in. We then have

$$H_i \text{ (from curve)} = -105 \text{ ampere-turns per in.}$$
$$H_i l_i = (-105)(21.75) = -2285 \text{ ampere-turns.}$$

The value of $H_a l_a$ will be increased in direct proportion to the flux density so that

$$H_a l_a = {}^{30}/_{20} \times 1567 = 2350 \text{ ampere-turns.}$$

These values satisfy Equation (9.2) within the allowable limits for magnetic calculations.

Problems

(15-IX) An air gap 0.2 in. long is cut in a ring of cobalt steel which has a mean diameter of 1.5 in. and a cross section of 0.25 sq in. The ring is magnetized to saturation with the air gap bridged. What will be the flux density in the air gap when the bridge is removed?

(16-IX) What would have been the flux density in the air gap of the ring described in Problem 15-IX if the material had been alnico?

(17-IX) The magnetic circuit of a D'Arsonval type meter consists of a permanent magnet of chrome steel, fitted with soft-iron pole pieces and core,

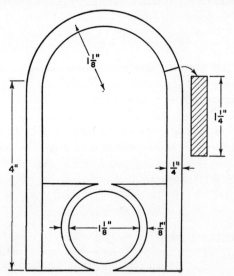

Fig. 9.13.

as shown in Fig. 9.13. What flux density could be expected in the air gaps following magnetization to saturation with the air gaps bridged? *Suggestion:* Modify Equation (9.3) to take account of the difference in cross section of the air gap and magnet. Neglect the ampere-turns required by the soft iron.

10. Magnetic cores having parallel branches. Just as a single source of emf may cause current in a number of parallel circuits to which it is connected, a single coil carrying current may supply the mmf to establish flux in several parallel branches of a magnetic circuit. The core shown in Fig. 9.14 is typical of the kind used in shell-type transformers and reactors, the windings being placed on the middle leg, and the other two legs serving as return paths for the flux.

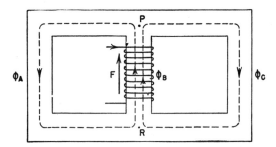

Fig. 9.14. Magnetic core with parallel branches.

Since magnetic lines are regarded as being always continuous, with no beginning and no end, it follows that in Fig. 9.14 the flux ϕ_B must be the sum of the fluxes ϕ_A and ϕ_C,

$$\phi_B = \phi_A + \phi_C. \qquad (9.4)$$

In general, the flux entering any region in a magnetic field must equal the flux emerging from that region. This relationship is very similar to Kirchhoff's current law, which is applied at junction points in electrical networks.

In order to establish a given amount of flux in the center leg, enough ampere-turns must be provided to give the required magnetic field intensities in the center leg and in either outside leg according to the equations

$$F = H_B l_B + H_A l_A \qquad (9.5)$$
and
$$F = H_B l_B + H_C l_C. \qquad (9.6)$$

The relation between the fluxes expressed by Equation 220 must also be satisfied. The simplest case is the one in which the outside legs are exactly alike, so that it may be assumed that the flux ϕ_B divides equally between them, making

$$\phi_A = \phi_C = \tfrac{1}{2}\phi_B. \qquad (9.7)$$

EXAMPLE 1: The dimensions of the magnetic core shown in Fig. 9.14 are as follows:

Over-all: 28 in. by 16 in.
Each window: 8 in sq.
Thickness of the core: 4 in.
Material: sheet-steel laminations.

Required: number of ampere-turns on center leg to establish a
flux $\phi_B = 1600$ kilolines.

SOLUTION: First we must determine the mean lengths and cross
sections of the flux paths in the various legs. In doing this, we may
consider each path to extend from point P to point R, midway of the
core sections. On this basis we have

$$l_A = l_C = 36 \text{ in.}$$
$$l_B = 12 \text{ in.}$$
$$A_A = A_B = A_C = 16 \text{ sq in.}$$

Now, $$B_B = \frac{\phi_B}{A_B} = \frac{1600}{16} = 100 \text{ kilolines per sq in.}$$

H_B (from curve) $= 65$ ampere-turns per in.

$$\phi_A = \phi_C = \frac{\phi_B}{2} = 800 \text{ kilolines.}$$

$$B_A = B_C = \frac{800}{16} = 50 \text{ kilolines per sq in.}$$

$H_A = H_C$ (from curve) $= 2.5$ ampere-turns per in.

From Equation (9.5) or (9.6),

$$F = (65 \times 12) + (2.5 \times 36) = 870 \text{ ampere-turns.}$$

If legs A and C are not identical, we cannot assume the flux ϕ_B to
divide equally, and the solution is more difficult.

EXAMPLE 2: The magnetic core in Example 1 has an air gap 0.05 in.
long cut in leg C. How many ampere-turns are now required to
establish a flux of 1600 kilolines in leg B?

SOLUTION: Cutting the air gap in leg C makes it necessary to modify
Equation (9.6), which now becomes

$$F = H_B l_B + H_C l_C + H_G l_G. \tag{9.8}$$

The flux density in leg B is 100 kilolines per sq in. as before, and the
magnetic field intensity H_B is 65 ampere-turns per in. It is obvious
that the air gap in leg C will increase the reluctance of that leg and
cause a decrease in the flux ϕ_C. We have no way of knowing in
advance how much the decrease will be, so we are forced to assume a
value. Let us assume $\phi_C = 400$ kilolines. Then,

$$B_C = \frac{400}{16} = 25 \text{ kilolines per sq in.}$$

H_C (from curve) $= 1.6$ ampere-turns per in.

$$H_C l_C = 1.6 \times 36 = 57.6 \text{ ampere-turns.}$$

The reluctance of the air gap is

$$\Re = \frac{l}{\mu_0 A} = \frac{\dfrac{.05}{39.37}}{(4\pi \times 10^{-7}) \dfrac{16}{(39.37)^2}} = 9.8 \times 10^4 \text{ MKS units.}$$

$$H_G l_G = \phi_G \Re_G = (4 \times 10^{-3})(9.8 \times 10^4) = 392 \text{ ampere-turns.}$$

Equating the right-hand side of (9.5) to the right-hand side of (9.8),

$$H_A l_A = H_C l_C + H_G l_G \tag{9.9}$$
$$= 57 + 392 = 449 \text{ ampere-turns.}$$
$$H_A = \frac{449}{36} = 12.5 \text{ ampere-turns per in.}$$

B_A (from curve) $= 84.4$ kilolines per sq in.

$$\phi_A = 84.4 \times 16 = 1350 \text{ kilolines.}$$

We can now check our assumption by substituting in Equation (9.4).

$$\phi_B = \phi_A + \phi_C = 1350 + 400 = 1750 \text{ kilolines.}$$

Since ϕ_B is to be only 1600 kilolines, we have evidently assumed too high a value for ϕ_C.

For our second trial let us assume $\phi_C = 320$ kilolines. We will then have

$$B_C = \frac{320}{16} = 20 \text{ kilolines per sq in.}$$

H_C (from curve) $= 1.5$ ampere-turns per in.

$$H_C l_C = 1.5 \times 36 = 54 \text{ ampere-turns.}$$
$$H_G l_G = \phi_G \Re_G = (3.2 \times 10^{-3})(9.8 \times 10^4) = 314 \quad \text{ampere-turns.}$$
$$H_A l_A = 54 + 314 = 368 \text{ ampere-turns.}$$
$$H_A = \frac{368}{36} = 10.2 \text{ ampere-turns per in.}$$

B_A (from curve) $= 82$ kilolines per sq in.

$$\phi_A = 82 \times 16 = 1310 \text{ kilolines.}$$
$$\phi_B = 1310 + 320 = 1630 \text{ kilolines.}$$

This is the required value of ϕ_B within the allowable limits of error. The ampere-turns required can now be found from either (9.5) or (9.8):

$$F = H_B l_B + H_A l_A \tag{221}$$
$$= (65 \times 12) + (10.2 \times 36) = 1147 \text{ ampere-turns.}$$

Problems

(**18-IX**) How many ampere-turns would have been required to establish a flux $\phi_C = 880$ kilolines in the magnetic core described in Example 1 if leg A had had a cross section of only 8 sq in.? What would have been the other fluxes?

(**19-IX**) How long an air gap should be cut in leg A of the magnetic circuit described in Example 1 in order that a mmf of 800 ampere-turns will establish a flux of 880 kilolines in leg C? What will be the other fluxes?

(**20-IX**) The following data are given on a magnetic core of the type shown in Fig. 9.14:

$l_A = l_C = 20$ in. Material: annealed sheet-steel laminations.
$l_B = 8$ in.
$A_A = A_C = 4$ sq in. Core wound on leg A instead of leg B.
$A_B = 1.5$ sq in.

What mmf F_A will be required to establish a flux $\phi_C = 280$ kilolines? What values will the other fluxes have?

(**21-IX**) A magnetic core similar to that shown in Fig. 9.14 has the following dimensions:

$l_A = l_C = 16$ in. Material: annealed sheet-steel laminations.
$l_B = 5$ in.
$A_A = A_B = A_C = 2.5$ sq in.

Windings are placed on leg A and also on leg B. The winding on leg B produces a mmf of 128 ampere-turns upward along the leg. What mmf on leg A will be required to establish a flux $\phi_B = 200$ kilolines? What will the other fluxes be?

(**22-IX**) Cores for small transformers and chokes are often built by stacking E-shaped laminations like those shown in Fig. 9.15. The completed coils are slipped on the center leg and the magnetic circuit closed by a stack of I-shaped laminations.

How many ampere-turns would be required to establish a flux of 50 kilolines in the center leg of a core 1 in. thick? Assume a stacking factor of 0.9 (that is, in a stack 1 in. thick, there is a 0.1-in. space between laminations) and assume a 0.015-in. air gap at each joint.

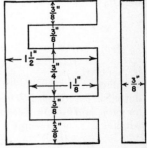

Fig. 9.15.

(**23-IX**) To what length would the air gaps of the core in Problem 22-IX have to be reduced in order that a flux of 50 kilolines in the center leg could be established by a current of 10 ma in a 4000-turn coil?

(**24-IX**) (a) The core described in Problem 22-IX is magnetized by a winding of 4000 turns carrying a direct current of 10 ma. What flux is established in the center leg? What is the permeability of the steel in MKS units?   (b) An alternating current ($i = 2 \sin 5000t$) is superimposed upon the direct current in the winding.   What flux is established when the alternating current is maximum in the direction of the direct current?   What is the incremental permeability (increase in B divided by increase in H) in MKS units?

(25-IX) (a) The core described in Problem 23-IX is modified by reducing the air gaps at the joints to 0.0015 in.   It is magnetized by a winding of 4000 turns carrying a direct current of 10 ma.   What flux is established in the center leg?   What is the permeability of the steel in MKS units?   (b) An alternating current ($i = 2 \sin 5000t$) is superimposed upon the direct current in the winding.   What flux is established when the alternating current is maximum in the direction of the direct current?   What is the incremental permeability (increase in B divided by increase in H) in MKS units?

(26-IX) The magnetic circuit of a four-pole d-c dynamo is shown in Fig. 9.16.   The poles, marked $N,S,\ N,S$, are bolted to the frame, and the armature

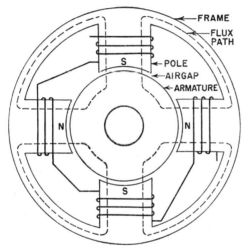

Fig. 9.16.

is mounted upon a shaft so it may rotate in the space between the poles. Windings on each pole set up mmf's which establish flux, as shown by the dotted lines.   Each flux path includes a section of the frame, two poles, two air gaps, and a section of the armature, and is acted upon by the mmf's of two windings.   The dimensions shown below refer to one flux path.

Part	Material	Cross Section of Path	Length of Path
Frame	Cast steel	15 sq in.	$17\frac{1}{2}$ in.
1 pole	Cast steel	36 sq in.	$4\frac{3}{4}$ in.
1 air gap		36 sq in.	$\frac{1}{8}$ in.
Armature	Sheet steel	16 sq in.	7 in.

How many ampere-turns per pole are required to set up a flux of 2500 kilolines per pole?

(27-IX) What change in the magnetic circuit of the dynamo described in Problem 26-IX should be considered if it is required to radically reduce the ampere-turns per pole? Make calculations to justify your answer.

(28-IX) Calculate the composite magnetization curve for the magnetic circuit of the four-pole dynamo described in Problem 26-IX, and from it determine the flux per pole that would be established by a mmf of 2000 ampere-turns per pole.

(29-IX) The armature of the d-c dynamo described in Problem 26-IX carries windings that set up a mmf of 250 ampere-turns per pole when the dynamo is operating under rated load. This armature mmf, known as armature reaction, opposes that of the poles. Plot the composite magnetization curve of the dynamo and use it to calculate the percentage of change in flux per pole due to armature reaction when the number of ampere-turns per pole produced by the windings on the poles is (a) 2000, (b) 3500.

Study Questions

1. What magnetic flux density will be established in sheet steel by a magnetic field intensity of: (a) 1 ampere-turn per in., (b) 5 ampere-turns per in. (c) 20 ampere-turns per in., (d) 100 ampere-turns per in.? Use the curves on p. 204.

2. For each of the four magnetic materials for which curves are shown on p. 204, look up the magnetic flux density produced by a magnetic field intensity of 10 ampere-turns per in.

3. For each of the four magnetic materials for which curves are shown on p. 204 look up the magnetic field intensity required to produce a magnetic flux density of 50 kilolines per sq in.

4. Why is it necessary to use a trial-and-error procedure when it is desired to find the flux established by a certain magnetomotive force in a magnetic circuit made up of two or more parts in series?

5. Comment on the correctness of this statement: if a magnetic circuit has in it one or more very short air gaps these may be neglected without seriously affecting the results of a calculation of the number of ampere-turns required to establish a certain flux.

6. In general, what effect will the cutting of an air gap in a magnetic circuit have upon the shape of the composite magnetization curve?

7. It is known that a magnetomotive force F_1 will establish a flux ϕ_1 in a certain magnetic circuit, and that a magnetomotive force F_2 will establish a flux ϕ_2 in the same magnetic circuit. What is wrong with the assumption that the two magnetomotive forces acting in conjunction, will establish a flux $\phi_R = \phi_1 + \phi_2$?

8. The same magnetomotive force can be produced by a 1000-turn coil carrying 1 amp or by a 40-turn coil carrying 25 amp or by a 10-turn coil carrying 100 amp. What considerations will determine which coil is best suited in a particular case?

9. The number of ampere-turns needed to establish a certain flux in an iron ring is calculated in the usual way. What assumption is made here as to how the turns are to be distributed around the ring? What would happen if the turns were all concentrated in a small space? Explain.

10. Why does leakage flux in magnetic calculations often turn out to be an important factor, whereas in most electrical problems leakage current can be neglected?

11. Why is alnico a better permanent magnet material than chrome steel, which has greater retentivity?   Explain.

12. In a magnetic circuit in the form of a ring of the same material and cross section throughout and magnetized by a uniformly distributed winding, a flux ϕ is established by a magnetomotive force F.   How would the flux be affected by increasing the cross section of the ring from A to $2A$?

13. In the magnetic core shown in Fig. 9.14 the magnetomotive force set up by the winding on leg B establishes fluxes ϕ_A, ϕ_B and ϕ_C in legs A, B, and C, respectively.   What would be the effect upon each of these fluxes of cutting an air gap in leg C?

CHAPTER X

ELECTROMAGNETIC FORCES

1. Force acting to close the air gap in a magnetic circuit—Magnetic pull. When an air gap exists in a magnetic circuit, forces act which tend to close the gap. The iron faces between which the air gap lies are magnetic poles, the north-seeking pole being the one at which the magnetic flux passes from iron to air, and the south-seeking pole the

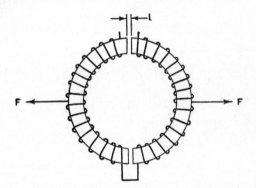

Fig. 10.1. Magnetic pull between halves of a magnetized iron ring.

one at which it passes from air to iron. The force that tends to close the air gap may be regarded as being in part the attraction between the unlike magnetic poles, and it is sometimes referred to as **magnetic pull.**

In order to get a mathematical expression for calculating such a force, let us consider a magnetic circuit formed by cutting an iron ring into two halves and separating the halves to form two short air gaps of equal length, as shown in Fig. 10.1. Let the cross section of the ring be A square meters and the length of each air gap L meters. The winding carries a current which establishes a flux density of B webers per square meter in each air gap and results in forces which tend to pull the two halves of the ring together. There will be energy stored in the air gaps in amount

$$W = \frac{1}{2}\frac{B^2}{\mu} \text{ joules per cu m.} \tag{7.46}$$

Since the volume of each air gap is LA cubic meters, the total energy stored in the air gaps is

$$W = \frac{B^2 LA}{\mu_0} \text{ joules.} \qquad (10.1)$$

Now, suppose a force of F newtons is applied which overcomes the forces of attraction, and lengthens each air gap by an amount ΔL. Meanwhile, the current in the windings is increased in order to maintain the flux density exactly constant. The work done by this force is

$$\Delta W = F \Delta L \text{ joules.} \qquad (10.2)$$

This work will appear as additional energy stored in the lengthened air gaps:

$$\Delta W = \frac{B^2 \Delta LA}{\mu_0} \text{ joules.} \qquad (10.3)$$

Equating the right-hand side of (10.2) to the right-hand side of (10.3) and solving for F we obtain

$$F = \frac{B^2 A}{\mu_0} \text{ newtons.} \qquad (10.4)$$

This force is divided equally between the two air gaps. Consequently, the magnetic pull at each air gap is

$$\frac{1}{2} F = \frac{B^2 A}{2\mu_0} \text{ newtons.} \qquad (10.5)$$

It can be seen from this equation that the magnetic pull might actually be increased in some instances by decreasing the cross section of the air gap. If the amount of magnetic flux remains constant, then since

$$B = \frac{\phi}{A}, \qquad (7.28)$$

a decrease in cross section would mean an increase in the flux density. Since flux density appears to the second power in Equation (10.5), and cross section to the first power only, a decrease in cross section means an increase in magnetic pull.

We now have an equation for calculating the pull exerted by all sorts of magnets, both permanent magnets and electromagnets, upon pieces of ferromagnetic material, provided there is a complete magnetic circuit and relatively short air gaps. The calculation of the pull of a lifting magnet, for instance, or of the magnets of an electric bell, can be made by use of this equation. Calculations for bar magnets and solenoids can seldom be made by Equation (10.5) because of the difficulty of determining flux density in cases where a larger part of the length of the magnetic path is in air.

EXAMPLE: A wrought-iron ring having a mean diameter of 7 in. and a circular cross section of 1 sq in. is cut in half, as in Fig. 10.1, and each half is uniformly wound with 760 turns of wire. With the halves separated 0.05 in., what will be the attractive force when the current in the windings is 2 amp?

SOLUTION: Solving for the flux density in the air gaps in the usual way, we find it to be 1.395 webers per sq m.

The area of the faces between which the pull is exerted is

$$\frac{1}{(39.37)^2} = 6.45 \times 10^{-4} \text{ sq m.}$$

The attractive force, by Equation (10.4), is

$$F = \frac{B^2 A}{\mu_0} = \frac{(1.395)^2 (6.45 \times 10^{-4})}{4\pi \times 10^{-7}} = 1000 \text{ newtons}$$
$$= 224 \text{ lb (total for both air gaps).}$$

Problems

(1-X) The magnetic circuit of a telegraph relay is constructed of wrought iron, with dimensions in inches as shown in Fig. 10.2. There are 1100 turns

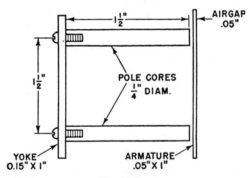

Fig. 10.2.

on each pole core. To attract the armature and close the relay against the pull of the spring requires a force of 5 g. What current in the winding will be necessary to close the relay? Neglect leakage flux.

(2-X) The magnetic circuit of a small lifting magnet is constructed of wrought iron with dimensions in centimeters as shown in Fig. 10.3. A 100-turn coil around the central core establishes flux over paths indicated by dotted lines. Assume that the surfaces of the magnet and armature are smooth enough to permit the armature and magnet to be fitted together with an effective air gap of 0.005 in. Determine the current in the coil to enable the magnet to exert a pull of 200 lb on the armature.

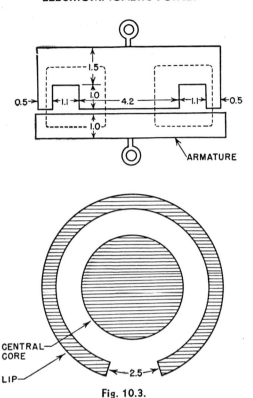

Fig. 10.3.

2. **The magnetic field about a long, straight conductor.** If the magnetic field in the vicinity of a long, straight conductor is investigated by any of the means described in Chapter VII (exploring coil or magnetic needle), it is found that it can be represented by circles having the wire as their center, and lying in planes perpendicular to the wire. A number of such circles are shown in Fig. 10.4 with the conductor shown in cross section at the center. The direction of the field at any point is a tangent to one of these circles, and its sense is that given by the right-hand rule. The magnetic field intensity at a

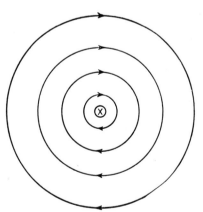

Fig. 10.4. Magnetic field surrounding a long straight conductor.

given point will depend upon the current in the wire and upon the perpendicular distance from the point to the wire, becoming less as the distance from the wire increases.

The magnetic field intensity at all points a specified distance from the wire (that is, all points on a particular circle of the field map) must be the same. The mmf required for a particular circle of radius S is, therefore, the product of H, the magnetic field intensity at distance S from the wire, and $2\pi S$, the distance around the circle.

$$F = 2\pi SH. \tag{10.6}$$

This is exactly like calculating the ampere-turns required for an iron ring which is of uniform cross section throughout. The circle may be considered to be a flux path of extremely small cross section, around which we take the product of magnetic field intensity and length of path to find the mmf required.

A straight wire, in order to carry current, must be part of a circuit. As previously explained, a long, straight conductor merely means that the rest of the circuit is far enough away so that its magnetic effect can be neglected in the region studied. A straight wire, therefore, is to be regarded as one turn, and to produce a mmf numerically equal to the current it carries. Consequently, we may write

$$2\pi SH = I \tag{10.7}$$

or

$$H = \frac{I}{2\pi S}, \tag{10.8}$$

and

$$B = \mu H = \frac{\mu I}{2\pi S}. \tag{10.9}$$

3. Force upon a current-carrying conductor in a magnetic field. The force between long, parallel conductors was used as the basis for defining the unit of current, the equation being

$$F = \frac{\mu L I_1 I_2}{2\pi S} = \left(\frac{\mu I_1}{2\pi S}\right)(L I_2). \tag{2.8}$$

We have just shown, however, in Equation 10.9, that $\mu I/2\pi S$ gives the flux density at a distance S from a long, straight conductor carrying a current of I amperes. Hence, we may regard the first factor of (2.8) as being B, the flux density produced by the current in the first conductor at a distance S meters (that is, in the region occupied by the second conductor). We may, therefore, write the expression for the force acting on a current-carrying conductor in a magnetic field as

$$F = BLI, \tag{10.10}$$

where F is the force in newtons.

B is the flux density in webers per square meter.

L is length of the conductor in meters.

I is the current in amperes.

It is not necessary, in order to use Equation (10.10), that the field be produced by a parallel conductor or that the conductor upon which the force acts be long. It is only necessary that the conductor be perpendicular to the magnetic lines or have a component of length perpendicular to them. The magnetic field may be produced by a permanent magnet or by any arrangement of current-carrying conductors. The conductor upon which the force acts may be any length so long as there is a finite length or component of length perpendicular to the magnetic lines. In the case of short conductors, however, there will usually be forces acting upon adjacent sections of the circuit, which must be taken into account.

A rule for finding the direction of the force may be obtained by a consideration of Fig. 10.5. These conductors carry current in the same direction, and hence the force is attraction, conductor No. 1 being pushed toward the right and conductor No. 2 toward the left. By the right-hand rule, the magnetic field produced by conductor No. 1 in the vicinity of conductor No. 2 is downward, as indicated by the arrows. By the same rule, the magnetic field produced by conductor No. 2 in its own vicinity is clockwise, as indicated by the arrows on the closed

Fig. 10.5. Strengthened and weakened field method of determining the direction of the force on a current-carrying conductor.

lines. Hence, the effect of conductor No. 2 is to modify the field produced by conductor No. 1, strengthening it on the right and weakening it on the left. The force on conductor No. 2, therefore, tends to move it from the strengthened toward the weakened part of the field. We may state the rule as follows: *A current-carrying conductor modifies a magnetic field in which it is placed, and is acted upon by a force which tends to move it from the strengthened toward the weakened part of the field.*

Problems

(3-X) What is the magnetic field intensity at a distance of 1 in. from the center of a long, straight wire carrying a current of 100 amp? What is the magnetic flux density?

(4-X) What current must flow in a long, straight wire in order to set up a magnetic flux density of 50 gausses at a distance of 10 cm from the center of the wire?

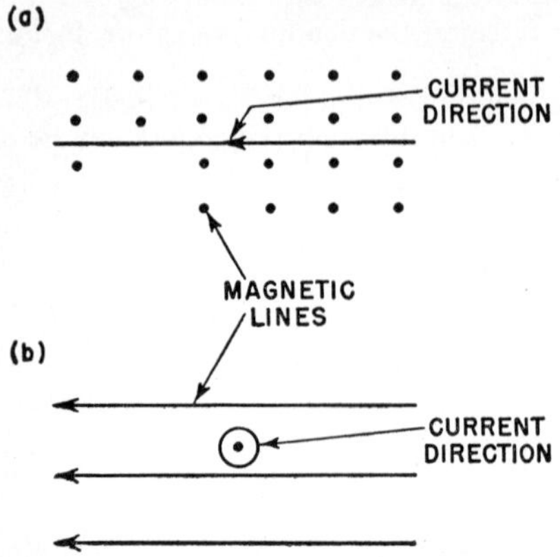

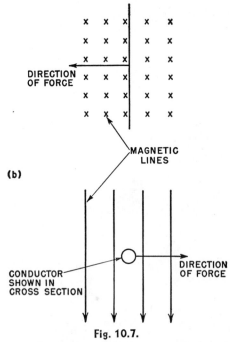

(a)

CURRENT DIRECTION

MAGNETIC LINES

(b)

CURRENT DIRECTION

Fig. 10.6.

density is 0.8 weber per sq m.

(5-X) Two long, straight conductors lie parallel to each other, 2½ in. apart. The current in each conductor is 75 amp. (a) Find the force per meter length which acts between the conductors, using the defining equation of current (Equation 2.8). (b) Find the magnetic flux density at the center of one conductor due to current in the other conductor by Equation (10.9), then find the force on the first conductor by applying Equation (10.10).

(6-X) A straight conductor which carries a current of 50 amp lies perpendicular to the lines of a magnetic field in which the flux Calculate the force per meter of conductor.

(a)

X X X X X

X X X X X

X X X X X

DIRECTION OF FORCE X X X X X

X X X X X

X X X X X

MAGNETIC LINES

(b)

CONDUCTOR SHOWN IN CROSS SECTION

DIRECTION OF FORCE

Fig. 10.7.

(7-X) What is the force on a conductor 50 in. long which carries a current of 100 amp and which lies perpendicular to the lines of a magnetic field in which the flux density is 1.5 kilolines per sq in.?

(**8-X**) What would be the force on the conductor in Problem 7-X if it lay at an angle of 37 degrees with the lines of the field?

(**9-X**) Determine the direction of force on the conductors shown in Fig. 10.6.

(**10-X**) Determine the direction of current in conductors shown in Fig. 10.7.

(**11-X**) Determine the direction of the field in which the conductors lie in Fig. 10.8.

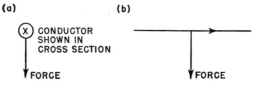

Fig. 10.8.

4. Force upon a charged particle moving in a magnetic field. Suppose a stream of small particles, such as electrons or charged atoms, consists of n particles per meter, each carrying a charge of e coulombs and moving with a velocity of v meters per second, at right angles to a magnetic field in which the flux density is B webers per square meter. The number of particles passing a reference point per second is

$$Z = nv, \tag{10.11}$$

and the quantity of electricity passing the reference point per second is

$$q = Ze = nve. \tag{10.12}$$

But quantity of electricity passing the reference point per second is current, so we may write

$$I = nve. \tag{10.13}$$

If we now substitute this expression for current into Equation (10.10) and put L equal to unity (because n is the number of particles *per meter*), we get

$$f = BLI = Bnve, \tag{10.14}$$

where f is the force in newtons acting upon a stream consisting of n particles. By putting $n = 1$, Equation (10.14) becomes

$$f = Bve, \tag{10.15}$$

where f is the force acting upon a single particle.

The direction of the force on a particle depends on the sign of its charge. A positive particle in motion is the equivalent of current, and the local field about it may be determined by the right-hand rule.   The direction of the force is, then, from the strengthened toward the weakened part of the field in which the particle moves.   A negative particle in motion is the equivalent of current in the *opposite* direction and, consequently, in applying the right-hand rule, the thumb must be pointed in the direction opposite to the motion.

Problems

(**12-X**) Determine the force which acts upon an electron moving with a velocity of 30,000 m per sec perpendicular to a magnetic field in which the flux density is 1.5 webers per sq m.

(**13-X**) Determine the force which acts upon a positive particle having a charge equivalent in magnitude to one electron and moving with a velocity of 10^6 m per sec perpendicular to a magnetic field in which the flux density is 10,000 gausses.

5. Electromagnetic torque.   We can now consider the effect of electromagnetic forces in causing rotation of a coil placed in a magnetic field.   This is the underlying principle of the electric motor, and of

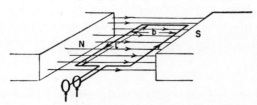

Fig. 10.9.   Elementary a-c motor.

D'Arsonval type electric meters, as was explained in Chapter V.   In Fig. 10.9, a rectangular coil consisting of a single turn of wire lies in a magnetic field of uniform flux density of B webers per square meter. The coil has a length of L meters, a breadth of b meters, and it carries a current of I amperes.   The coil is mounted so that it may rotate about its long axis, and its initial position is such that none of the magnetic lines link it.   Fig. 10.10a shows the sides of the coil in cross section as it lies in the initial position.   Each of the long sides of the coil will experience a force, according to Equation (10.10), of

$$f = BLI \text{ newtons.}$$

These forces each act at right angles to a moment arm of $b/2$ m, and, as a consequence, the coil experiences a torque of

$$T = 2BLI\,\frac{b}{2} = BLbI \text{ newton-m,} \tag{10.16}$$

tending to rotate it clockwise about its axis.   As it rotates from its

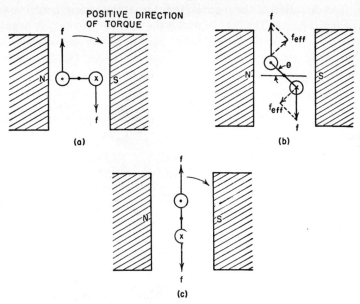

Fig. 10.10. Effect of coil position on torque.

initial position, the forces acting on the coil sides remain constant, but they are no longer at right angles to the moment arms, and, therefore, the torque decreases. After the coil has rotated through an angle θ, as shown in Fig. 10.10b, the component of force at right angles to the radius arm is

$$f_{effective} = f \cos \theta, \tag{10.17}$$

and the torque is

$$T = BLbI \cos \theta. \tag{10.18}$$

When the angle of rotation becomes 90°, as in Fig. 10.10c, the effective component of the force is zero and the coil, therefore, locks in this

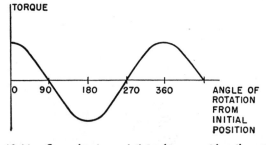

Fig. 10.11. Curve showing variation of torque with coil position.

position. As may be seen, it is the position in which the coil is linked by the most magnetic lines.

If the coil is forced past the 90° position by an external torque, it will tend to return. The electromagnetic torque is negative (the clockwise direction being considered positive). We may plot the torque against angle of rotation from the initial position, obtaining a curve like that shown in Fig. 10.11. At the 270° position, there exists a condition of unstable equilibrium. As long as the angle is exactly 270°, there is no torque, and the coil remains at rest. But a small displacement either way gives rise to a positive or negative torque which, if unopposed, rotates the coil back to the 90° position.

Problems

(14-X) A 1-turn coil, 20 by 30 cm is mounted as in Fig. 10.9 so that it may rotate about its long axis in a uniform magnetic field of 0.2 weber per sq m. The coil carries a current of $+100$ amp. Calculate the torque at 30° intervals of displacement of the coil from the reference position from 0 to 360°. Use positive directions and reference position as in Fig. 10.10. Plot torque against displacement angle.

(15-X) Recalculate the torques and plot torque against displacement using the data in Problem 14-X and the positive directions and reference position shown in Fig. 10.12.

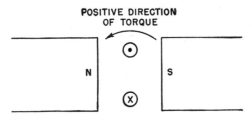

Fig. 10.12.

6. Electric motors. It is apparent that if continuous rotation of a coil like that in Fig. 10.10 is to be produced, there must be some means of reversing the current in the coil, and thereby maintaining the torque in the positive direction after the coil passes the 90° position. The simplest possible way of doing this is to use alternating current. This arrangement is not self-starting, because with the coil in the 90° position, there would be no torque, no matter what the magnitude and direction of the current. If, however, the coil be set in rotation by some means, without current flowing in it, at a speed equal to the frequency of the current to be used, and then the switch be closed at precisely the correct time (so that the current is positive maximum when the coil is in the initial position, as in Fig. 10.13a), torque will be developed always in the same direction, and the device will continue to run.[1]   This is an elementary **synchronous motor.**   If it is to run at all, its time of rotation must be the same as the period of the alternating current which energizes it.

In order to obtain continuous rotation of the coil with direct current, it is necessary to provide a **commutator,** or switching device, to

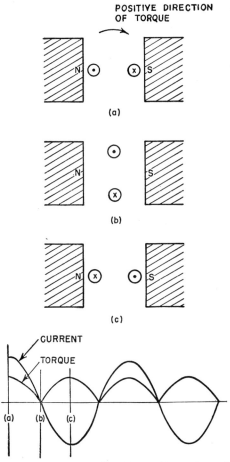

Fig. 10.13.   Relation between current, coil position and torque in an elementary a-c motor.

reverse the current in the coil at the proper time.   The commutator is a metal ring, cut into two or more insulated segments, and mounted so that it rotates with the coil as in Fig. 10.14.   The ends of the coil are

[1] Note that the current directions marked in Figs. 10.13 and 10.15 are the directions selected as positive; not actual directions.   The instantaneous values of current and torque corresponding to coil positions a, b and c are shown by the graphs.

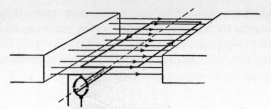

Fig. 10.14.   Elementary d-c motor.

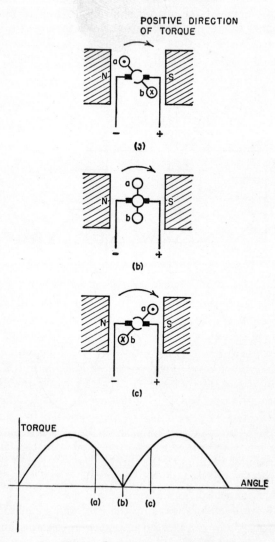

Fig. 10.15.   Commutation in a d-c motor.

connected to the commutator segments, and connection with the source of energy is through the **brushes** which maintain sliding contact with the commutator segments.   In Fig. 10.15a, current flows through the coil in the direction marked as positive, which tends to rotate the coil clockwise in the direction selected as positive.

In Fig. 10.15b, both commutator segments are in contact with both brushes, and the coil is short-circuited.   The current in the coil is effecting its change in direction during the time of short circuit, and is considered to be zero at the instant shown.   In Fig. 10.15c, the short circuit no longer exists, and the current flows through the coil sides in the direction *opposite* to that selected as positive, thus maintaining torque in the clockwise direction.[1]

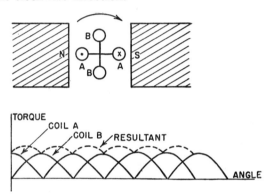

Fig. 10.16.   Torque in a multicoil d-c motor.

Motors like those shown in Figs. 10.13 and 10.15 are not practical for several reasons.   First, the torque of any single-coil motor is pulsating, and even though it is never in the negative direction, its magnitude falls to zero twice during a revolution.   Such a motor cannot successfully deliver much mechanical power, and is able to run at all only because the inertia of the rotating parts carries it over the dead points, where no torque is developed.   By using two coils having the same axis of rotation, but with their planes perpendicular to each other, as in Fig. 10.16, it is possible to eliminate the dead points and make the torque much more uniform, for when one coil is in the 90° position, where it contributes nothing to the torque, the other is in the position to develop maximum torque.   In practical motors, the number of coils is further increased, and the resultant torque made still more uniform.   The problem of arranging the coils and connecting them to form a practical **winding** is treated in books on electrical machinery.

[1] For footnote see page 239.

The production of any considerable torque also requires that the magnetic paths of the flux be mostly in iron, in order that large flux densities may be produced in the region occupied by the coils. This is accomplished by placing the coil sides in slots cut lengthwise in the surface of a cylindrical iron core, shaping the pole faces to conform to this cylinder, and completing the magnetic path through the frame of the machine. Magnetic problems involving such flux paths have already been considered in a previous chapter.

Problems

(16-X) The armature of a d-c motor has 36 slots, in each of which there are two coil sides. There are 9 turns per coil, making a total of 18 conductors per slot, each of which carries a current of 50 amp. Of the 36 slots, 28 lie under the pole faces in a uniform flux density of 1.08 webers per sq m. The other 8 slots lie opposite the interpolar spaces, and the flux density will be considered to be zero. The flux entering the armature may be considered as perpendicular to the surface and to the conductors in the slots. The effective length of the armature conductors is 30 cm, and the effective radius of the armature is 25 cm. Calculate:
  (a) The force on each armature conductor.
  (b) The force on all the conductors in a slot.
  (c) The torque due to all the conductors in a single slot.
  (d) The total torque due to all the slots under the poles.

Study Questions

1. What would be the effect on magnetic pull of chamfering the pole faces?
2. From Equation (10.4) it would seem that magnetic pull does not depend upon the distance between the pole faces. Explain.
3. In deriving the expression for magnetic pull it is assumed that all the additional energy stored in the air gaps when the pole faces are separated by an additional distance ΔL comes from the agency that causes the separation. How can we be sure none of it comes from increasing the current in the winding?
4. How do we know that the magnetic field intensity is the same at all points which are equidistant from a very long straight wire which carries current? Why would it not be true for a short straight wire which carried current?
5. The expression $F = BLI$ was developed for long parallel conductors. Is its use limited to the calculation of forces on such conductors? Why?
6. Would parallel streams of like-charged particles moving in free space be attracted as would current-carrying conductors? Explain.
7. Devise a simple statement of how a current-carrying loop will orient itself in a magnetic field.

8. The running of an elementary single-coil motor can sometimes be improved by adding a flywheel.   Explain.

9. What is the function of the commutator in an elementary d-c motor? Why is it not required on an a-c motor?

10. In starting an elementary synchronous motor it is noticed that sometimes several trials are necessary.   At other times the motor starts immediately.   Explain.

CHAPTER XI

ELECTROMAGNETIC INDUCTION AND MOTIONAL ELECTROMOTIVE FORCE

1. Electromotive force caused by a changing magnetic field. Faraday's experiments in 1831 led him to the concept of lines of magnetic flux as a means of explaining how it was possible for a change in current in one circuit to cause a current in another circuit with which no electrical connections existed. This concept proved so useful that it has continued to occupy a principal place throughout the history of electrical science. Faraday's law of electromagnetic induction, which expresses the relationship between electromotive force and rate of change of magnetic flux,

$$E = N \frac{\Delta \phi}{\Delta T}, \tag{7.12}$$

served as the basis of our definition of magnetic flux and its unit (Chapter VII). We shall now study this law more carefully, with the object of determining its usefulness and limitations, and also of trying to gain a better understanding of the magnetic flux concept itself.

In Faraday's original experiments, the changes in flux were basically changes in flux density, brought about by changing the current in some neighboring circuit. To illustrate this, let A and B in Fig. 11.1 represent circular turns of wire, fixed in position relative to one another and having a common axis. With the switch open in circuit A, no magnetic field exists in the region of the coils because no current is flowing. Upon closing the switch, current begins to flow in circuit A, establishing a magnetic field, some of the lines of which link circuit B. As the current in circuit A increases, the magnetic field intensity and magnetic flux density in all the space surrounding circuit A will increase, which will result in an increase in the number of magnetic lines linking circuit B, and, conse-

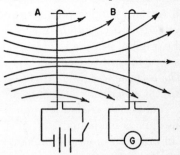

Fig. 11.1. Emf induced by a changing magnetic field.

quently, in an emf induced in circuit B, which causes current to flow, and the galvanometer to be deflected.

That an emf will likewise be induced in circuit A is evident from the same reasoning. Its effect is not so readily detected because there is another source of emf (the battery) in that circuit. The effect of this emf will be studied in more detail in Section 15. The emf in circuit B is called an **emf of mutual induction,** that in circuit A is called an **emf of self-induction.** These emf's, of course, will persist only as long as the current continues to change in circuit A. When the current reaches its Ohm's law value (usually in a very short time), the flux ceases to increase and the induced emf's become zero.

If the switch is opened, or if any change is made in the current which flows in circuit A, emf's appear in both circuits and persist as long as the change continues. Thus, if a source of alternating current were substituted for the battery in circuit A, the current in that circuit would be continually changing, and both self and mutual emf's would always be present. Our two circuits would then function as a **transformer,** which we will consider in more detail in Section 18.

2. Lenz's law. We must now find some way to determine the **direction** of an induced emf. Let us first suppose that the emf in circuit B, Fig. 11.1, acts to send current in the same direction as the current in circuit A. Such a current would further strengthen the original magnetic field set up by the increasing current in circuit A, and thus increase the induced emf, which would increase the current, and so forth endlessly. This is obviously impossible. Consequently, we must have been wrong when we supposed the induced emf to be in the direction we did. It is in the contrary direction, and acts to send current around circuit B in such a direction as to oppose the increase in the original field, not aid it. This reasoning leads to **Lenz's law,** which is a statement in electrical terms of the law of conservation of energy: *The emf induced in a circuit by a change in flux will be in the direction current would have to flow in order to oppose the change in flux.*

Lenz's law is readily applied to any complete circuit through which the flux is changing. It must be carefully noted that the law says "in order to oppose the **change** of flux," not "in order to oppose the flux." If the flux is decreasing, the emf is in the direction in which current must flow to aid the flux, and tends to prevent its decrease. Thus, referring again to Fig. 11.1, if the switch in circuit A is opened, the current and, therefore, the flux, must decrease to zero. The emf induced in circuit B will now actually be in such a direction as to send current in the same direction as the current in circuit A, thus aiding the flux and opposing its decrease.

The direction of the emf of self-induction set up in circuit A may likewise be determined by Lenz's law. It must always "be in the direction current would have to flow in order to oppose the **change** in flux." When the switch is closed and flux is increasing, the induced emf in circuit A opposes the battery emf, tending to prevent the increase in the current that is causing the flux. When the switch is opened and flux is decreasing, the induced emf in circuit A aids the battery emf, tending to maintain the current and prevent the decrease in flux.

Problems

(**1-XI**) Determine the actual direction of the induced emf in Fig. 11.2a and b.

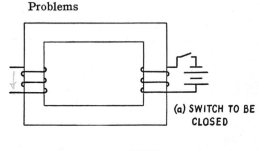

(a) SWITCH TO BE CLOSED

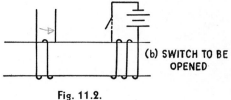

(b) SWITCH TO BE OPENED

Fig. 11.2.

(**2-XI**) Determine the actual direction of the induced emf in Fig. 11.3a and b.

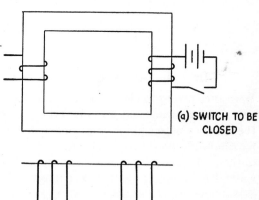

(a) SWITCH TO BE CLOSED

(b) SLIDER TO BE MOVED DOWN

Fig. 11.3.

(3-XI) Determine the actual direction of the induced emf in Fig. 11.4a and b.

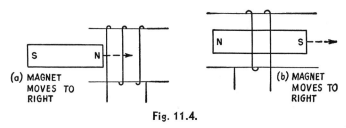

Fig. 11.4.

3. Emf caused by a conductor moving in a magnetic field. It can be readily demonstrated that any change in the flux linking a circuit as a consequence of its motion in the magnetic field will also cause an emf. Such emf's are called **motional,** or **generated,** emf's as distinguished from induced emf's as discussed in the preceding section. Suppose, for example, that circuit B in Fig. 11.1 were pivoted so that it could be rotated about a diameter into the position shown in Fig. 11.5.

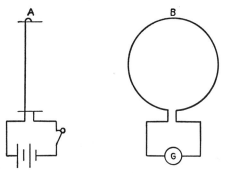

Fig. 11.5.   Emf induced in a coil rotated in a fixed magnetic field.

With the current in circuit A, and, therefore, the magnetic field intensity and flux density at all points in the region remaining unchanged, the number of magnetic lines linking circuit B will decrease from a maximum, when it is in the position shown in Fig. 11.1, to a minimum in the position shown in Fig. 11.5, and an emf will be set up in the coil while it is in motion, as will be demonstrated by the deflection of the galvanometer. Experiments show that Faraday's law is valid for motional emf's as it was for those induced by magnetic fields which varied in intensity.

It is not necessary that the entire circuit shift in position relative to the magnetic field. If any part of it move in such a way as to increase or decrease the total number of magnetic lines linked, the effect is the same. Suppose a uniform magnetic field (that is, one having the same flux density at every point) is established perpendicular to the plane of the paper as indicated by the x arrows in Fig. 11.6. The circuit lies in the plane of the paper, and consists of two metal rails R, R, connected at the upper end by the galvanometer. A movable conductor M is arranged to slide along the rails, maintaining contact with them, and keeping always parallel to its initial position. As M moves from position A to position B, there is, obviously, an increase in the number of magnetic lines linking the loop, and, consequently, an emf (evidenced by the deflection of the galvanometer), and again found to be in accordance with Faraday's law.

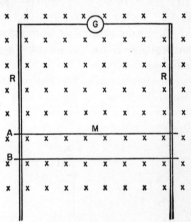

Now the only way in which additional lines can be admitted to link the circuit is by the movement of the sliding conductor M. As it moves lines are **cut** by it— that is, they are transferred from one side of it to the other, and are admitted to link the circuit. Thus, in the particular case under consideration, the rate of increase of flux linking the loop,[1] and the electromotive force may be calculated on this basis.

Fig. 11.6. Emf induced in a conductor which cuts magnetic lines.

4. The BLV Rule. Since the rate at which the moving conductor is cutting flux (for an arrangement such as that shown in Fig. 11.6) is equal to the rate of change of flux linking the circuit, we can obtain an expression for motional emf in terms of magnetic flux density, the length of the moving conductor, and its velocity relative to the field. Suppose the length of the moving conductor in Fig. 11.6 is L meters, and the distance traversed as it moves from position A to position B is ΔS meters. Then, if the magnetic flux density is B webers per square meter, the change in flux linking the loop is

$$\Delta\phi = BL\Delta S. \tag{11.1}$$

If the average velocity at which the conductor moves is V meters per second, then the time required to move from position A to position B is

$$\Delta T = \frac{\Delta S}{V}. \tag{11.2}$$

---

[1] This is true provided the ends of the moving conductor do not project beyond the rails R, R, and provided, of course, there is no change in flux density.

Substituting (11.1) and (11.2) into the Faraday's law equation, we obtain

$$E = N \frac{\Delta \phi}{\Delta T} = \frac{BL\Delta S}{\frac{\Delta S}{V}} = BLV. \tag{11.3}$$

To illustrate the equivalence of the two methods, we shall now consider a numerical example.

EXAMPLE: A conductor 10 cm long moves as in Fig. 11.6, requiring 10^{-4} sec to move 2 cm from position A to position B. The flux density is 10^{-6} weber per sq m perpendicular to the paper. Determine the average emf generated in the conductor as it moves from position A to position B by (a) change-of-flux-linkage method and (b) flux-cut method.

SOLUTION: (a) The change in flux linking the loop is

$$\Delta \phi = BL\Delta S$$
$$= (10^{-6})(0.1 \times 0.02) = 2 \times 10^{-9} \text{ weber.}$$
$$E = N \frac{\Delta \phi}{\Delta T}$$
$$= 1 \frac{2 \times 10^{-9}}{10^{-4}} = 2 \times 10^{-5} \text{ v.}$$

(b) The velocity at which the conductor moves is

$$V = \frac{\Delta S}{\Delta T} = \frac{0.02}{10^{-4}} = 200 \text{ m per sec.}$$
$$E = BLV$$
$$= (10^{-6})(0.1)(200) = 2 \times 10^{-5} \text{ v.}$$

Equation (11.3) is based on a straight conductor that moves in a direction at right angles to the magnetic lines. If this condition is not met in a particular problem, it is necessary to find a component of flux density, or a component of the velocity, such that they are at right angles. Suppose the magnetic lines in Fig. 11.6 were not perpendicular, but inclined to the left, making an angle of θ degrees with the surface of the paper. The component of flux density perpendicular to the paper would be, then,

$$B_P = B \sin \theta, \tag{11.4}$$

as can be seen from a study of Fig. 11.7. In like manner, it can be seen that if the flux lines are perpendicular to the paper but both rails are tilted so that the plane in which the conductor moves makes an angle of α degrees with the paper, then a component of velocity

$$V_P = V \cos \alpha \tag{11.5}$$

would have to be used.

In the form in which it was stated in Section 2, Lenz's law cannot be applied to conductors that are not part of a complete circuit.

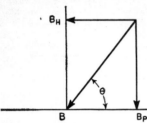

Therefore, various rules of thumb have been devised which do apply to such conductors, and three such rules are given below.

1. *The emf in the moving conductor will be in such direction as to cause a current which would strengthen the field on the leading side of the conductor.*

Fig. 11.7. Components of magnetic flux density.

2. *The emf will be in the direction pointed by the thumb if the conductor is allowed to strike the palm of the open right hand held with the fingers in the direction of the magnetic lines.*

3. *The emf will be in the direction pointed by the middle finger of the right hand held with the thumb, forefinger, and middle finger mutually perpendicular, the thumb pointing in the direction of motion and the forefinger pointing in the direction of the magnetic lines.*

There is no derivation for these rules: they simply are used because they happen to give the correct results. The student should verify all of them by applying them to Fig. 11.6.

Problems

(**4-XI**) In an apparatus like that in Fig. 11.6, the slide rails are 10 in. apart. The distance from the cross connection to the moving conductor in position A is 20 in.; to position B, 22 in. The lines of a uniform magnetic field in which the flux density is 5×10^{-7} weber per sq m are perpendicular to the plane of the apparatus. Calculate by Faraday's law the emf generated in the circuit if the conductor moves from A to B in 10^{-3} sec.

(**5-XI**) Recalculate the emf in Problem 4-XI, using the BLV rule.

(**6-XI**) What would have been the emf in Problem 5-XI if the lines had inclined to the right, making an angle of 50° with the paper? Use the BLV rule.

(**7-XI**) What would have been the emf in Problem 5-XI if the conductor were moved in a direction which makes an angle of 30° with the perpendicular to its length? Use the BLV rule.

(**8-XI**) The magnetic lines of the earth's field in a certain locality make an angle of 65° with the surface of the earth, entering the earth from the south. The flux density is 0.6 gauss. What emf would be generated in an axle of a railway train moving north at a speed of 75 mph? Take the length of the axle as 4 ft, $8\frac{1}{2}$ in.

(**9-XI**) What emf would be generated in a vertical antenna 2 m long on an automobile going north at a speed of 75 mph in the locality of Problem 8-XI? What emf would be generated if the automobile were going east?

(**10-XI**) What is the direction of the emf induced in a loop of wire that is raised from a position flat on the floor to a position in an E-W vertical plane?

(**11-XI**) Work out the thing called for in each of the cases of a conductor moving in magnetic field as shown in Fig. 11.8.

5. Limitations of the BLV rule. The questions may be asked, "Is an emf developed in a moving conductor that is not part of a loop? When is Equation (11.3) applicable?" It would seem that the answer to the first question could readily be found by experiment. However, when we connect a galvanometer or other measuring instrument to the ends of the moving conductor, we complete a circuit, and any emf that is measured could be attributed to a change of flux linking this circuit, unless it could be shown there were no such change. In certain arrangements of moving conductors, as in a Faraday disk generator (Sec. 10), it is possible to produce and measure an electromotive force in a loop when no change in the flux linking the loop is taking place. In such a case, Faraday's law would not give the right result: since there is no change in the

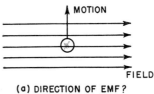

(a) DIRECTION OF EMF?

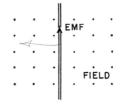

(b) DIRECTION OF FIELD?

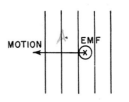

(c) DIRECTION OF MOTION?

Fig. 11.8.

flux linking the circuit, Faraday's law would give zero for the emf when actually an emf is being measured. We may conclude, therefore, that a change in flux linkages is not essential, and an emf will be generated when flux is cut by a conductor that is not part of a complete circuit. To calculate the magnitude of such an emf, the BLV rule must be used.

It is easy to see that Equation (11.3) would not be applicable to the calculation of an emf caused by a change in flux density. In Fig. 11.6, if there is no motion of the conductor M, Equation (11.3) would give zero for the emf when actually an emf would exist if the flux density were increasing or decreasing. To calculate the magnitude of such an emf, Faraday's law must be used.

Suppose now that in the arrangement shown in Fig. 11.6, the flux density were made to increase and the conductor M were moved downward at the same time. We would thus have the amount of flux linking the loop increasing for two reasons. Nevertheless, Faraday's law holds, and if we divide the change in flux by the time it took to bring it about, we find the average emf generated in the loop due to both motion and change in flux density. But using Equation (11.3) (after having determined the average flux density for the period of time the conductor M was in motion) will give the average emf due to motion only.

Thus we see that Equation (11.3) is applicable to the calculation of a motional emf when the conductor moves at right angles to a uniform magnetic field and to its own length.

Numerous paradoxical circuits and arrangements can be devised in which an emf might be predicted by one of the rules and experiment prove the emf non-existent, or on the other hand no emf might be predicted and experiment prove one to exist. In problems where both Faraday's law and the BLV rule give the same result, there is little question about its validity. If they do not give the same result the problem needs to be studied further to see whether in fact it involves a change of flux density, a conductor cutting flux, or a combination of the two.

6. Physical interpretation of emf's. We have seen that an emf may be produced by: (1) a change in the amount of magnetic flux linking a circuit, brought about by either: (a) a change in the magnetic flux density or (b) a change in position of the circuit or some part of it relative to the magnetic field; or by (2) cutting of magnetic flux by a moving conductor. Actually (1b) and (2) may be regarded as two ways of dealing with the same phenomenon. Let us now see whether we can find reasons why an emf should appear as a consequence of either a variation of magnetic flux density or a cutting of magnetic lines.

Let us begin with the flux-cut idea. In Fig. 11.9, a conductor M is represented as moving downward in a magnetic field perpendicular to the page, keeping always parallel to its initial position, exactly as described in Section 3. In the space lattice of the conductor are free electrons, which of necessity move downward as parts of the conductor itself. Now, any moving charge is the equivalent of a current, and in a magnetic field will experience a force at right angles to its direction of motion and to the lines of the field. An electron moving downward is the equivalent of current upward, and will create a local field about itself which will strengthen the main field in Fig. 11.9 on the right and weaken it on the left, resulting in a force acting to move the electron to the left along the conductor. If the conductor is part of a complete circuit, as it is here, electrons are put in motion all the way around the circuit, and current will flow as long as the motion continues. The direction of the emf and the current will be contrary to the electron flow as shown, and will be found to agree with the direction as found by Lenz's law or by any of the various hand rules.   The energy expended in maintaining the current through the resistance of the circuit can be shown to be equal to the energy required to move the conductor against the emf owing to its carrying current in a magnetic field, and, therefore, comes from the source that moves the conductor, not from the field.

If the conductor is insulated from the rails on which it slides, the free electrons will experience forces as before, and will move to the left until there is established throughout the length of the conductor an electric field of intensity $\mathcal{E}$[1] just sufficient to prevent any further

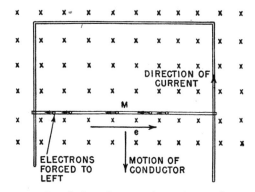

Fig. 11.9.   Forces exerted on the free electrons of a moving conductor in a magnetic field.

motion of electrons.   There would then exist between the ends of the conductor an emf,

$$E = BLV. \tag{11.6}$$

We have thus explained motional emf as being the direct consequence of the forces that act upon moving charges in a magnetic field and, therefore, of the forces that act between charges moving relative to one another.   The concept of change of flux linkages, although valid in cases where the moving conductor is part of a complete circuit, is seen to be a somewhat indirect way of explaining the phenomenon, though the laws of Faraday and of Lenz are nearly always the best and most convenient means of actually calculating the emf.

We now have to consider the origin of emf's that appear as a consequence of a change in the flux density of a magnetic field.   Suppose the conductor M in Fig. 11.9 and all parts of the circuit remain at rest with respect to the field, but that the flux density increases owing to an

[1] Section 3, Chapter XII.

increase in current in the circuit that establishes the flux. Since there is now no relative motion between the field and the circuit, our explanation of the emf as being due to magnetic forces acting upon moving electrons is no longer valid. We know, however, that electrons will experience forces in an *electric* field, regardless of whether they are in motion or at rest with respect to the field. We may, therefore, resolve our difficulty by supposing that a magnetic field in which the flux density varies with time gives rise to an electric field. The free electrons of the circuit would then experience electric forces, which, if the circuit were so placed that it coincided with the electric field throughout its length, would result in an emf which would act to cause a flow of current. In fact, it is not necessary that the circuit *coincide* with the field at every point, but simply that if we divide the circuit into segments, take the product of every segment's length by the component of the electric field intensity in the direction of the segment, and then sum up all these products, the summation should not be zero.

We need to emphasize at this point that we do not induce current: we induce emf, and the current that flows then depends upon the resistance of the circuit provided. Suppose we made up a circuit of glass tubing instead of wire. The emf induced in it (that is, the summation of the products of electric field intensity by length) would be precisely the same as for a copper conductor. Of course no current could be made to flow in such a circuit because of its enormous resistance.

When it comes to the matter of placing the circuit in the electric field to the best advantage (that is, so that it shall coincide as nearly as possible with the field) we usually find it expedient to make use again of the concept of lines of magnetic flux, and simply place the circuit so that the variation in the number of magnetic lines linking it will be a maximum. One thing is equivalent to the other, and the geometry of the varying magnetic field is usually more apparent than that of the associated electric field.

7. Representation of emf's. As we have already learned, the direction of a current is conveyed to a reader by telling him if it is positive or negative, and drawing an arrow to indicate which direction we are calling positive. Both these things are necessary: a statement that a certain current is positive is meaningless unless there is an indication of *which* direction is positive. These same statements may be made regarding emf's set up in coils and conductors. We select a direction in which the emf will be designated as positive, and plainly indicate this **positive direction** by placing an arrow beside the coil or conductor. We then proceed to apply Lenz's law to determine the actual direction of the emf. If the actual direction of the emf turns out to be in the arrow direction, it is accordingly written as positive; if opposite to the arrow, it is designated as negative. To illustrate this procedure, let us consider a coil like that shown in Fig. 11.10 which is linked by magnetic flux as shown, owing to current either in the coil itself, or in a neighboring circuit. The direction chosen as positive for the emf is indicated by the arrow marked e and placed alongside the coil. This arrow denotes that a rise of potential in the direction it points (from the right-hand terminal toward the left-hand terminal of the coil) will be considered positive.

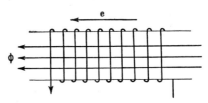

Fig. 11.10. Positive direction for induced electromotive force.

Now, let us suppose that the flux linking the coil is increasing. Lenz's law tells us that the induced emf is actually in the direction selected as positive, tending to cause current to flow out at the left-hand terminal, thereby opposing the increase in the flux. The emf is, therefore, positive, and we write

$$E = +N \frac{\Delta \phi}{\Delta T}. \tag{11.7}$$

If by chance we had selected the other direction as positive, it should be clear that since the actual direction of the emf is *not* the direction selected as positive, we would have had to write

$$E = -N \frac{\Delta \phi}{\Delta T}. \tag{11.8}$$

Let us now suppose that the flux linking the coil is decreasing. By applying Lenz's law, we find that the induced emf is actually in the direction opposite to that selected as positive, since it must tend to cause current to flow out at the right-hand terminal of the coil, thereby opposing the decrease in flux that is taking place. It is plain, then, that the emf is negative, but before writing it down, we must remember that in this case (flux decreasing) $\Delta \phi / \Delta T$ is itself a negative quantity, and the use of the minus sign is not only unnecessary, but wrong. Accordingly, we write

$$E = +N \frac{\Delta \phi}{\Delta T}. \tag{11.9}$$

It appears then, since (11.9) is identical with (11.7), that whether the flux is increasing or decreasing makes no difference in the expression to be used. The emf is actually in one direction for increasing flux and in the opposite direction for decreasing flux. The expression to be used is the same because $\Delta\phi/\Delta T$ itself is positive or negative according to whether the flux is increasing or decreasing.

To make the illustration complete, let us suppose we had taken the positive direction opposite to that in Fig. 11.10. With the flux decreasing, the emf would then actually be in the direction selected as positive and must, therefore, be represented as positive. But $\Delta\phi/\Delta T$ is itself negative. The correct expression is, therefore,

$$E = -N\frac{\Delta\phi}{\Delta T}.$$ (11.10)

The student may ask why we select a positive direction in advance at all. Why not apply Lenz's law at once and determine the actual direction in each case, then let this be the direction selected as positive? The answer to this is rather obvious. In a-c circuits, the flux linking the circuit first increases, then decreases, then increases in the opposite direction, then decreases, and so forth, repeating this cycle of variation over and over. The actual direction of the emf is not the same at every instant, and we have nothing to recommend the choice of one direction any more than the other as being the direction to consider positive. But a choice must be made if we are to speak intelligibly of positive or negative values of an emf. Even in problems where the flux change is limited to an increase or a decrease, the choice of a positive direction is arbitrary. In many textbooks the law is consistently written

$$E = -N\frac{\Delta\phi}{\Delta T},$$

which implies that the positive direction of the induced electromotive force was selected to agree with the direction of a current which is related to the changing flux by the right-hand rule.[1] Unfortunately, the positive direction is not always marked, and the student is sometimes given rather vague reasons why the law should be written with the minus sign. There is, of course, no objection to this particular choice; it is as logical as any other, but no more so, and it is essential

---

[1] This is particularly true of books on electromagnetic theory. In electrical engineering books the positive directions of emf's are often chosen as best suits the immediate purpose of the writer, with the result that Faraday's law may sometimes have a negative, sometimes a positive sign. A further result is that on vector diagrams for alternating current circuits and machines, an emf may either lead or lag by 90° the sinusoidal flux which produced it. If the positive directions for emf's were always chosen so that $E = -N\dfrac{\Delta\phi}{\Delta T}$, then the emf would in every case lag the sinusoidal flux by 90°.

for the student to know that the minus sign results from a choice of positive direction and to know which direction was chosen. The student will do well never to write the expression at all without first marking a positive direction and then using Lenz's law to determine the actual direction of the emf. If this is done there will never be any doubt as to the sign of the expression.

Problems

(12-XI) Write Faraday's law with the proper sign for the positive direction indicated in Fig. 11.11a and b.

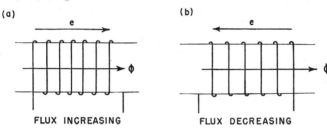

Fig. 11.11.

(13-XI) What positive directions must have been assumed in Fig. 11.12a and b in order for the sign used in Faraday's law to be correct?

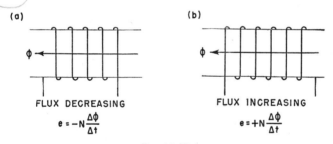

Fig. 11.12.

(14-XI) Determine whether or not the emf is actually in the direction selected as positive in Fig. 11.13a and b.

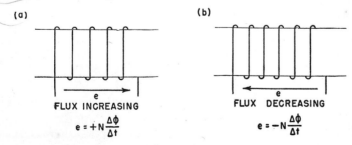

Fig. 11.13.

8. Average, instantaneous, maximum, and effective values of emf.

The emf's calculated in the present chapter thus far have been **average** for finite periods of time. If we use

$$E = N \frac{\Delta \phi}{\Delta T}, \qquad (7.12)$$

we obtain the average value for E over the period of time ΔT.[1] Now, the rate of change of flux (and consequently the emf) seldom remains the same for any time ΔT, and it is often necessary to determine **instantaneous** rates of change of flux and instantaneous emf's. If we take the limit of (7.12) as ΔT approaches zero, we obtain the instantaneous emf, designated usually by a small letter.

$$e = \lim_{\Delta T \to 0} N \frac{\Delta \phi}{\Delta T} = N \frac{d\phi}{dt}. \qquad (11.11)$$

This is seen to be simply the derivative of the flux with respect to time. To actually calculate instantaneous values of e from this equation, it is, of course, necessary that we know the manner in which flux varies with time and that we be able to express the variation mathematically and perform the differentiation indicated in (11.11).

The **maximum,** or **peak,** value of an emf is the maximum instantaneous value which it has during a given period of time—usually one cycle.

The **effective,** or **root mean square,** value of an emf is the square root of the average squared value of the emf during a given period of time, usually one cycle. This is the value read by an a-c voltmeter. Any statement as to an a-c potential difference, unless it expressly says average, instantaneous, or maximum, is understood to mean effective value.

9. An elementary a-c generator.

Suppose a conductor bent to form a one-turn rectangular coil is rotated in a uniform magnetic field, as shown in Fig. 11.14. In its initial position (shown in cross section in Fig. 11.15), the plane of the coil is perpendicular to the magnetic field, and it is linked by the maximum flux, ϕ_M. The directions assumed as positive for the generated emf's are marked beside the conductors which form the coil sides. As the coil rotates, it is linked by less and less flux, until the angle θ, through which it has rotated, becomes 90°. The flux linking the coil for any position from $\theta = 0°$ to $\theta = 90°$ is obviously given by the equation

$$\phi = \phi_M \cos \theta. \qquad (11.12)$$

[1] In finding the average value of an alternating emf, ΔT is arbitrarily taken to correspond to a half cycle. The average value for one cycle is obviously zero.

For angles from 90° to 270°, the cosine is negative, and Equation (11.12) gives negative values for the flux through the coil. This can be interpreted to mean that flux that passes through the coil in the reference position from the face indicated by solid line to the face indicated by dotted line is positive, and that flux that passes through the coil in the opposite direction is negative. For angles from 270° to

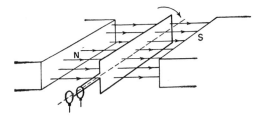

Fig. 11.14.   Elementary a-c generator.

360°, the cosine of θ is again positive, and the flux linking the coil is also positive.

Application of Lenz's law or any of the rules given in Section 4 shows that the actual emf is in the direction selected as positive as the coil moves from the position $\theta = 0°$ to the position $\theta = 90°$. Since

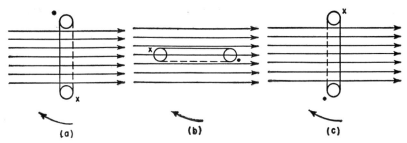

(a)   (b)   (c)

Fig. 11.15.   Rotating coil of elementary alternator.

$\Delta\phi/\Delta T$ is negative for flux decreasing, we must write the equation for the average emf as

$$E = -N \frac{\Delta\phi}{\Delta T}.$$ ·(11.13)

By considering various cases, the student may readily convince himself that (11.13) holds for any change in the position of the coil.

In order to find instantaneous emf's corresponding to various positions of the coil, we must take the limit of (11.13) as ΔT approaches zero, which is

$$e = -N \frac{d\phi}{dt}.$$ (11.14)

By substituting (11.12) in (11.14), we obtain

$$e = -N \frac{d(\phi_M \cos \theta)}{dt}.$$ (11.15)

If the coil is rotating at a uniform angular velocity of ω radians per second, where

$$\omega = 2\pi \times \frac{\text{revolutions per minute}}{60},$$ (11.16)

the angle through which the coil has rotated from the reference position is given by

$$\theta = \omega t,$$ (11.17)

where t is the time in seconds elapsed since the coil passed through the reference position.

Substituting (11.17) in (11.15) gives

$$e = -N \frac{d(\phi_M \cos \omega t)}{dt}$$

and carrying out the differentiation, we obtain

$$e = N\omega\phi_M \sin \omega t.$$ (11.18)

If we plot the instantaneous emf against time (or against the angle ωt), we obtain a wave like that shown in Fig. 11.16.

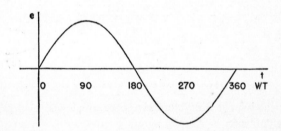

Fig. 11.16.   Sine wave of emf produced by elementary alternator.

The greatest value the sine of an angle can have is 1; consequently, the maximum value of the emf is

$$E_M = N\omega\phi_M,$$ (11.19)

and we may write the equation for emf simply

$$e = E_M \sin \omega t$$ (11.20)

Such an emf is called a sinusoidal emf, and would give rise to sinusoidal currents in any linear bilateral network. The effective value of a sinusoidal emf can be shown to be $1/\sqrt{2}$ times its maximum value.

EXAMPLE: An elementary a-c generator like that shown in Fig. 11.14 has a single-turn coil 40 by 50 cm which rotates at a uniform angular speed of 1200 rpm in a uniform magnetic field in which the flux density is 15×10^{-5} weber per sq m. (a) What is the average emf as the coil rotates from the position $\theta = 0°$ to the position $\theta = 90°$? (b) What is the average emf as the coil rotates from $\theta = 45°$ to $\theta = 135°$? (c) What is the maximum emf? (d) What is the instantaneous emf at each of the following positions: 0, 45, 90, 135°? (e) What is the effective value of the emf?

SOLUTION: (a) When $\theta = 0°$,

$$\phi_1 = \phi_M = {}^{40}\!/_{100} \times {}^{50}\!/_{100} \times 15 \times 10^{-5} = 3 \times 10^{-5} \text{ weber.}$$

When $\theta = 90°$,

$$\phi_2 = \phi_M \cos 90° = 0,$$
$$\Delta\phi = 0 - (3 \times 10^{-5}) = -3 \times 10^{-5} \text{ weber,}$$
$$\Delta T = {}^{60}\!/_{1200} \times {}^{90}\!/_{360} = 0.0125 \text{ sec,}$$
$$E_{aver} = -1 \frac{(-3 \times 10^{-5})}{0.0125} = 2.4 \times 10^{-3} \text{ v.}$$

(b) When $\theta = 45°$,

$$\phi_1 = \phi_M \cos 45° = 2.121 \times 10^{-5} \text{ weber.}$$

When $\theta = 135°$,

$$\phi_2 = \phi_M \cos 135 = -2.121 \times 10^{-5} \text{ weber,}$$
$$\Delta\phi = (-2.121 \times 10^{-5}) - (2.121 \times 10^{-5}) = -4.242 \times 10^{-5} \text{ weber,}$$
$$\Delta T = 0.0125 \text{ sec. [same as in part (a)],}$$
$$E_{aver} = -1 \frac{(-4.242 \times 10^{-5})}{0.0125} = 3.39 \times 10^{-3} \text{ v.}$$

(c) $E_{max} = N\omega\phi_M$ (11.19)

$$= (1) \left(\frac{2\pi \times 1200}{60}\right) (3 \times 10^{-5}) = 3.77 \times 10^{-3} \text{ v.}$$

(d) When $\theta = 0$ $e = 3.77 \times 10^{-3} \sin 0° = 0.$
     When $\theta = 45°$ $e = 3.77 \times 10^{-3} \sin 45° = 2.67 \times 10^{-3}$ v.
     When $\theta = 90°$ $e = 3.77 \times 10^{-3} \sin 90° = 3.77 \times 10^{-3}$ v.
     When $\theta = 135°$ $e = 3.77 \times 10^{-3} \sin 135° = 2.67 \times 10^{-3}$ v.

(e) $E_{effective} = 1/\sqrt{2}\, E_{max} = 1/\sqrt{2} \times 3.77 \times 10^{-3} = 2.67 \times 10^{-3}$ v.

Problems

(15-XI) An elementary alternator has a one-turn coil 40 by 50 cm which rotates at a uniform speed of 1200 rpm in a uniform magnetic field in which the flux density is 15×10^{-5} weber per sq m. The reference position of the coil and the directions selected as positive for the emf are as shown in Fig. 11.17. (a) What is the average emf as the coil rotates from the reference position ($\theta = 0°$) to the position $\theta = 30°$? (b) What is the average emf as

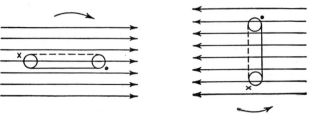

Fig. 11.17.   Fig. 11.18.

the coil rotates from $\theta = 30°$ to $\theta = 60°$? (c) What is the average emf as the coil rotates from $\theta = 60°$ to $\theta = 90°$? (d) What is the average emf as the coil rotates from 90° to 180°?

(16-XI) Find the equation for the instantaneous emf of the generator in Problem 15-XI. Plot the emf against angle and compare with Fig. 11.16.

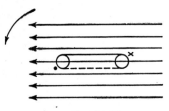

Fig. 11.19.

(17-XI) An elementary alternator has a 50-turn coil 10 by 20 cm which rotates at a uniform speed of 900 rpm in a uniform magnetic field in which the flux density is 30 gausses. The reference position of the coil and the directions selected as positive for the emf are as shown in Fig. 11.18. Find the equation for the instantaneous emf, and plot emf against angle.

(18-XI) An elementary alternator has a 1-turn circular coil 25 cm in diameter which rotates at a uniform speed of 1500 rpm in a uniform magnetic field in which the flux density is 30 gausses. The reference position of the coil and the directions selected as positive for the emf are as shown in Fig. 11.19. Find the equation for the instantaneous emf, and plot emf against angle.

10. Elementary d-c generators.

If a metal disk is mounted on a shaft and rotated between the poles of a magnet, as shown in Fig. 11.20, an emf, constant in magnitude and direction, is developed between the shaft and the rim of the disk. This apparatus, first devised by Faraday, is a true d-c generator. The emf must be regarded as due to the cutting of flux by radial filaments of the disk: there is here no change in the flux linking the circuit.

An emf, always in the same direction though not constant in magnitude, can be readily obtained by adding a commutator to an elementary a-c generator like that described in Section 9. The emf's developed in the coil sides are alternating, the commutator serving as a switching device to keep the coil connected to the external circuit in such a way as to maintain current always in the same direction. Fig. 11.21 shows three positions of the coil as it rotates in the field. The rotation of the commutator serves to keep the right-hand brush positive regardless of the position of the coil. The emf of such a generator pulsates, as shown graphically in Fig. 11.22.

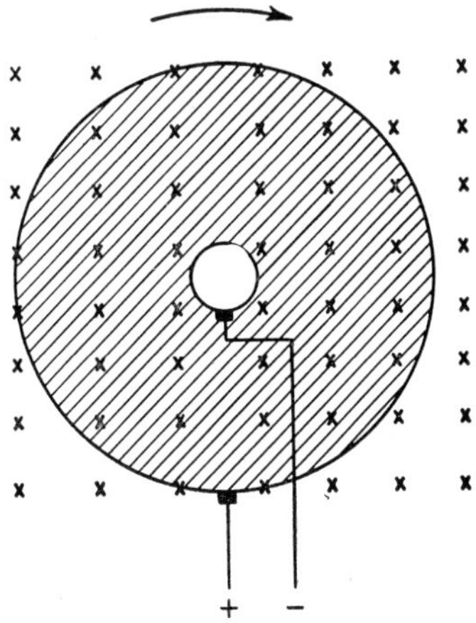

11. Practical generators. In order

Fig. 11.20. Faraday's disc generator.

that the emf's produced shall be of sufficient magnitude for practical purposes, two principal modifications must be made in the elementary generators described in the

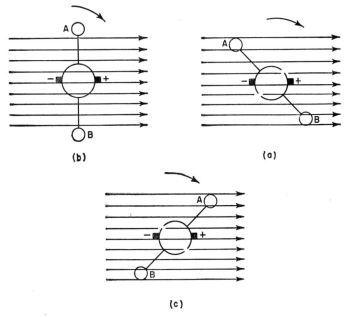

(b)

(a)

(c)

Fig. 11.21. Rotating coil and commutator of elementary d-c generator.

preceding sections. First, in order that high flux densities may be produced economically, the path of the magnetic lines must be principally in iron, the air gaps being only long enough to give the required clearance for the rotating parts. Second, practical generators must not be limited to one single-turn coil; there must usually be a number

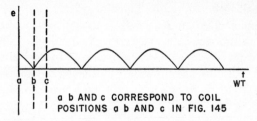

a b AND c CORRESPOND TO COIL
POSITIONS a b AND c IN FIG. 145

Fig. 11.22.   Wave of emf produced by elementary d-c generator.

of coils, each consisting of several turns, and connected in series or series-parallel between the terminals.

The magnetic circuit and arrangement of the coil sides in a modern d-c generator is shown in Fig. 11.23.   The magnetic circuit consists of the **yoke,** or **frame,** of the machine; the **poles,** on which are wound

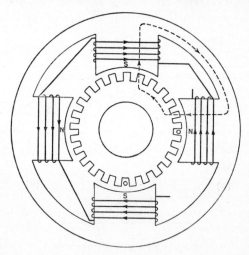

Fig. 11.23.   Construction of a 4-pole d-c generator.

the **field coils** which supply the necessary mmf to set up the magnetic flux; the **air gaps;** and the **armature.** Typical flux paths are indicated by the dotted lines. The armature conductors, or coil sides, are placed in slots in the surface of the armature. Each coil is of the proper pitch, or width, so that when one of its sides is under an N

pole, the other side will be in the corresponding position under an
S pole, and thus the generated emf's will be additive around the coil.
As many as half of the coils on the armature may be connected in
series to obtain the required voltage.   The various schemes of inter-
connecting the coils and making connections to the commutator are
treated in detail in books on d-c machinery.

Another effect of connecting coils in series is to make the voltage
of the machine more nearly constant.   Instead of a single coil, the
instantaneous emf of which will vary from zero to maximum depending
upon position, we now have a number of coils, so distributed around
the armature that their emf's do not become zero simultaneously.

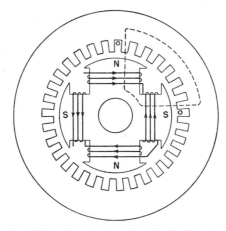

Fig. 11.24.   Construction of a 4-pole alternator.

Thus, in a practical machine, the terminal emf, although still pulsating, is much nearer constant than that shown in Fig. 11.22, for a
single-coil machine.

It is interesting to note that although considerable work has been
done in trying to develop a true d-c generator (one in which the emf
in the moving conductors is always in the same direction) that would
be commercially practicable, none was ever evolved that was as
satisfactory as the conventional commutator-type machine.   Work
on such machines, known as **homopolar,** or **unipolar,** generators, has
been abandoned.

In the design of a-c generators, or **alternators** as they are called,
it has proved best to place the coils in slots in the stationary part of
the machine and the field poles upon the rotating member, as shown
in Fig. 11.24.   This could not be done in the conventional d-c generator
because the commutator must rotate and must be connected at many

points with the winding. The coils of alternators, like those of d-c
generators, are formed so that their sides are approximately one pole
pitch apart, thus making the generated emf's additive around the coil.
The coils may all be connected in series to form a **single-phase** winding
(in which case only about $\frac{2}{3}$ of the slots are used) or they may be
connected into two or more groups to form a **polyphase** winding.
Practically all present-day alternators have three such winding groups,
so arranged that the emf of each group will pass through zero at a
time $\frac{1}{3}$ of a period earlier or later than the emf's of the other two

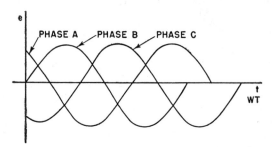

Fig. 11.25.   Emf waves produced by a 3-phase alternator.

groups. The emf's of such a three-phase alternator are shown in
Fig. 11.25.

Problems

(**19-XI**) An elementary d-c generator has a 25-turn coil 20 by 40 cm which
rotates at a speed of 1200 rpm in a uniform magnetic field of 5×10^{-4} weber
per sq m.   What is the maximum instantaneous emf of this generator?   What
is the average emf?

(**20-XI**) A practical d-c generator has an armature winding consisting of
30 coils of 5 turns each, making a total 300 armature conductors.   The coils
are distributed uniformly around the circumference of the armature, and are
so connected that there are two circuits, each having 15 coils in series.   During
each revolution, each armature conductor cuts all of the flux under each of
the 4 poles.   The speed of the generator is 1200 rpm and the flux per pole is
3×10^{-2} weber.   Calculate the average emf of the generator.

12. Inductance—The henry. When the flux linking a circuit is
changing as a consequence of a changing current, either in some
neighboring circuit or in the circuit itself, the induced emf may be
expressed as a function of the rate of change of current. If the
changing current is in a neighboring circuit, the relation is written

$$e_1 = \pm M \frac{di_2}{dt}, \tag{11.21}$$

where the subscripts refer to circuits 1 and 2 respectively, and M is called the **mutual inductance** of the two circuits. If the changing current is in the circuit itself, the relation is written

$$e = \pm L \frac{di}{dt},\qquad(11.22)$$

and L is called the **self-inductance** of the circuit. The proper sign has to be determined in either case by first selecting a positive direction and then applying Lenz's law.

Both mutual inductance and self-inductance are measured in the same unit, the **henry**, defined as follows: *The inductance is one henry if current changing at the rate of 1 amp per sec induces an emf of 1 v.*

definition

The inductance concept is extremely useful because it enables us to express an induced emf directly in terms of changing current, rather than having to go through the intermediate step of calculating the flux caused by the current, and then applying Faraday's law.

13. Factors affecting mutual inductance. Let us again consider two coils arranged as in Fig. 11.26, so that when coil No. 1 carries

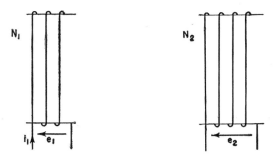

Fig. 11.26. Coils having mutual inductance.

current, some of the magnetic flux established by this current will link coil No. 2. Any change in the current in No. 1 will result in a change in the flux linking No. 2 and, therefore, an emf will be set up in No. 2 according to Faraday's law:

$$e_2 = +N_2 \frac{d\phi_{12}}{dt}.\qquad(11.23)$$

The subscript after ϕ denotes it as the flux produced by coil No. 1 which links coil No. 2. The emf can also be found directly from the rate of change of current:

$$e_2 = +M \frac{di_1}{dt}.\qquad(11.24)$$

Equating (11.23) and (11.24),

$$N_2 \frac{d\phi_{12}}{dt} = M \frac{di_1}{dt}, \qquad (11.25)$$

from which

$$M = N_2 \frac{d\phi_{12}}{di_1}. \qquad (11.26)$$

If the flux path is in air, then ϕ_{12} will be zero when i_1 is zero, and will be always in direct proportion to i_1, and we may write

$$M = \frac{N_2 \phi_{12}}{i_1}. \qquad (11.27)$$

This equation tells us the mutual inductance is the flux-turns formed with coil No. 2, per ampere in coil No. 1. Obviously, then,

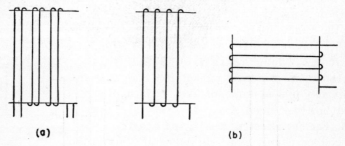

(a)   **(b)**

Fig. 11.27. Effect of coil arrangement on mutual inductance: (a) maximum mutual inductance; (b) minimum mutual inductance.

if we want two circuits to have relatively great mutual inductance, we must place them so that one circuit is linked by a large percentage of the flux lines produced by the other circuit. This can be accomplished by making the two windings occupy the same space as nearly as possible, as in Fig. 11.27a. Conversely, if we want to avoid mutual inductance, we place the circuits so that few or no flux lines from one circuit can link the other, as in Fig. 11.27b.

Now, the flux is determined by the mmf $N_1 i_1$ of coil No. 1 and by the reluctance $\Re$ of the path taken by the flux:

$$\phi_{12} = \frac{N_1 i_1}{\Re}. \qquad (11.28)$$

Substituting in (11.26), we obtain

$$M = N_2 \frac{d\left(\dfrac{N_1 i_1}{\Re}\right)}{di_1}. \qquad (11.29)$$

If the flux path is in air, the reluctance is not a function of the current, and we may carry out the differentiation to obtain

$$M = \frac{N_1 N_2}{\Re}. \tag{11.30}$$

This equation tells us that mutual inductance varies as the product of the number of turns in each circuit and inversely as the reluctance. This assumes, however, that the percentage of the flux due to current in circuit No. 1 and linking circuit No. 2 is independent of the number of turns in both circuits. It is not always possible to change the number of turns and maintain this percentage constant; hence, in practice Equation (11.30) is an approximation only.

Finally, we see that by substituting a ferromagnetic material for air as the flux path through which the circuits are linked, we may very greatly decrease the reluctance and increase the mutual inductance. Since the reluctance of an iron flux path is a function of flux, however, and therefore of current, we see that mutual inductance is a function of current. A numerical value for the mutual inductance of two coils on an iron core is meaningless unless corresponding values of current are also given.

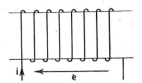

Fig. 11.28. Coil having self-inductance.

14. Factors affecting self-inductance. Any coil or circuit which is linked by flux due to current in its own turns will have an emf induced in it whenever the current is changing. Thus, in the coil in Fig. 11.28, a change in current will cause a change in flux, and an emf will be induced in the coil itself. According to Faraday's law, this emf is

$$e = +N \frac{d\phi}{dt}. \tag{11.31}$$

The emf can also be found directly from the rate of change of current:

$$e = +L \frac{di}{dt}. \tag{11.32}$$

Equating (11.31) and (11.32),

$$N \frac{d\phi}{dt} = L \frac{di}{dt}, \tag{11.33}$$

from which

$$L = N \frac{d\phi}{di}. \tag{11.34}$$

If the flux path is in air, ϕ will be directly proportional to i at all times, and we may write

$$L = \frac{N\phi}{i}. \tag{11.35}$$

According to this equation, self-inductance is flux-turns per ampere. For a given number of turns, then, the self-inductance would be greatest when the turns were so arranged that all the flux linked all the turns. This condition can be most nearly realized by making a concentrated coil like that in Fig. 11.29a. Such a coil would have more self-inductance than a distributed coil of the same number of turns, as shown in Fig. 11.29b.

Equation (11.35) also indicates how we can wind a coil which has no self-inductance. If, after winding any number of turns, we double

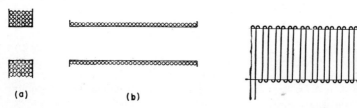

(a)   **(b)**

Fig. 11.29. Effect of distribution of turns on self-inductance: (a) maximum self-inductance; (b) minimum self-inductance.

Fig. 11.30. Coil wound to have zero self-inductance.

back and wind an equal number in the opposite direction, as in Fig. 11.30, the net mmf caused by a current in the winding will be zero. Consequently, no flux will link the turns, and the coil will have no self-inductance.

The flux linking the coil in Equation (11.35) may be expressed in terms of mmf and reluctance of the flux path as

$$\phi = \frac{Ni}{\mathcal{R}}. \tag{11.36}$$

Substituting in (11.35), we obtain

$$L = \frac{N\left(\dfrac{Ni}{\mathcal{R}}\right)}{i} = \frac{N^2}{\mathcal{R}}. \tag{11.37}$$

Thus, we see that the self-inductance varies as the square of the number of turns and inversely as the reluctance of the flux path. As in the case of Equation (11.30), the relation between self-inductance and turns is strictly true only when all the turns are linked by all the flux, though it is a useful approximation in the case of concentrated coils generally. The possibility of greatly increasing self-inductance by providing a flux path through iron is also obvious from (11.37). The inductance of any iron-cored coil, however, is a function of current, for the reason that the reluctance of the flux path varies with flux, which in turn depends upon current.

Equations (11.30) and (11.37) are of little use for actually calculating the self-inductance of a given coil. For such calculations, various empirical formulas have been devised.[1]

Problems

(**21-XI**) Current changing at the rate of 1000 amp per sec in circuit No. 1 induces an emf of 1.5 v in circuit No. 2. What is the mutual inductance of the circuits? What rate of change of current in circuit No. 1 would induce an emf of 0.3 v in circuit No. 2?

(**22-XI**) The self-inductance of a circuit is 0.15 h. What emf would be induced in the circuit by current changing at the rate of 400 amp per sec?

(**23-XI**) Two coils are wound side by side on a paper-tube form. An emf of 0.25 v is induced in coil A when the flux linking it changes at the rate of 10^{-3} weber per sec. A current of 2 amp in circuit B causes a flux of 10^{-5} weber to link coil A. What is the mutual inductance of the coils?

(**24-XI**) A coil of 250 turns has a self-inductance of 0.0145. Assuming that all the turns are linked by all the flux, what flux would be established by a current of 5 amp in this coil?

(**25-XI**) A concentrated coil of 250 turns has a self-inductance of 19 mh. How many turns should be added to increase the self-inductance to 25 mh? Assume that all the turns are linked by all the flux.

(**26-XI**) An air-cored toroid having a mean diameter of 20 cm and a diameter of cross section of 2.5 cm is provided with two uniform windings. Winding A consists of 1125 turns, and winding B consists of 775 turns. Calculate (a) self-inductance of coil A, (b) self-inductance of coil B, (c) mutual inductance of the coils, and (d) total inductance with coils connected in series.

(**27-XI**) A choke coil consists of 4000 turns of wire wound on the center leg of a magnetic core, such as that shown in Fig. 9.15. The thickness of core, stacking factor, and air gaps are as given in Problem 22-IX. Determine the self-inductance of the choke for (a) current of 10 ma and (b) current of 20 ma.

15. The effect of self-inductance in a circuit. Though self-inductance is a property of a circuit, just as resistance is, its effect is felt only when the current in the circuit is changing. For steady currents, the behavior of a circuit having self-inductance is no different from that of a circuit which is noninductive. Any change in current, however, will cause an emf to be set up in an inductive circuit, in such

---

[1] Terman, F. E., *Radio Engineer's Handbook*, Section 2. New York: McGraw-Hill Book Co., Inc., 1943.

a direction as to oppose the change in current, and thus tend to prolong the time required for a given change to take place.

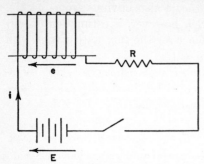

Fig. 11.31. Circuit consisting of resistance and self-inductance in series.

Let us consider the circuit shown in Fig. 11.31, which consists of a coil of wire having a self-inductance of L henrys and a resistance of R ohms connected to a battery of E volts. The resistance is indicated as apart from the coil itself, even though it is, in fact, distributed throughout the turns themselves, the connecting wires, and the battery. The procedure of representing all the resistance of a circuit as lumped together in a certain part and all the inductance as lumped together at another point is a convenient one, and much used in circuit analysis.

When the switch is closed, a current i begins to flow, and increases toward its limiting value

$$i = \frac{E}{R}.$$
(11.38)

The increasing current gives rise to an emf,

$$e = +L\frac{di}{dt},$$
(11.39)

due to the self-inductance of the coil. Applying Kirchhoff's second law to the circuit gives

$$E - L\frac{di}{dt} = Ri.$$
(11.40)

This is a differential equation which may be readily solved to obtain an expression for the current at any instant following the closing of the switch.[1] The current is found to be

$$i = \frac{E}{R}[1 - \epsilon^{-\frac{Rt}{L}}].$$
(11.45)

Study of this equation shows that the current does not increase instantaneously from zero to its final value, but increases according

---

[1] The solution of (11.40) can be carried out by various methods, one of which is that of separating the variables. By this method, (11.40) is first manipulated to

to an exponential law as shown graphically in Fig. 11.32. Greatest
at the instant of closing the switch, the rate of increase diminishes

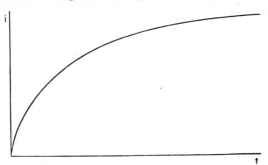

Fig. 11.32.   Graph showing exponential increase of current in an inductive circuit.

as time goes on, eventually becoming so small the current may be
regarded as steady.

The time required for the current to reach any given percentage
of its final value can be seen from Equation (11.45) to depend upon the
self-inductance of the circuit.   The larger the value of L, the greater
is the value of t required for the exponential term to become negligible.
A value of t equal to L/R is defined as the **time constant** of the circuit.
It is the time required for the current to reach 63.2 per cent of its

get it into the form

$$\frac{di}{i - \dfrac{E}{R}} = -\frac{R\,dt}{L}. \tag{11.41}$$

Both sides of (11.41) are then integrated to obtain

$$\log_\epsilon\left(i - \frac{E}{R}\right) = -\frac{Rt}{L} + K, \tag{11.42}$$

or

$$i - \frac{E}{R} = \epsilon^{\left(-\frac{Rt}{L}+K\right)} = \epsilon^{-\frac{Rt}{L}}\epsilon^{k}. \tag{11.43}$$

To evaluate ϵ^{k}, we take advantage of the known fact that at the instant of closing
the switch ($t = 0$), the current is zero.   This gives

$$\epsilon^{k} = -\frac{E}{R}, \tag{11.44}$$

which, substituted in (11.43), gives

$$i - \frac{E}{R} = -\frac{E}{R}\epsilon^{-\frac{Rt}{L}}.$$

$$i = \frac{E}{R}\left[1 - \epsilon^{-\frac{Rt}{L}}\right]. \tag{11.45}$$

final value following the closing of the switch, as may be readily seen by putting L/R for t in Equation (11.45). The exponent becomes -1, and the current is

$$i = \frac{E}{R}[1 - \epsilon^{-1}] = \frac{E}{R}\left(1 - \frac{1}{\epsilon}\right) = 0.632\frac{E}{R}. \qquad (11.46)$$

16. Energy storage in the magnetic field of an inductive circuit. It was shown in Chapter VII that energy was stored in any magnetic field. When the field is due to a current of I amperes flowing in a circuit of self-inductance L henrys, the amount of energy stored can be shown to be[1]

$$W = \frac{LI^2}{2}. \qquad (11.50)$$

This way of expressing the energy stored is extremely convenient. Since magnetic fields are generally indefinite in extent and vary in intensity from point to point, any attempt to calculate the total energy by using the expression for energy stored per unit volume would be hopeless. Equation (11.50) expresses it in terms of readily measurable quantities and avoids the difficulty entirely.

[1] This energy is furnished by the battery or other source that maintains the current I, and its storage is a direct consequence of establishing the current I in the circuit against the opposition of the self-induced emf. At any instant while the current is being established (Fig. 11.33), the emf is

$$e = +L\frac{di}{dt}. \qquad (11.47)$$

The rate at which energy is being supplied is

$$p = ei = L\frac{di}{dt}i. \qquad (11.48)$$

The energy supplied during an infinitesimal time dt is

$$dw = pdt = Lidi. \qquad (11.49)$$

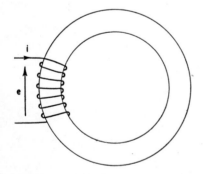

Fig. 11.33. Storage of energy in the magnetic field of an inductive circuit.

The total energy supplied while the current is being increased from zero to I is then found by summing up all the dw's as i varies from 0 to I. This is the definite integral,

$$W = \int_0^I Lidi = \frac{LI^2}{2}. \qquad (11.50)$$

The energy represented by Equation (11.50) is partly recoverable. The arc which occurs upon opening an inductive circuit is made possible by the self-induced emf set up by the decreasing current, and the energy dissipated in the heat of the arc is in part the stored energy of the magnetic field.

Problems

(**28-XI**) A series circuit contains a coil having a self-inductance of 0.2 henry and negligible resistance, and a noninductive resistance of 50 ohms. This circuit is connected to a 10-v battery. (a) Determine the value of the current 0.004 sec later. (b) Repeat for time intervals of 0.008, 0.012, 0.016, 0.02, and 0.04 sec. (c) Plot the current against time.

(**29-XI**) (a) In Problem 28-XI, what is the initial rate of increase of current? (b) What is the initial induced emf? (c) What is the initial rate of energy storage? (d) What is the rate of increase of current 0.004 sec after connecting the circuit to the battery? (e) What is the induced emf after 0.004 sec? (f) What is the rate of energy storage after 0.004 sec?

(**30-XI**) A series circuit consists of a coil having a self-inductance of 1 h and a resistance of 5 ohms, and a 50-v battery. (a) Determine the value of the current 0.01 sec after closing the circuit. (b) Repeat for time intervals 0.03, 0.05, 0.1, 0.2, 0.3, 0.4, 0.5, and 1 sec. (c) Plot the curve of current against time.

(**31-XI**) (a) How long does it take the current in the above circuit to drop to 5 amp, after the battery is short-circuited? (b) Repeat for 1 amp, 0.1 amp, 0.01 amp.

(**32-XI**) How much energy is stored in the magnetic field of the coil in Problem 30-XI, when the current is 10 amp?

17. Self-inductance in a-c circuits—Reactance. Since self-inductance manifests itself by opposing and slowing up any change in cur-

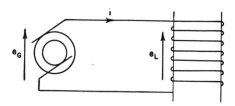

Fig. 11.34. Alternating emf applied to an inductive circuit.

rent, its effect will be most striking in a-c circuits. Suppose an a-c generator is connected to a coil having a self-inductance L and negligible resistance, as in Fig. 11.34. The emf of the alternator is adjusted to a value e_G, which causes a current

$$i = I_{max} \sin \omega t \qquad (11.51)$$

to flow in the circuit. This varying current gives rise to a self-induced emf

$$e_L = +L\frac{di}{dt} = L\frac{d[I_{max} \sin \omega t]}{dt} \qquad (11.52)$$

$$= \omega L I_{max} \cos \omega t. \qquad (11.53)$$

Since the largest possible value of $\cos \omega t$ is unity for values of ωt equal to $0°$, $180°$, $360°$, and so forth, the largest possible value of e_L is, obviously,

$$E_{L_{max}} = \omega L I_{max}, \qquad (11.54)$$

or

$$\frac{E_{L_{max}}}{I_{max}} = \frac{E_{L_{effective}}}{I_{effective}} = \omega L. \qquad (11.55)$$

The quantity ωL is called *inductive reactance*. Since it is the ratio of potential difference to current, it is dimensionally the same as resistance, and is expressed in ohms. It is commonly represented by the symbol X_L.

$$X_L = \omega L = 2\pi f L, \qquad (11.56)$$

where X_L is inductive reactance in ohms.

    f is frequency in cycles per second.

    L is self-inductance in henrys.

It is seen that, whereas self-inductance (when no iron is in the vicinity of the circuit) is a constant independent of frequency[1] and current, reactance depends upon frequency directly. Thus, with direct current (frequency zero), a circuit with negligible resistance would permit the flow of an extremely large current when even a small voltage was applied. With alternating current (frequency $= f$), the current would be limited by reactance to a value inversely proportional to the frequency. A device known as a **choke coil,** consisting of a number of turns of copper wire (sometimes on an iron core) is often used in a branch of a network to impede the flow of alternating current while permitting direct current to flow unhindered.

Equation (11.55) gives a clue as to how self-inductance may be measured provided resistance is negligible. We may obtain readings of voltage and current when the coil or circuit carries alternating current of known frequency. We then divide voltage by current to obtain reactance, according to Equation (11.55). Maximum values of voltage and current are not readily measured directly, but the corre-

[1] Not strictly true at high frequencies.

sponding effective values can be read with ordinary iron-vane type voltmeters and ammeters, and are in the same ratio one to the other as are the maximum values. If the resistance of the circuit is not negligible, then Equation (11.55) gives **impedance,** not reactance, and the procedure outlined above is no longer valid.

EXAMPLE: When an alternating emf of 50 v is impressed across a coil of negligible resistance, a current of 2.5 amp flows. The frequency of emf is 60 cycles per sec. What is the self-inductance of the coil? What current would have flowed if the frequency of the impressed emf had been 400 cycles per sec?

SOLUTION:

$$X_L = \frac{E}{I} = \frac{50}{2.5} = 20 \text{ ohms at 60 cycles per sec.}$$

$$L = \frac{X_L}{2\pi f} = \frac{20}{2\pi \times 60} = 0.0531 \text{ h.}$$

$$X_L = 2\pi fL$$
$$= 2\pi \times 400 \times 0.0531 = 133.5 \text{ ohms at 400 cycles per sec.}$$

$$I = \frac{E}{X_L} = \frac{50}{133.5} = 0.375 \text{ amp.}$$

Problems

(**33-XI**) Calculate the reactance of a 1 microhenry (μh) inductance at frequencies of 0, 10, 10^2, and so forth, up to 10^9 cycles per sec.

(**34-XI**) The voltage drop across a coil of negligible resistance is found to be 105 v when the current is 2.1 amp. These measurements were made with a-c instruments at a frequency of 60 cycles per sec. What is the self-inductance of the coil?

18. The transformer. A transformer consists of two or more coils so placed that mutual inductance exists between them. The coils may be wound upon a ferromagnetic core that forms part of a magnetic circuit, as shown in Fig. 11.35a, or they may be wound upon a non-magnetic form, such as a paper tube, as shown in Fig. 11.35b. All transformers designed for use at power frequencies and audio frequencies are built with ferromagnetic cores, and the windings are usually placed so that, as nearly as possible, both windings are linked by all of the flux. If we assume that this can be perfectly done (that is, that the leakage flux can be made negligible), we may analyze the operation of the transformer as follows:

Suppose an alternating emf of frequency f cycles per second is applied to one of the windings called the **primary** (Fig. 11.36). An alternating current is caused to flow in this winding, and it in turn causes an alternating flux, which links both windings and causes emf's to be induced in them. The emf set up in the primary winding

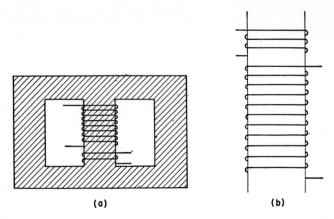

Fig. 11.35. Transformers: (a) iron-cored power transformer; (b) air-cored transformer for radio-frequency circuits.

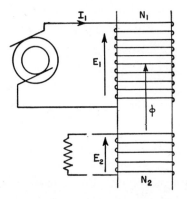

Fig. 11.36. Relation of induced emf's to turn ratio in an iron-cored transformer.

(which has N_1 turns) will be

$$e_1 = N_1 \frac{d\phi}{dt}, \tag{11.57}$$

and the emf set up in the secondary winding (which has N_2 turns) will be

$$e_2 = N_2 \frac{d\phi}{dt}. \tag{11.58}$$

Let the flux be assumed to vary sinusoidally according to the equation

$$\phi = \phi_{max} \sin \omega t. \tag{11.59}$$

Substituting (11.59) in (11.57) and (11.58) and performing the differentiations gives

$$e_1 = N_1 \omega \phi_{max} \cos \omega t. \tag{11.60}$$
$$e_2 = N_2 \omega \phi_{max} \cos \omega t. \tag{11.61}$$

Since $\cos \omega t$ can never exceed unity,

$$E_{1_{max}} = N_1 \omega \phi_{max}. \tag{11.62}$$
$$E_{2_{max}} = N_2 \omega \phi_{max}. \tag{11.63}$$

Dividing (11.62) by (11.63) gives

$$\frac{E_{1_{max}}}{E_{2_{max}}} = \frac{E_{1_{effective}}}{E_{2_{effective}}} = \frac{N_1}{N_2}. \tag{11.64}$$

The effective values of the emf's will be in the same ratio as the maximum values—that is, in the same ratio as the turns. If we may further assume the resistances of the windings to be negligible, so that there are no internal resistance drops to be taken into consideration, the terminal voltages will also be in the same ratio as the turns:

$$\frac{V_1}{V_2} = \frac{N_1}{N_2}. \tag{11.65}$$

When $N_1 > N_2$, we have a **step-down** transformer—that is, the voltage V_2 at the secondary terminals is less than the applied voltage V_1. When $N_1 < N_2$, we have a **step-up** transformer, with V_2 greater than V_1.

The use of the transformer as a means of stepping voltages up or down makes possible the present-day power systems. Large a-c generators may operate at 12,000 v, which has been found to be most satisfactory for such machines. For long-distance transmission, the voltage may be stepped up by means of transformers to, say, 160,000 v, thus taking advantage of the smaller losses and higher efficiency associated with high-voltage transmission. For use by consumers, the voltage is again stepped down to 12,000, 2400, 240, or 120, since these are the voltages at which consumers' apparatus operates most satisfactorily. Since transformers are, as a rule, very efficient, these various voltage changes can be made without the loss of any considerable part of the energy generated.

In communication engineering, we usually do not think of a transformer as a device for stepping voltage up or down, but as a device for making a certain resistance (or impedance) appear greater (or less) than it really is. An ideal transformer (one in which there are no losses and in which the magnetic flux can be produced by a negligible current) would step the current up or down in the inverse ratio of the turns:

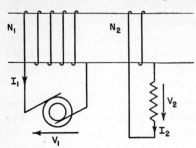

$$\frac{I_1}{I_2} = \frac{N_2}{N_1}. \tag{11.66}$$

Fig. 11.37. Transformer used for imped-ance matching.

If the voltage is stepped up by an ideal transformer, the current is stepped down in the same ratio, keeping the product of volts × amperes the same. Suppose, now, that a resistance connected to the secondary terminals of a transformer, as in Fig. 11.37, has a current of I_2 amperes (effective value) flowing in it, and a voltage V_2 (effective value) across its terminals. The resistance then has an actual value of

$$R = \frac{V_2}{I_2} \text{ ohms.} \tag{11.67}$$

But by Equation (11.65), the voltage at the primary terminals of the transformer is

$$V_1 = \frac{N_1}{N_2} V_2,$$

and by Equation (11.66), the current flowing in the primary winding is

$$I_1 = \frac{N_2}{N_1} I_2.$$

The apparent resistance, then, measured on the primary side of the transformer, is

$$R_A = \frac{V_1}{I_1} = \frac{\dfrac{N_1}{N_2} V_2}{\dfrac{N_2}{N_1} I_2} \tag{11.68}$$

$$= \left(\frac{N_1}{N_2}\right)^2 \frac{V_2}{I_2} = \left(\frac{N_1}{N_2}\right)^2 R. \tag{11.69}$$

The apparent resistance on the primary side is equal to the actual resistance times the turn ratio squared. If, for example, the transformer ratio was 5 to 2 step-down, as shown, and the actual value of R was 10 ohms, then the apparent value of R, as measured on the primary side of the transformer, would be

$$(5\!/\!2)^2 \times 10 = 62.5 \text{ ohms.}$$

This use of the transformer is especially important in case maximum power transfer is required.   The actual resistance of a load, such as a loud-speaker, can be **matched** to the resistance of a source, such as an amplifier, to obtain maximum power transfer.

In actual transformers, either for power or communication circuits, there is more or less departure from the ideal conditions discussed above.   Leakage flux cannot be avoided, the windings necessarily have some resistance, the current required to produce the flux is not negligible (particularly in air-cored transformers), and the hysteresis and eddy-current losses in an iron-cored transformer must be taken into account.   The complete analysis of the transformer, taking all these things into account, may be found in any book on a-c machinery.

Problems

(**35-XI**) What should be the approximate turn ratio of (a) an ordinary distribution transformer $\frac{2400}{120}$-v step-down, (b) a step-up transformer to obtain 100,000 v from a 120-v lighting circuit for operating an X-ray tube, and (c) a 2.5-v filament transformer in an ordinary radio receiver?

(**36-XI**) (a) What should be the approximate turn ratio to match a 5-ohm load to a 250-ohm generator?   (b) To match a 500-ohm load to a 50-ohm generator?

Study Questions

1. In what two ways may we bring about a change in the magnetic flux linking a circuit?

2. A student offers the following as a statement of Lenz's law: The electromotive force induced in a circuit by a change in flux will be in the direction current would have to flow in order to oppose the flux.   What is wrong? For what percent of all flux changes would the statement be correct?

3. It is stated at the end of Art. 1 that if alternating current flows in circuit *A* then both self and mutual electromotive forces would always be present.   Is this literally true?   Why?

4. Why is it not possible to measure directly the electromotive force generated in a straight piece of wire moving across a magnetic field.

5. Is it possible to have a conductor in motion in a steady magnetic field and yet have no electromotive force generated in it?   Explain.

6. What is the physical explanation of the generation of an electromotive force in a conductor in motion in a magnetic field?

7. What is the physical explanation of the induction of an electromotive force in a loop of wire placed in a magnetic field in which the flux density is increasing or decreasing?

8. The terms "generator emf" and "transformer emf" are often used in analyzing the operation of electrical machinery.   What distinction do you think is intended?

9. A spring clip like a bicylist's trouser-guard is slipped over one pole of a U-shaped permanent magnet (Fig. 11.38*a*).   The clip is then pulled to the right so that its ends spring apart (Fig. 11.38b) and it is removed from the magnet (Fig. 11.38c). A closed circuit is maintained at all times. Is an electromotive force induced in the clip? Why?

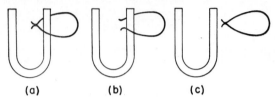

(a)   (b)   (c)

Fig. 11.38.

10. The spring clip in Question 9 is slipped off over the end of the magnet instead of springing the ends apart. Will an electromotive force be induced in the clip? Why?

11. What is the significance of the positive direction arrow for an electromotive force? Without a positive direction arrow, what would be the significance of a $+$ or a $-$ sign before the expression $N\dfrac{\Delta\phi}{\Delta T}$?

12. Is it possible that $-N\dfrac{\Delta\phi}{\Delta T}$ could be a positive quantity? Explain.

13. The BLV rule as explained in Art. 4 gives average electromotive force. How could it be modified to find instantaneous electromotive force? Under what circumstances will they be the same?

14. In an elementary alternating current generator like the one described in Art. 9, the electromotive force is zero at the instant the flux linking the coil is maximum and maximum at the instant the flux linking the coil is zero. Explain.

15. In early direct current generators the armature coils were mounted on the surface of a smooth cylindrical iron core. Placing the coils in axial slots in the armature core was a radical improvement in generator design and the size and cost of a generator of a given rating were radically reduced. Why?

16. Equations (11.30) and (11.37) are useful in that they show approximately how inductance depends upon turns. They are not of much practical value for calculating inductance. Why?

17. Given a 100 foot length of copper wire, how would you arrange it to have maximum self-inductance? Minimum self-inductance?

18. Two direct current circuits have equal resistances, and equal voltages are applied to their terminals. One circuit is known to be non-inductive, the other highly inductive. The circuits themselves are concealed and cannot be examined, but they may be opened and closed at will, and electrical instruments may be connected at the terminals. Could the inductive circuit be distinguished? How?

19. A coil that is designed to be connected across a 115 volt a-c circuit is accidentally connected across a 115 volt d-c circuit and immediately smoke begins to appear. Explain.

20. If there were no transformers, power systems would be severely limited in size, serving only one building or one small town. Explain.

CHAPTER XII

ELECTRIC FIELD CONCEPTS—CAPACITANCE

1. Charged bodies. A body that has either a deficiency or an excess of electrons is said to be **charged.** The charging of amber by friction is the earliest electrical phenomenon of which we have any record, and experiments with charged bodies were well advanced before anything was known of electric current. The outstanding property of charged bodies is, of course, that of attracting and repelling other charged bodies. A body that has an excess of electrons is arbitrarily designated as negatively charged and is repelled by any other body having a negative charge. A body that has a deficiency of electrons is designated as positively charged and is repelled by any other body having a positive charge. But a body that has a negative charge is attracted by any other body that has a positive charge.

Forces are continually at work in nature which tend to cause the molecules of all gases to lose electrons and, therefore, to become positively charged particles. The electrons thus lost attach themselves to other molecules which become negatively charged particles. Other forces in nature result in the separation of positive and negative electricity between the upper and lower strata of clouds, thus giving rise to the charges that produce lightning.

The charged bodies with which we work in electrical engineering usually become charged as a result of being connected to some source of emf, such as a battery or generator. Suppose, for example, the terminals of a battery to be connected to two well-insulated, parallel metal plates as in Fig. 12.1. The emf of the battery will cause electrons to move off plate A, onto plate B, leaving plate A with a deficiency of electrons and, therefore, positively charged, whereas plate B, with an excess of electrons, will be negatively charged.

This transfer of electrons constitutes a current in the connecting wires of momentary duration only, because every electron that moves toward plate B does so against the repelling force of all those which preceded it, and an equilibrium condition is soon reached where the battery is unable to move any more electrons against this opposing force. The potential difference between the plates is now equal to the emf of the battery. They may be disconnected from the battery, and if they are perfectly insulated, as we assumed them to be, they will maintain their charges and their potential difference indefinitely.

We have here a means of actually storing energy in electrical form. Energy had to be supplied by the battery to effect the removal of electrons from one plate to the other, and this energy is stored, just as energy is stored when a mass is raised to an elevation above the earth. In that case, mass is raised through a gravitational

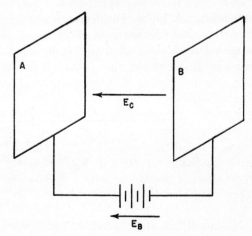

Fig. 12.1. Electrically charged parallel plates.

potential difference; in the electrical case, charge is raised through an electrical potential difference.[1]

The energy stored can be recovered by connecting a wire from one plate to the other. The displaced electrons then move back to their normal positions, constituting a current in the wire and dissipating the stored energy as I^2R loss. The plates are then said to be **discharged**.

Problems

(**1-XII**) To transfer a quantity of electricity equivalent to 500 microcoulombs from one insulated conductor to another requires energy equivalent to 1 joule. What potential difference exists between the charged conductors?

(**2-XII**) What amount of heat energy could be realized by discharging a parallel-plate arrangement charged with 0.0025 coulomb at 25,000 v?

2. The electric field. Suppose a very small, light ball be suspended by a thread and given a positive charge, either by friction or by allowing it to touch a larger object that is positively charged.

[1] To be consistent with conventional rise in potential we will have to think of a positive charge as having been moved from plate B to plate A.

If this charged ball is brought into the region between the charged plates shown in Fig. 12.1, it will be repelled by the positive plate and attracted by the negative plate, and will tend to move accordingly. Provided the battery used to charge the plates has sufficient emf and the ball is not too heavy, the motion can be readily observed, and the positively charged ball thus becomes a means of exploring the space between the plates, just as the compass needle was a device for exploring the space around a wire carrying current.   The region between the plates is said to be an **electric field.**   *Any region in which charged bodies are acted upon by forces is an electric field, and the direction in which a positive test charge is urged is the direction of the field.*

If the force acting upon the test charge is observed in successive positions, taking care to move the charge always in the direction of

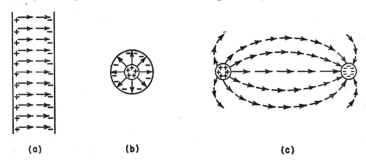

(a)   **(b)**   **(c)**

Fig. 12.2.   Typical electric fields: (a) between oppositely charged parallel plates; (b) between oppositely charged coaxial cylinders; (c) between oppositely charged parallel wires.

the indicated force, we may map an electric field in much the same way that we mapped magnetic fields with an exploring coil or compass needle.   The field between oppositely charged parallel plates that are separated by a distance that is small compared with the dimensions of the plates themselves is found to be directed at every point perpendicularly away from the positive and toward the negative plate, as indicated in Fig. 12.2a.   The field between oppositely charged coaxial cylinders is found to be *radial*, as shown in Fig. 12.2b.   This is typical of the field in coaxial cables used in high-frequency transmission.   The field in the vicinity of two oppositely charged, parallel wires is shown in Fig. 12.2c.   Here the description of the field is not so easy, since its direction changes from point to point, and it is not limited strictly to the space between the conductors.

It will be remembered that in formulating the magnetic field concepts we made use of the uniformly wound toroid because of the geometrical simplicity of its field.   In formulating the electric field concepts, we make use of parallel flat plates for precisely the same reason: the field in this case is the simplest electric field we can set up. Between the plates, it is uniform and unidirectional; beyond the edges of the plates, it soon becomes too feeble to detect.

3. Electric field intensity.   To describe an electric field completely, we may specify its intensity at every point.   The intensity may be defined in terms of the magnitude and direction of the force which acts upon a unit test charge placed at the point as follows: *The electric field intensity at a point has a value of 1 MKS unit if a 1-coulomb test charge placed at the point is acted upon by a force of 1 newton.   The direction of the electric field intensity is the direction of the force on a positive test charge.*

A descriptive name for the unit would therefore be the newton per coulomb.   This name, although perfectly correct, is little used because, as we shall see, the unit may be described by another name to better advantage.   The symbol most commonly used is $\mathcal{E}$ and the defining equation is

$$F = \mathcal{E}Q, \tag{12.1}$$

where F is force in newtons.

$\mathcal{E}$ is electric field intensity in newtons per coulomb.

Q is charge in coulombs.

In general, electric field intensity is a vector quantity which varies from point to point both in magnitude and in direction.   Consider a test charge of $+Q$ coulombs to be moved along a path *a-b-c-d-e* (Fig. 12.3) arbitrarily drawn between the faces of two oppositely charged parallel plates.

At every point on the path there will be an electric field intensity which can be represented by a vector $\mathcal{E}$ in the figure.   Now suppose the path to be divided up into short segments Δl, so short that for the accuracy required, $\mathcal{E}$ may be considered the same in magnitude and direction all along a segment.   Let us then form products by multiplying the length of each segment by the component of $\mathcal{E}$ that lies along the segment, and by Q, the magnitude of the test charge.   Each of these products will be an amount of

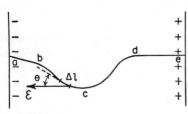

Fig. 12.3. The summation of $\mathcal{E} \cos \theta \Delta l$ along the path a-b-c-d-e is equal to the potential difference between the charged plates.

work done in moving the test charge through a length Δl, and if we take the summation of all such amounts of work, we will find the total work done in moving the test charge from one plate to the other

$$\sum_{a}^{e} \varepsilon \cos \theta Q \, \Delta l = W. \tag{12.2}^{[1]}$$

But the work done in moving the test charge from one plate to the other is also given by

$$W = VQ, \tag{2.16}$$

where V is the potential difference between the plates. If we equate these two expressions and solve for V we obtain

$$\sum_{a}^{e} \varepsilon \cos \theta \, \Delta l = V. \tag{12.3}$$

In other words, the summation of the products of electric field intensity by Δl taken as described above gives the potential difference between the extremities of the path specified.

For the special case of oppositely charged parallel plates here considered, the electric field intensity is the same at every point along the path, and the summation becomes simply the product of ε by the distance S between the plates.

$$\varepsilon S = V \tag{12.4}$$

or

$$\varepsilon = \frac{V}{S} \tag{12.5}$$

Electric field intensity can, therefore, be expressed also in **volts per meter,** and this is the name most often used. For the simple field used in this instance, it is equal to the potential difference between the plates divided by the distance by which the plates are separated. In general, the electric field intensity varies from point to point, as we go from one extremity of the field to the other, and Equation (12.5) would yield **average** field intensity.

EXAMPLE: Parallel plates 10 cm apart are maintained at a potential difference of 5000 v. What is the electric field intensity? What force would act upon a 10^{-2}-microcoulomb charge placed in the field?

SOLUTION: By Equation (12.5), electric field intensity is

$$\varepsilon = \frac{V}{S} = \frac{5000}{0.1} = 50,000 \text{ v per m.}$$

By Equation (12.1), the force on the charge is

$$F = \varepsilon Q = 50,000 \times 10^{-8} = 0.0005 \text{ newton.}$$

[1] More rigorously $\displaystyle\int_{a}^{e} \varepsilon \cos \theta Q \, \Delta l = W$ as Δl is allowed to approach zero.

Problems

(3-XII) What is the electric field intensity between parallel plates 1 cm apart and maintained at a potential difference of 250 v? What force would act upon an electron placed in this field?

(4-XII) A test charge of 10^{-10} coulomb in a uniform field is acted upon by a force of 10^{-7} newton. What is the potential difference between points 7.5 cm apart measured in the direction of the field?

4. Equipotential surfaces. The potential difference between two points is measured by the work done in moving a unit charge from one point to the other. If a unit positive charge is moved from the surface of the negative plate in Fig. 12.3 to a point x meters to the right, the work done and, therefore, the potential difference moved through, is

$$V_x = W_x = \mathcal{E}x. \tag{12.6}$$

The path taken in moving the charge would be immaterial, since work is only being done when the charge is being moved against the force of the electric field. Moving the charge at right angles to the field requires no work. Therefore, we may move the charge to *any* point x meters to the right of the negative plate with the same amount of work. Consequently, we see that all points in a parallel plane x meters to the right of the negative plate have the same potential difference with respect to it, and no potential difference with respect to one another. Such a plane is called an **equipotential surface.** Any number of equipotential surfaces may be drawn in a field, each containing those points which are at a certain potential difference with respect to another plane or with respect to one of the terminal electrodes of the field. A number of such surfaces for the field between parallel plates are indicated by the dotted lines in Fig. 12.4a.

Equipotential surfaces are not always planes. For the radial field between oppositely charged coaxial cylinders, the equipotential surfaces would also be cylinders, as represented by the dotted lines in Fig. 12.4b. For oppositely charged parallel wires, the equipotential surfaces are also circles, the centers of which are displaced from the centers of the wires, as in Fig. 12.4c. It will be noticed that in every instance the equipotential surfaces are perpendicular to the direction of the field.

By drawing the equipotential surfaces so that the potential difference between successive surfaces is the same, we obtain a sort of contour map of the electric field. Where the equipotential surfaces are close together, potential is changing rapidly, and there is considerable electric field intensity. Where the surfaces are far apart, the potential is changing slowly, and the electric field intensity is small. This is exactly like a topographical contour map where closely spaced contours indicate rapid change in elevation (that is, steep grades).

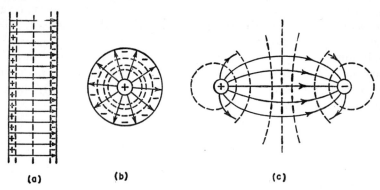

(a)   (b)   (c)

Fig. 12.4. Equipotential surfaces: (a) between oppositely charge parallel plates; (b) between oppositely charged coaxial cylinders; (c) between oppositely charged parallel wires.

5. Metal conductors in electric fields. Any metal is characterized by the presence in its atomic structure of free electrons which are capable, when acted upon by certain forces, of drifting through the space lattice of the substance. When a conductor, not part of a circuit, is placed in an electric field, all of its free electrons will be urged in the direction opposite to the direction of the field, thereby causing a momentary current in the conductor.

In Fig. 12.5, a straight conductor has been placed in the field between a pair of charged plates. The free electrons have moved to the left end of the conductor, nearest the positive plate, making that end negatively charged with respect to the right end, which is positively charged. The charges are referred to as **induced charges,** since they were caused without any contact with the conductor itself. The effect of the charges at the ends of the conductor is to establish within the conductor an electric field equal and opposite to the field due to the charged plates, thus bringing to zero the net field that exists within the conductor itself. That this must be so is evident from the consideration that as long as any electric field exists within the conductor, the free electrons will experience forces which cause them to move in such a direction as to neutralize the field. We are thus led to the conclusion that *no steady electric field can be maintained within an isolated conductor.*

Any change in the electric field between the plates will result in a momentary current while the free electrons rearrange themselves. If the electric field between the plates were continually varying, as would be the case if the battery were replaced by an a-c generator, a varying field would exist in the conductor, under the influence of which the free electrons would be moving, first to the left, then to the right, and so forth, constituting an alternating current in the conductor. This is exactly what happens in radio reception. The transmitting antenna maintains a varying electric field in the vicinity of the receiving antenna. The free electrons in the receiving antenna, under the influence of this field, move back and forth, and thus establish in it an alternating current of the frequency of the transmitter.

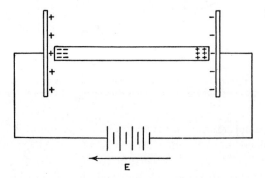

Fig. 12.5.   Insulated metal rod in an electric field.

A steady electric field may, and in fact always does, exist in a conductor which carries direct current. The free electrons of the conductor are continually acted upon by this field, giving rise to the forces that urge them along. The field required to do this is never of very great intensity, since it is only necessary for it to overcome the IR drop along the conductor. For example, the resistance of No. 10 copper wire is about 1 ohm per 1000 ft, or about 0.00328 ohm per m. To maintain a current of 25 amp in this wire thus requires an electric field intensity of $25 \times 0.00328 = 0.082$ v per m in the direction in which current flows along the wire.

In studying the function of the battery in an electric circuit in Chapter II, we spoke of it as supplying energy to the electrons as they passed through it. We may now take the optional viewpoint that the function of the battery is to maintain an electric field intensity along the circuit sufficient to maintain the desired current. The energy to maintain the current must, of course, come from the battery in the final analysis.

6. Insulators in electric fields.   Substances act as insulators primarily because there are few, if any, free electrons in their structure. Such substances, collectively called **dielectrics,** include solids, liquids, and gases.   When subjected to electric fields of less than a certain intensity, dielectrics permit only negligible current to flow.   The molecules of the material, however, appear to be distorted by the field so that, in effect, the center of positive charge of a molecule no longer coincides with the center of negative charge.   The dielectric and the molecules themselves are then said to be **polarized.**   Fig. 12.6a represents schematically a section of a dielectric in its normal state, and Fig. 12.6b shows the same section under the influence of an electric field.   The degree of polarization depends upon the intensity of the

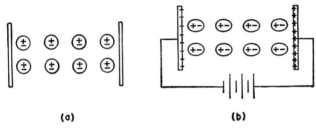

(a)   **(b)**

Fig. 12.6.   Polarization of molecules of an insulating substance in an electric field: (a) molecules in normal state; (b) polarized molecules.

field, the polarization increasing with electric field intensity up to the critical value.

A gaseous dielectric, once the field is removed, immediately returns to its normal state.   In liquid and solid dielectrics, particularly in the latter, the state of polarization may continue for an appreciable time after the field is removed, the molecules returning gradually to their normal state.   We have here, temporarily at least, a sort of electrical counterpart of residual magnetism.

A dielectric that is subjected to an alternating electric field would be polarized first in one direction, then in the other, at the frequency of the field.   In the case of liquid and solid dielectrics, in which the polarized molecules do not relax instantaneously, there occurs a certain **dielectric loss,** not unlike hysteresis loss in magnetic materials. This loss is so large in some otherwise good insulating materials as to preclude their use in high-frequency apparatus.   For very-high-frequency apparatus, it has been necessary to develop new synthetic insulations, such as polystyrene, in which the dielectric loss is low.

7. Dielectric strength.   If the critical electric field intensity of a dielectric substance be exceeded, the molecules distorted by polarization are no longer able to hold together, and their breakdown into charged particles changes the nature of the substance from insulator to conductor. The electric field intensity at which breakdown occurs is known as the **dielectric strength** of the substance.

The dielectric strength of any particular insulating material depends upon attendant conditions, such as temperature, thickness of specimen, and length of time the specimen is subjected to the electric field. A surge voltage applied to a specimen of insulating material for a few microseconds might leave it unharmed, whereas a lesser voltage applied for several seconds might cause breakdown. In using published figures of dielectric strength, it is, therefore, necessary to know the conditions that prevailed when the tests were made. The values given in Table VI are for steady voltages applied to specimens not exceeding 1 mm in thickness.

The breakdown of a solid insulating material usually renders it unfit for further use by puncturing, burning, cracking, or otherwise damaging it. Gaseous and liquid dielectrics are self-healing and may be used repeatedly following breakdown.

Problems

(**5-XII**) What thickness of rubber insulation, allowing a safety factor of 2, is required between metal surfaces for a potential of 4000 v?

(**6-XII**) The windings of a certain transformer are insulated from the core by a layer of varnished cambric 0.036 in. thick. What voltage could be safely applied between windings and core?

(**7-XII**) What should be the minimum thickness of oiled-paper insulation to withstand a potential difference of 600 v?

TABLE VI
DIELECTRIC STRENGTH OF MATERIALS

Material	Dielectric Strength (kv per mm)	Dielectric Constant
Air	3	1
Glass	80–150	5–9
Vulcanized rubber	15–30	2–3
Mica	50–200	5–7
Paper, paraffined	40–60	2–3
Varnished cambric	50–70	2–3
Transformer oil	12–20	2–3
Pure water	......	81

8. Electric flux. As was previously explained in Section 3, an electric field may be described by specifying the electric field intensity

for various points in the field.   For a simple field such as that between parallel flat plates, the electric field intensity was seen to depend primarily on the potential difference E which was established between the plates.   For some purposes, it would be con-
venient if we were also able to describe an electric field by specifying some quantity which depended upon the charge Q existing on the plates.   With this in mind, we begin by defining **electric flux.** We may think of electric flux as emerging from every positive charge in amount depending upon the charge, and as terminating on negative charges likewise.   The concept can best be visualized by thinking of the flux as lines, the number of lines emerging from a positive charge or terminating on a negative charge being always proportional to the magnitude of the charge.

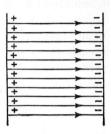

Fig. 12.7. Lines of electric flux between oppositely charged parallel plates.

The MKS unit of flux, which has been given no special name, is defined as follows: *One MKS unit of electric flux is the amount which is associated with a charge of 1 coulomb.*

The symbol is ψ, and the defining equation is

$$\psi = Q, \tag{12.7}$$

where ψ is electric flux in MKS units, and
    Q is charge in coulombs.
When electric flux is visualized as lines, we may arbitrarily assign any amount of flux to be represented by each line, as 1 MKS unit or 10^{-2} MKS unit or 10^{-8} MKS unit, as is most convenient.

9. Gauss's law.   Suppose a closed surface is drawn so that it encloses a net charge of $+Q$ coulombs, as in Fig. 12.8a.   There would emerge from this charge, according to the defining equation in Section 8, an electric flux

$$\psi = Q \text{ MKS units}, \tag{12.7}$$

all of which would pass outward through the specified surface.   If the surface were drawn to enclose a net charge of $-Q$ coulombs, as in Fig. 12.8b, an electric flux

$$\psi = Q \text{ MKS units} \tag{12.7}$$

would pass inward through the surface and terminate upon the charge. If the surface were so drawn that the net charge enclosed were equal to zero, the net flux passing in or out through the surface would be zero. Even if there were other charges in the vicinity, lines entering the specified surface due to these could not terminate within it (since it contains no net charge), but must again pass through the surface outward, as in Fig. 12.8c. These self-evident statements are summed up in Gauss's law as follows: *The net amount of electric flux passing through any closed surface is numerically equal to the net charge enclosed by the surface.*

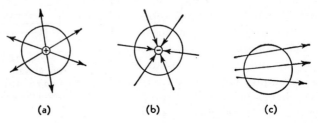

(a)   (b)   (c)

Fig. 12.8. Lines of electric flux penetrating a closed surface within which is: (a) a positive charge; (b) a negative charge; (c) no charge.

10. Electric flux density. Just as a magnetic field might be described by specifying for each point either the magnetic field intensity or the magnetic flux density, so an electric field may be described by specifying for each point either the electric field intensity or the electric flux density. Electric flux density is a vector quantity which may vary from point to point both in direction and in magnitude. Let us consider a surface *a-b-c-d* (Fig. 12.9), which is in an electric field

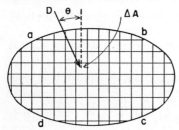

Fig. 12.9. The summation of $D \cos \theta \Delta A$ over the surface is equal to the total electric flux penetrating the surface.

and which is penetrated by the lines of electric flux. At every point there will be an electric flux density which can be represented by a vector such as D directed into the paper. The direction of the vector is the direction of the field at the point and its length is proportional to the flux density. Now suppose the surface to be divided into small areas ΔA, so small that the flux density may be considered as uniform over ΔA. Then suppose we form products such as $D \cos \theta \, \Delta A$ by multiplying the area by the component of the flux density perpendicular to the area, and finally that we sum up all such products over a specified surface and equate this to the electric flux ψ which penetrates the surface

$$\sum^{A} D \cos \theta \, \Delta A = \psi. \tag{12.8}[1]$$

This equation will serve as our definition of electric flux density. *Electric flux density is that quantity which, if its products with elements of area be taken as described above and summed up over any given surface, the summation is equal to the amount of electric flux penetrating the surface.*

In the simple case of the field between oppositely charged parallel plates, the summation would become simply

$$DA = \psi \tag{12.9}$$

or

$$D = \frac{\psi}{A}. \tag{12.10}$$

Electric flux density is in this case seen to be electric flux per unit area, and so far as dimensions are concerned this is true in general. It must be remembered, however, that it is not usually possible to find the electric flux density at a point by simply dividing an electric flux by an area. This is valid only if the flux density is uniform over the area, or if average flux density is wanted.

The MKS unit of electric flux density has no special name and electric flux densities are expressed as so many MKS units of electric flux per square meter.

The difference between electric field intensity and electric flux density may be brought out by two experiments. First, suppose two flat plates, maintained parallel at a fixed distance apart, are connected to a battery and then immersed in an oil bath as shown in Fig. 12.10a. The electric field intensity remains unchanged, since the potential difference between the plates is fixed by the battery. The charge on the plates, however, increases, as may be demonstrated by connecting a ballistic galvanometer in series with the battery, and therefore the electric flux and the electric flux density increase also. This may be explained by assuming that under the influence of the field, the molecules of oil become polarized, and in effect, but not actually, diminish the charges on the plates. The battery is then able to crowd more charge onto the plates.

Now, suppose that after charging the plates (which are assumed to be perfectly insulated), the battery is disconnected and the plates immersed in the oil bath as in Fig. 12.10b. The charge on the plates

[1] To be rigorously correct we must, of course, let ΔA approach zero. As the elemental areas are made smaller and smaller, and ΔA approaches zero, the summation of Equation (12.8) becomes the definite integral $\int^{A} D \cos \theta \, dA = \psi$.

is now fixed, as are the electric flux and electric flux density.   There is nothing to maintain the plates at a constant potential difference, however, and an electrostatic voltmeter connected to the plates would indicate a decrease in potential difference as the plates are lowered into the oil.   The explanation again depends upon the polarized molecules of oil, which set up an electric field in opposition to the

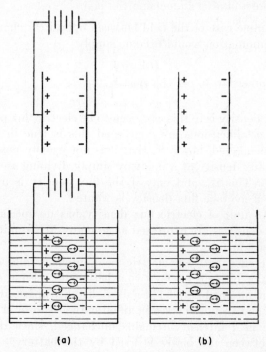

Fig. 12.10.   Effect of immersing a pair of oppositely charged parallel plates in a liquid dielectric: (a) plates maintained at constant potential difference; (b) plates maintained at constant charge.

field of the plates, and thus reduce the electric field intensity and the potential difference.

In the first experiment, where the electric field intensity was fixed, the electric flux density was seen to depend upon the medium in which the field is established.   Electric flux density would be least in free space and would become greater in any material dielectric.   In the second experiment, where the charge was fixed, the electric field intensity was seen to depend upon the medium in which the field was established.   Electric field intensity would be greatest in free space and would decrease in any material dielectric.

EXAMPLE 1: Two parallel plates, each 20 cm square and spaced 2 cm apart in air, are connected to a 1000-v battery and a transfer of charge of 1.77×10^{-8} coulomb takes place from one plate to the other. While still connected to the battery, the plates are lowered into oil, and the charge on the plates is observed to increase to 4.42×10^{-8} coulomb. Determine the electric field intensity and the electric flux density before and after immersing the plates in oil.

SOLUTION: The electric field intensity remains constant at a value of

$$\mathcal{E} = \frac{V}{S} = \frac{1000}{0.02} = 50,000 \text{ v per m.}$$

Before immersion in oil, the electric flux is

$$\psi = Q = 1.77 \times 10^{-8} \text{ MKS unit,}$$

and the electric flux density is

$$D = \frac{\psi}{A} = \frac{1.77 \times 10^{-8}}{0.2 \times 0.2} = 44.2 \times 10^{-8} \text{ MKS unit per sq m.}$$

After immersion in oil, the electric flux is

$$\psi = Q = 4.42 \times 10^{-8} \text{ MKS unit,}$$

and the electric flux density is

$$D = \frac{\psi}{A} = \frac{4.42 \times 10^{-8}}{0.2 \times 0.2} = 110.2 \times 10^{-8} \text{ MKS unit per sq m.}$$

EXAMPLE 2: The parallel plates described in Example 1 are charged from a 1000-v battery which is then disconnected. The plates, charged with 1.77×10^{-8} coulomb, are now immersed in oil, and the potential difference between them is observed to decrease to 400 v. Determine the electric field intensity and electric flux density before and after immersing the plates in oil.

SOLUTION: The electric flux remains constant at a value of

$$\psi = Q = 1.77 \times 10^{-8} \text{ MKS unit,}$$

and the electric flux density also remains constant at a value of

$$D = \frac{\psi}{A} = \frac{1.77 \times 10^{-8}}{0.2 \times 0.2} = 44.2 \times 10^{-8} \text{ MKS unit.}$$

The electric field intensity before immersing in oil is

$$\mathcal{E} = \frac{V}{S} = \frac{1000}{0.02} = 50,000 \text{ v per m.}$$

The electric field intensity, after immersing in oil, is

$$\mathcal{E} = \frac{V}{S} = \frac{400}{0.02} = 20,000 \text{ v per m.}$$

Problems

(**8-XII**) Two parallel flat plates, each 10 by 5 cm and separated by 1 cm, are charged by transferring 0.1 microcoulomb from one plate to the other. What electric flux is established between the plates? What is the electric flux density?

(**9-XII**) What charge would be required to establish an electric flux density of 2×10^{-5} MKS unit per sq m between parallel flat plates 20 cm in diameter?

(**10-XII**) What is the electric flux entering (leaving) a surface which encloses (a) the positive plate in Problem 9-XII, (b) the negative plate in Problem 9-XII, and (c) both plates in Problem 9-XII?

(**11-XII**) A spherical surface 50 cm in diameter is penetrated by an inward electric flux uniformly distributed over the surface, the electric flux density being 2.5×10^{-7} MKS unit per sq m. What is the sign and magnitude of the charge enclosed by this surface?

11. Permittivity. We have now defined two concepts—electric field intensity and electric flux density—either of which may be used in describing an electric field. The first was seen to be proportional to the potential difference between the two extremities of the field, and the second was seen to be proportional to the charges on the electrodes between which the field is established. We now wish to find a relationship between the two concepts. The problem is similar to the one we encountered in defining the magnetic field concepts. After defining magnetic field intensity and magnetic flux density independently, we proceeded to show that they were related through permeability, which depended upon a property of the medium in which the field existed. We now find that the relationship between electric field intensity and electric flux density also depends upon a property of the medium. As was demonstrated in Section 10, with fixed electric field intensity, the electric flux density depends upon the medium in which the field exists, whereas for fixed electric flux density, the electric field intensity depends upon the medium.

The property of a dielectric which determines the relation of electric flux density and electric field intensity is known as **permittivity**, defined by the equation

$$\epsilon = \frac{D}{\mathcal{E}}, \tag{12.11}$$

where ϵ is permittivity in MKS units.

   D is electric flux density in MKS units per square meter.

   $\mathcal{E}$ is electric field intensity in volts per meter.

The unit of permittivity is defined in words as follows: *The permittivity of a substance is 1 MKS unit if an electric field intensity of 1 v per m corresponds to an electric flux density of 1 MKS unit per sq m.*

No substance has a permittivity approaching unity. The permittivity of free space designated as ϵ_0 is determined experimentally to be 8.85 $\times$ 10^{-12} MKS unit, or very closely $\frac{1}{36\pi} \times$ 10^{-9} MKS unit. The permittivities of gases differ so slightly from this figure that extreme care is required in making the measurements if the difference is to be detected. Solid and liquid dielectrics have permittivities ranging from 2 to 80 times the permittivity of free space.

The ratio of the permittivity of any substance to the permittivity of free space is called **relative permittivity,** or more commonly, **dielectric constant,** and may be designated as ϵ_R. The actual permittivity of a substance in MKS units would then be

$$\epsilon = \epsilon_0 \epsilon_R.$$

The dielectric constants of several materials commonly used for insulation are given in Table VI.

Problems

(**12-XII**) What is the permittivity of a substance in which (a) an electric flux density of 1.018 $\times$ 10^{-7} MKS unit per sq m is established by an electric field intensity of 500 v per m, (b) an electric flux density of 1.145 $\times$ 10^{-6} MKS unit per sq m is established by an electric field intensity of 3.5 $\times$ 10^4 v per m, and (c) an electric flux density of 2.71 $\times$ 10^{-5} MKS unit per sq m is established by an electric field intensity of 6 $\times$ 10^5 v per m? What is the dielectric constant of each of these substances?

(**13-XII**) A potential difference of 7500 v is established between parallel plates 30 by 40 cm which are separated by a sheet of glass (dielectric constant 8.35) 0.062 in. thick. Determine the charge on the plates.

(**14-XII**) What potential difference would be required to transfer a charge of 1 microcoulomb between parallel plates 25 cm in diameter which are spaced 1.5 cm apart and immersed in glycerin (dielectric constant 25)?

(**15-XII**) What is the maximum charge that can be transferred without causing breakdown of the air between parallel plates 5 cm in diameter and spaced 1 cm apart?

12. Electric fields in nonhomogeneous dielectrics. Suppose an electric field is established between two plates which are separated by a layer of dielectric A, having a thickness S_A and a permittivity ϵ_A, and a layer of dielectric B, having a thickness S_B and permittivity ϵ_B, as shown in Fig. 12.11. Since there are no free charges within either layer of dielectric, nor at the boundary, lines of electric flux which originate on charges on the positive plate must be continuous through both layers and terminate on the negative plate. Since the cross section of the field is uniform, the electric density D must be the same in both layers:

$$D_A = D_B. \tag{12.12}$$

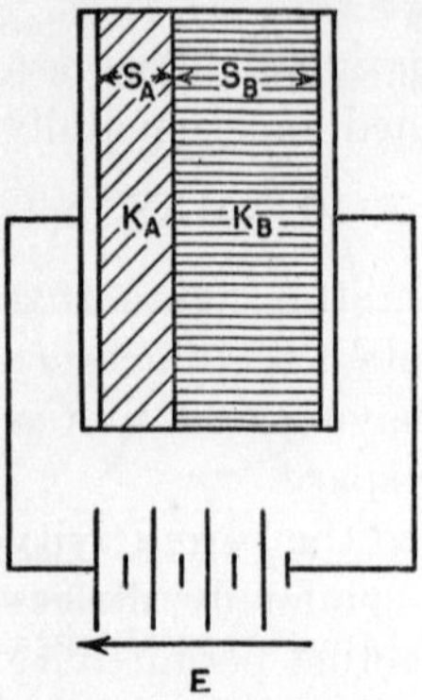

But since the permittivities are not the same, the electric field intensities must be different and must satisfy the equation

$$\epsilon_A \mathcal{E}_A = \epsilon_B \mathcal{E}_B \tag{12.13}$$

or, since $\epsilon_A = \epsilon_0 \epsilon_{RA}$ and $\epsilon_B = \epsilon_0 \epsilon_{RB}$,

$$\epsilon_{RA} \mathcal{E}_A = \epsilon_{RB} \mathcal{E}_B. \tag{12.14}$$

Fig. 12.11. Parallel plates insulated by slabs of two different dielectric substances. Also, the summation of the products of electric field intensity by thickness of the dielectric must equal the potential difference between the plates at the extremities of the field:

$$\mathcal{E}_A S_A + \mathcal{E}_B S_B = E. \tag{12.15}$$

If the dielectric constants, thicknesses, and potential difference are known, we may solve (12.14) and (12.15) to obtain the electric field intensity in each dielectric.

It is obvious from Equation (12.14) that the highest electric field intensity must exist in the medium of smallest dielectric constant. This is often of practical importance in the design of insulation, particularly if one of the layers is air. Air not only has a smaller dielectric constant, but also a smaller dielectric strength than most insulating materials and, consequently, an air film trapped between layers of other insulation is likely to break down, even when the stress in the other insulation is nominal. The heat resulting from breakdown of the air film may cause eventual deterioration and failure of the other insulation.

Problems

(**16-XII**) Two parallel plates are separated by a sheet of plate glass (dielectric constant 7.57) $\frac{3}{16}$ in. thick and a sheet of rubber (dielectric constant 2.3) $\frac{1}{4}$ in. thick. A potential difference of 50,000 v is established between the plates. Determine the electric field intensity in each substance.

(**17-XII**) The potential difference between the plates in Problem 16-XII is gradually raised until failure of one of the dielectrics occurs. Which dielectric fails first, and what will be the potential difference between the plates when failure occurs?   Assume the dielectric strength of each substance to be the lower figure given in Table VI.

(18-XII) A sheet of fiber (dielectric constant 5) 0.23 cm thick is inserted between parallel plates 0.25 cm apart.   A potential difference of 2500 v is applied between the plates.   Determine the electric field intensity in the fiber and in the air film between the fiber and the plate.   Will the air break down?

Fig. 12.12.   Electric flux emerging from a positive point charge.

13. Electric field intensity due to point charges. If a charge of $+Q$ coulombs is concentrated at a point in space remote from other charges, an electric flux $\psi = Q$ MKS units will emerge radially in all directions.   If we imagine this charge to be surrounded by a sphere of radius S meters, with the charge at the center, the electric flux will be distributed uniformly over the sphere, penetrating the surface perpendicularly, as shown in Fig. 12.12.   The electric flux density at any point on the surface will be

$$D = \frac{\psi}{A} = \frac{Q}{4\pi S^2} \text{ MKS units per sq m.} \qquad (12.16)$$

The electric field intensity at any point on the surface will be

$$\mathcal{E} = \frac{D}{\epsilon_0} = \frac{Q}{4\pi \epsilon_0 S^2} \text{ v per m,} \qquad (12.17)$$

where ϵ_0 is the permittivity of free space.   Equation (12.17) enables us to calculate the electric field intensity at any distance S from a point charge in free space.   It must be remembered that $\mathcal{E}$ is a vector quantity and, therefore, its direction as well as its magnitude must be stated.   The direction of the field due to a positive charge at a point is away from the point; that due to a negative charge at a point is toward the point.

If two or more point charges are present in a certain region, the electric field intensity at any specified point can be found by taking the resultant of the electric field intensities at this point due to the individual charges.   That this is so will be clear when we remember that electric field intensity is measured by the force acting upon a unit positive charge placed at the point in question.   When we add electric field intensities, we are, in effect, adding forces on a charge, and the resultant force will be the resultant electric field intensity.

EXAMPLE: In a system of plane rectangular coordinates, charge A is $+2 \times 10^{-6}$ coulomb and is located at the point (0, 2), as shown in Fig. 12.13.   Charge B is $+5 \times 10^{-6}$ coulomb and is located at the point (3, 0).   The coordinates are expressed in meters.   Determine the electric field intensity at the origin due to each charge and the resultant electric field intensity.

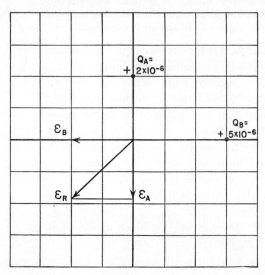

Fig. 12.13. Graphical determination of the electric field intensity due to two point charges.

SOLUTION: Electric field intensity at the origin due to charge A is

$$\mathcal{E}_A = \frac{2 \times 10^{-6}}{4\pi \left(\dfrac{1}{36\pi} \times 10^{-9}\right)(2)^2} = 4500 \text{ v per m}$$

directed along the negative y axis as shown.

Electric field intensity at the origin due to charge B is

$$\mathcal{E}_B = \frac{5 \times 10^{-6}}{4\pi \left(\dfrac{1}{36\pi} \times 10^{-9}\right)(3)^2} = 5000 \text{ v per m}$$

directed along the negative x axis as shown.

	x Component	y Component
$\mathcal{E}_A$	0	-4500
$\mathcal{E}_B$	-5000	0
$\mathcal{E}_R$	-5000	-4500

$$\mathcal{E}_R = \sqrt{(5000)^2 + (4500)^2} = 6740 \text{ v per m.}$$

There is no limit to the number of point charges that may be taken into account by this method, nor is it necessary that all the charges lie in the same plane. If we are given the sign; magnitude; and x, y, and z coordinates of n point charges, we can find the electric field intensity at the origin, or at any specified point in space. Practically, the procedure is too laborious to apply to any but the simplest cases.

Point charges are, of course, fictitious, because any charge is distributed more or less uniformly over the surface of the body with which it is associated. Distributed charges may sometimes be replaced for purposes of calculation, however, by point charges properly placed. For instance, a charge uniformly distributed over the surface of a sphere can be replaced by an equal point charge placed at the center. A charged surface of any kind may be broken down into elements of area, and the charge on each element regarded as a point charge for the purpose of calculating electric field intensity by the method outlined above. The resultant field intensity would then be found as the vector summation of all the field intensities due to the elemental areas with their associated charges. However, this procedure, as indicated above, is too laborious to be very useful.

Problems

(**19-XII**) What is the electric field intensity in space 25 cm from a point charge of $+10^{-6}$ coulomb?

(**20-XII**) What is the electric field intensity at the origin if a point charge of $+2 \times 10^{-7}$ coulomb is located at the coordinate (30, 40) and a charge of -3×10^{-7} coulomb is located at the coordinate $(-60, 80)$? Coordinates are expressed in centimeters.

(**21-XII**) Calculate the electric field intensity at the point (20, -20) due to the arrangement of point charges described in Problem 20-XII.

(**22-XII**) What is the maximum charge which may be placed upon a sphere 1 cm in diameter, located in air, before breakdown occurs?

14. Coulomb's law. An expression for calculating the forces that would act between point charges can readily be obtained from Equation (12.17). Consider two point charges of Q_1 and Q_2 coulombs, respectively, located S meters apart in free space. The electric field intensity produced by Q_1 at the point where Q_2 is located is given by

$$\mathcal{E} = \frac{Q_1}{4\pi\epsilon_0 S^2}. \tag{12.18}$$

The force acting upon the charge Q_2 is, therefore,

$$F = \mathcal{E}Q_2 \tag{12.19}$$

$$= \frac{Q_1 Q_2}{4\pi\epsilon_0 S^2}. \tag{12.20}$$

This relation is known as **Coulomb's law,** or the **inverse square law.** It serves as the defining equation for unit quantity of electricity in the CGS electrostatic system (see Appendix A).

Problem

(**23-XII**) What force would act between equal point charges of $+10^{-6}$ coulomb placed 20 cm apart in free space? What would be the force if the charges were immersed in alcohol (dielectric constant 23)?

15. Capacitance. In order to charge one conductor with respect to another, it is necessary to establish between the conductors a certain potential difference. Conversely, if a potential difference be established between two conductors, a certain quantity of electricity is transferred from one to the other. The one thing implies the other. We never have potential difference without charge, nor charge without potential difference. The charge divided by the corresponding potential difference is defined as the **capacitance** of the two conductors.

The unit of capacitance is the **farad,** defined as follows: *The capacitance of two conductors is 1 farad if a potential difference of 1 v corresponds to a charge of 1 coulomb.*

The definition in equation form is

$$C = \frac{Q}{V},$$ (12.21)

where C is the capacitance in farads.

Q is the charge in coulombs.

V is the potential difference in volts.

The farad is too large a unit to be convenient for practical measurements. The charge corresponding to 1 v potential difference will never exceed more than a very small fraction of a coulomb, even for the largest conductors. Consequently, capacitance is usually expressed in microfarads (μf) or micromicrofarads ($\mu\mu$f). In making calculations in MKS units, of course, farads must always be used.

Capacitance depends upon (a) the sizes and shapes of the two conductors, (b) their distance apart, and (c) the medium in which the conductors are located. In general, the larger the conductors and the closer together they are, the greater will be their capacitance. The capacitance will be several times as great if the conductors are separated by a solid or liquid dielectric as it will if the medium is air or free space.

Capacitance is frequently introduced deliberately into an electric circuit to secure certain desired behavior. On the other hand, it frequently occurs in circuits and apparatus as a consequence of other design considerations, without being particularly sought after. For example, the capacitance between the conductors of a transmission line, or a telephone cable, is an important factor in determining their performance characteristics, as is the capacitance between the various electrodes of any electronic tube. Often, the incidental capacitance is so high as to prevent the operation of the device as desired. For example, ordinary electronic tubes cannot be used at very high frequencies because of their too large interelectrode capacitances, and telephone conversations over ocean cables are not practicable because of the large capacitances between the conductors.

Problems

(24-XII) What is the capacitance of a parallel-plate arrangement if a potential difference of 2500 v corresponds to a charge of 10^{-4} coulomb? What would be the charge if the potential difference were 7500 v? What potential difference would correspond to a charge of 10^{-3} coulomb?

(25-XII) The capacitance of a line consisting of two No. 10 gage wires spaced 18 in. apart is given in tables as 0.00762 μf per mile of line. What charge per mile would appear on each wire if the potential difference between the wires were 2300 v?

(26-XII) The plate-cathode capacitance of a 2A3 vacuum tube is 5.5 $\mu\mu$f. The normal potential difference between plate and cathode is 250 v. What is the charge on these electrodes at normal voltage?

16. Calculation of capacitance of parallel plates. The relationships between the various electric field concepts and capacitance will

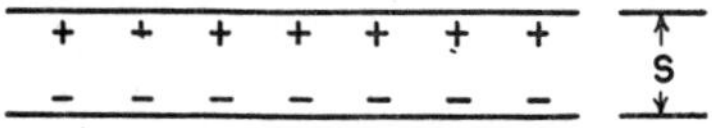

Fig. 12.14. Oppositely charged parallel plates.

be further illustrated by the calculation of the capacitance of two parallel, flat plates. Suppose a quantity of electricity equivalent to Q coulombs be moved from one plate to the other as in Fig. 12.14. If we assume the plates to be separated by a distance which is small compared to their other dimensions, we may neglect any edge effects and assume the charge to be distributed uniformly over the inner surface of each plate.

The electric flux emerging from the positive plate and terminating on the negative plate is

$$\psi = Q \text{ MKS units.} \tag{12.7}$$

Since the charge was assumed to be uniformly distributed, we may assume the electric flux to be uniformly distributed also. The electric flux density in any plane between the plates and parallel to them will, therefore, be

$$D = \frac{\psi}{A} = \frac{Q}{A} \text{ MKS units per sq m,} \qquad (12.22)$$

where A is the area in square meters of one side of one plate. If the plates are separated by a dielectric substance of permittivity ϵ, the electric field intensity will be

$$\mathcal{E} = \frac{D}{\epsilon} = \frac{Q}{\epsilon A} \text{ v per m.} \qquad (12.23)$$

The electric field intensity will be constant from the surface of the positive plate to the surface of the negative plate. The potential difference between the plates is, therefore,

$$V = \mathcal{E}S = \frac{QS}{\epsilon A} \text{ v,} \qquad (12.24)$$

where S is the plate separation in meters.

From the defining equation of capacitance, we then have

$$C = \frac{Q}{V} = \frac{Q}{\dfrac{QS}{\epsilon A}} = \frac{\epsilon A}{S} \text{ farads.} \qquad (12.25)$$

Equation (12.25) not only enables us to calculate the capacitance of parallel plates when the permittivity of the dielectric is known, but also makes it possible to determine permittivity. If we *measure* the capacitance of a parallel-plate arrangement the dimensions of which are accurately known, we may use (12.25) to determine the permittivity of the substance used as the dielectric.

Problems

(**27-XII**) What is the capacitance of 2 parallel plates 20 by 25 cm, separated by 0.5 cm of air?

(**28-XII**) What should be the area of a pair of plates separated by mica (dielectric constant 6.5) 0.005 in. thick in order that their capacitance shall be 0.001 μf?

(**29-XII**) Two parallel metal plates each having a surface area of 100 sq cm (one side) and separated by 1 mm are immersed in oil. The capacitance is measured and found to be 0.00213 μf. What is the permittivity of the oil? What is its dielectric constant?

17. Energy stored in an electric field. It was pointed out in Section 1 that the charging of conductors by removing electrons from one to the other requires the expenditure of energy. This energy is not lost, but is stored in the electric field established between the conductors, and is recoverable in the form of heat when the conductors are discharged.   We shall now look for a way to express the stored energy in terms of the electric field concepts.

As the potential difference between the conductors is increased, the charge increases in direct proportion, as shown by the graph in Fig. 12.15.   Corresponding to a potential difference e_1, there exists on each conductor a charge q_1.   If the potential difference is increased by an amount Δe to a value e_2, the charge on each conductor increases by an amount Δq to a value q_2. The work done in moving this additional quantity of electricity

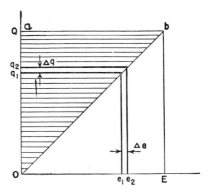

Fig. 12.15.   Graphical determination of the energy stored in an electric field.

Δq from one conductor to the other is, by the defining equation of potential difference, equal to the charge moved times the average potential difference that existed while it was being moved:

$$\Delta w = \frac{e_1 + e_2}{2} \Delta q. \qquad (12.26)$$

If Δe is made very small, we can consider $e_1 = e_2$ and

$$\Delta w = e_1 \Delta q. \qquad (12.27)$$

Graphically, Δw is represented in Fig. 12.15 by the area of the strip of width Δq and length e_1.   To find the total energy required to move a quantity of electricity Q from one plate to the other and thus establish a potential difference E between the plates, we have to sum up the area represented by all such strips from $e = 0$ to $e = E$:

$$W = \sum_{e=0}^{e=E} e \Delta q. \qquad (12.28)$$

Graphically, this energy is represented in Fig. 12.15 by the area of the triangle oab, which is

$$W = \frac{EQ}{2}. \qquad (12.29)$$

If the conductors are parallel plates, as used in defining the various electric field concepts, the field will be uniform, and we may write

$$E = (-) \, \mathcal{E}S, \tag{12.30}$$
$$Q = \psi = DA. \tag{12.31}$$

Upon substituting (12.30) and (12.31) in (12.29), we obtain

$$W = \frac{(\mathcal{E}S)(DA)}{2}. \tag{12.32}$$

The product SA is the volume of the space between the plates. Consequently, the energy stored per unit volume is

$$W = \frac{\mathcal{E}D}{2} \text{ joules per cu m.} \tag{12.33}$$

If the space between the plates is filled with a dielectric of permittivity ϵ, the energy storage per unit volume can also be expressed as

$$W = \frac{\mathcal{E}D}{2} = \frac{\mathcal{E}(\mathcal{E}\epsilon)}{2} = \frac{\mathcal{E}^2\epsilon}{2} \text{ joules per cu m,} \tag{12.34}$$

or

$$W = \frac{\mathcal{E}D}{2} = \left(\frac{D}{\epsilon}\right)\frac{D}{2} = \frac{D^2}{2\epsilon} \text{ joules per cu m.} \tag{12.35}$$

We may also obtain from (12.29) an expression for total stored energy in terms of capacitance and potential difference, because since

$$Q = CE,$$

substitution into (12.29) gives

$$W = \frac{E(CE)}{2} = \frac{CE^2}{2}. \tag{12.36}$$

The student will note the similarity between the expressions obtained in this article and the corresponding expressions for the energy stored in the magnetic field. Equations (12.34) and (12.35) should be compared with Equations (7.46) and (7.47) in Chapter VII. Equation (12.36) should be compared with Equation (11.50) in Chapter XI.

18. Force between charged plates. We can make use of the expression just derived for the energy stored in an electric field to calculate the force with which oppositely charged plates attract each other. Suppose the plates are arranged so that they may be separated a further distance ΔS by exerting a force F newtons to overcome the force of attraction between them.

Before the separation of the plates is increased, the energy stored in the field, according to Equation (12.32), is

$$W = \frac{\varepsilon SDA}{2} \text{ joules.}$$

Increasing the separation by an amount ΔS involves the storage of an additional amount of energy

$$\Delta W = \frac{\varepsilon \Delta SDA}{2} \text{ joules.} \qquad (12.37)$$

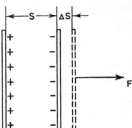

Fig. 12.16. Separation of oppositely charged parallel plates by an external force.

Since the charge on the plates is fixed, the electric flux, electric flux density, and electric field intensity remain constant.

All of the increase represented by Equation (12.37) must have come from the mechanical force that pulled the plates apart. The energy supplied from this source is

$$\Delta W = F \Delta S \text{ joules.} \qquad (12.38)$$

Equating (12.37) and (12.38) and solving for F, we obtain

$$F = \frac{\varepsilon DA}{2} \text{ newtons,} \qquad (12.39)$$

or

$$F = \frac{D^2 A}{2\epsilon} \text{ newtons.} \qquad (12.40)$$

Equation (12.40) may be compared with Equation (10.5), which gives the comparable magnetic force.

The force of attraction between charged plates may be utilized as a means of measuring potential difference. An instrument of this kind is known as an **electrostatic voltmeter.**

Problems

(30-XII) What is the energy storage per unit volume in an electric field in space where the intensity is 10^{-3} v per m? 10 v per m? 10^6 v per m?

(31-XII) How much energy is stored when a potential difference of 10,000 v is established between the plates of a parallel-plate arrangement which has a capacitance of 10^{-3} μf?

(32-XII) The capacitance of No. 10 wires spaced 18 in. apart in air is 0.00762 μf per mile. How much energy is stored in the electric field between the wires when the potential difference is 2300 v?

(33-XII) Parallel plates 10 cm in diameter are spaced 1 cm apart in air. With what force do the plates attract each other if the potential difference between them is 1500 v?   What would the force become if the plates were immersed in oil (dielectric constant 2.5)?

(**34-XII**) What is the maximum attractive force that could be attained without breakdown of the air dielectric in the parallel-plate arrangement described in Problem 33-XII?   Would this maximum force be more or less if the plates were immersed in oil (dielectric strength 100 kv per cm)?

19. Capacitors.   An arrangement of insulated plates for obtaining a required capacitance in a limited space is known as a **capacitor** or **condenser.**   The earliest capacitors were glass jars provided with inner and outer coatings of tin foil, and were called Leyden jars.   They were used in connection with early-day electrostatic machines to accumulate electric charge as it was separated by the machine, and thus make possible the production of more spectacular discharges than could be obtained from the machine alone.   No other form of capacitor was devised until about 1900 when the need for such a device in wireless telegraphy brought about the development of the parallel-plate type.

In present-day electrical engineering, immense numbers of capacitors of all types are used.   The multiple-plate type consists of a stack of alternate plates and pieces of a dielectric material, such as mica, the odd-numbered plates being connected together to one terminal of the capacitor, and the even-numbered to the other.   In other multiple-plate capacitors, the plates are held apart by spacers, and are so mounted that one group of plates may be moved relative to the other, and the groups interleaved to any desired extent.   This is the familiar tuning condenser in any radio receiver.

Probably the most-used capacitor is of the type in which long, alternate strips of paper and metal foil are rolled together to form a compact unit of considerable capacitance.   Paper capacitors are sometimes sealed into containers containing a liquid dielectric, which greatly improves the insulating qualities of the paper and makes the unit more reliable.

For applications in which a very large value of capacitance is required in small space, the electrolytic type of capacitor has been developed.   The dielectric in this type is an extremely thin film deposited on an aluminum plate by the action of an electrolyte.   The use of electrolytic capacitors is limited to d-c circuits and caution must be used to maintain the proper polarity.

A satisfactory explanation of the various uses to which capacitors are put is not easily made at this time.   Most of the applications are in a-c circuits, and although one or two explanations will be attempted in the following sections, a full appreciation of the usefulness of capacitors is not possible until the student has more knowledge of alternating currents.

20. Rating of capacitors. Any capacitor is designed with two objectives in mind: the capacitance required and the potential difference to which the insulation will be subjected. The insulation aspect of the problem is usually the first one to be considered. The dielectric must be of such material and such thickness that its dielectric strength will not be exceeded when the capacitor is put into service. Since the properties of insulating materials vary somewhat, and since a capacitor may be momentarily subjected to overvoltage, it should be designed for a maximum safe voltage greater than the working voltage for which it is intended.

After having selected the dielectric material and calculated the proper thickness, there remains the calculation of the plate area to give the required capacitance, and the determination of the number of plates and their size to give the required area. In multiple-plate capacitors, the total plate area is given by

$$A = a(N - 1), \tag{12.41}$$

where A is total required plate area.

    a is the area of one side of one plate.

    N is the number of plates used.

EXAMPLE: Design a capacitor that will have a capacitance of 0.01 μf and will work at a voltage of 2000.

SOLUTION: Let us consider mica as the dielectric. Table VI shows the dielectric strength of mica to be 50–200 kv per mm. Taking the minimum figure of 50 kv per mm and assuming that our capacitor may be subjected to as much as $1.5 \times 2000 = 3000$ v, we find the necessary thickness of the mica to be

$$\frac{3000}{50,000} \times 1 = 0.06 \text{ mm}$$

$$= 6 \times 10^{-5} \text{ m}.$$

The required plate area is given by Equation (12.25) for the capacitance of parallel flat plates:

$$C = \frac{\epsilon A}{S}.$$

From Table VI, we find the dielectric constant of mica to be 5–7. Again taking the minimum value, we find the permittivity of mica to be

$$\epsilon = \epsilon_0 \epsilon_R = 5 \times 8.85 \times 10^{-12} \text{ MKS unit.}$$

Substituting in Equation (12.25) and solving for A, we obtain

$$0.01 \times 10^{-6} = \frac{(5 \times 8.85 \times 10^{-12})A}{6 \times 10^{-5}}$$

$$A = 136 \text{ sq cm.}$$

If we use 11 plates, then each plate must have an area of 13.6 sq cm.

Problems

(35-XII) What should be the effective surface area of each plate of a 1-μf paper-insulated capacitor using paper 2 mils thick? What would be the maximum voltage rating of such a capacitor?

✓ **(36-XII)** A mica-insulated capacitor is to have a rating of 0.001 μf, 1000 v. What should be the effective area of the plates if a safety factor of 2 is allowed? If the capacitor is to be built up of alternate mica and metal disks, determine a suitable diameter and number of plates to give the proper area.

21. Capacitors in parallel and in series. Consider three capacitors having values of C_1, C_2, and C_3 farads, respectively, connected in

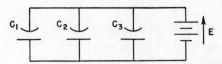

Fig. 12.17. Capacitors in parallel.

parallel as shown in Fig. 12.17, and charged by a battery of constant voltage E. The final charges on the various capacitors will be

$$Q_1 = C_1 E \text{ coulombs.} \tag{12.42}$$
$$Q_2 = C_2 E \text{ coulombs.} \tag{12.43}$$
$$Q_3 = C_3 E \text{ coulombs.} \tag{12.44}$$

The total charge Q_0, transferred through the battery from the positive to the negative plates of the capacitors, will be the sum of the charges on the individual capacitors:

$$Q_0 = Q_1 + Q_2 + Q_3 \tag{12.45}$$
$$= C_1 E + C_2 E + C_3 E \tag{12.46}$$
$$= [C_1 + C_2 + C_3]E. \tag{12.47}$$

The total capacitance of the group is, therefore,

$$C_0 = \frac{Q_0}{E} = C_1 + C_2 + C_3. \tag{12.48}$$

Now, suppose three capacitors having capacitances C_1, C_2, and C_3 farads, respectively, are connected in series, as shown in Fig. 12.18, and charged from a battery of constant emf E_0. The charge on each capacitor in this case will be the same. The negative charge forced on to the right-hand plate of C_3 will result in the displacement of an equal negative charge on to the right-hand plate of C_2 and finally of C_1, leaving the left-hand plate of each capacitor positively charged.

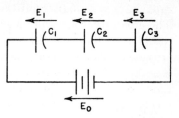

Fig. 12.18.   Capacitors in series.

In general, the emf's of the various capacitors will not be the same, since in each case the emf is determined by the charge and the capacitance. They are:

$$E_1 = \frac{Q}{C_1} \text{ v.} \tag{12.49}$$

$$E_2 = \frac{Q}{C_2} \text{ v.} \tag{12.50}$$

$$E_3 = \frac{Q}{C_3} \text{ v, respectively.} \tag{12.51}$$

By Kirchhoff's voltage law, the total voltage is

$$E_0 = E_1 + E_2 + E_3 \tag{12.52}$$

$$= \frac{Q}{C_1} + \frac{Q}{C_2} + \frac{Q}{C_3} = \left[\frac{1}{C_1} + \frac{1}{C_2} + \frac{1}{C_3} \right] Q. \tag{12.53}$$

Then the total capacitance is

$$C_0 = \frac{Q}{E_0} = \frac{Q}{\left[\dfrac{1}{C_1} + \dfrac{1}{C_2} + \dfrac{1}{C_3} \right] Q} = \frac{1}{\dfrac{1}{C_1} + \dfrac{1}{C_2} + \dfrac{1}{C_3}}, \tag{12.54}$$

or

$$\frac{1}{C_0} = \frac{1}{C_1} + \frac{1}{C_2} + \frac{1}{C_3}. \tag{12.55}$$

We may, therefore, state the rules for capacitors in parallel and series as follows:

The capacitance of a number of capacitors in parallel is the sum of the individual capacitances.

The capacitance of a number of capacitors in series is the reciprocal of the sum of the reciprocals of the individual capacitances.

Capacitors may be connected in parallel to obtain larger values of capacitance than are available from individual units. They are sometimes connected in series when the circuit voltage exceeds the

working voltage of the individual units. In using the series connection, it is important to keep in mind that the voltages across
capacitors in series are not the same unless the capacitances are equal.
The greater voltage will be across the smaller capacitance, which may
result in its failure if the capacitances differ very much.

One method of obtaining very high voltages in so-called "lightning
generators" involves the charging of a number of capacitors in parallel,
then reconnecting them in series for discharge. The reconnection
is accomplished automatically by properly placed insulating gaps
which break down when a predetermined voltage is reached.

Problems

(**37-XII**) Three capacitors of 2 μf, 3 μf, and 5 μf, respectively, are connected
in parallel and charged from a 200-v battery. What is the group capaci-
tance? What is the charge on each capacitor? What is the total charge?

(**38-XII**) Three capacitors of 2 μf, 3 μf, and 5 μf, respectively, are connected
in series and charged from a 200-v battery. What is the group capacitance?
What is the voltage across each capacitor? What is the charge on each
capacitor? What is the total charge?

(**39-XII**) Three capacitors rated 1 μf, 300 v; 2 μf, 200 v; and 1.5 μf, 450 v
are connected in series across a variable voltage, which is increased until one
capacitor fails. Assume any capacitor will break down at 2 times its rated
voltage. Which capacitor fails first, and what is the voltage across the group
when failure occurs?

(**40-XII**) What will be the total capacitance of a parallel group made up of
three capacitors having ratings of 20 μf, 30 μf, and 5 μf, respectively? What
would be the total capacitance of a series group made up of these capacitors?

(**41-XII**) A laboratory capacitor is made up of four units arranged in a box,
as in Fig. 12.19, so that various capacitances may be obtained by inserting
plugs in positions A, B, C, . . . J. What capacitances are obtainable?
Capacitances are expressed in μf.

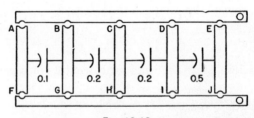

Fig. 12.19.

(**42-XII**) A 2-μf capacitor is charged from a 100-v source. It is then connected, without loss of charge, to an uncharged 5-μf capacitor. What will be
the final charge on each capacitor and the potential difference between their
terminals?

(**43-XII**) Calculate the energy stored in the 2-μf capacitor in Problem
42-XII before it is connected to the other capacitor. Calculate the total

energy stored in both capacitors after they are connected.   Account for any discrepancy.

(**44-XII**) A 2-μf capacitor and a 5-μf capacitor are connected in series and charged from a 500-v battery.   They are then disconnected from the battery and connected together, positive to positive and negative to negative.   What will be the final charge on each capacitor and the potential difference at their terminals?

(**45-XII**) A 2-μf capacitor and a 5-μf capacitor are connected in series and charged from a 500-v battery.   They are then disconnected from the battery and connected together, positive to negative and negative to positive.   What will be the final charge on each capacitor and the potential difference at their terminals?

(**46-XII**) A surge generator consists of fifty 0.5-μf capacitors which are charged in parallel to 50,000 v.   They are then reconnected in series and discharged.   What is the charge on each capacitor and the total charge?   What is the potential difference between terminals when the capacitors are reconnected in series?   What quantity of electricity is available on discharge?

(**47-XII**) Calculate the total energy stored in the capacitors in Problem 46-XII during the charging period.   Calculate the energy available on discharge.   Account for any discrepancy.

22. Charging a capacitor.   When a potential difference is applied to the terminals of a capacitor or to any conductors between which capacitance exists, electrons move as explained in Section 1 to charge the capacitor and establish at its terminals a potential difference equal to that applied.   If the charging circuit contained no resistance, the charge would be completed instantaneously, and motion of electrons would cease.   If, however, the charging circuit contains resistance, the rate at which charge can be transferred is limited, and electrons continue to move for an appreciable time before equilibrium is established.   The movement of electrons in the charging circuit constitutes a measurable current which flows while the charging continues.

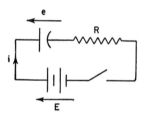

Fig. 12.20.   Capacitor charged through a resistance by a source of constant emf.

Suppose a capacitor of C farads capacitance is being charged from a battery of E volts as indicated in Fig. 12.20.   The circuit also contains a resistance of R ohms, as shown.   At the instant of closing the switch, there is no charge on the plates of the capacitor, and the current is limited only by the resistance of the circuit:

$$i = \frac{E}{R}. \tag{12.56}$$

Electrons are thus transferred from the left-hand plate through the battery and resistance to the right-hand plate, charging it negatively

and leaving the left-hand plate positive.   The accumulation of charge
on the plates establishes between them a potential difference

$$e = \frac{q}{C} \tag{12.57}$$

which opposes the emf of the battery and thus decreases the current.
If we apply Kirchhoff's voltage law to the circuit,

$$E - e = Ri. \tag{12.58}$$

Current is the time rate of transfer of charge and can be expressed as

$$I = \frac{\Delta Q}{\Delta T} \tag{12.59}$$

if average current for a period of time ΔT is wanted, or

$$i = \frac{dq}{dt} \tag{12.60}$$

if instantaneous current is wanted, as in this instance.   Substituting
in (12.58) the values of e and i from Equations (12.57) and (12.60),
we have

$$E - \frac{q}{C} = R\frac{dq}{dt}. \tag{12.61}$$

This is a differential equation which may be solved[1] to obtain an

[1] The solution of (12.61) may be carried out by various methods, one of which is
that of separating the variables.   By this method, (12.61) is first manipulated to
get it into the form

$$\frac{dq}{q - CE} = -\frac{dt}{RC} \tag{12.62}$$

Both sides of (12.62) are then integrated to obtain

$$\log_\epsilon (q - CE) = -\frac{t}{RC} + K, \tag{12.63}$$

or $\qquad q - CE = \epsilon^{\left(-\frac{t}{RC}+K\right)} = \epsilon^{-\frac{t}{RC}}\epsilon^K. \tag{12.64}$

To evaluate ϵ^K, we take advantage of the known fact that at the instant of closing
the switch $(t = 0)$, the charge on the plates is zero.   This gives

$$\epsilon^K = -CE, \tag{12.65}$$

which, substituted in (12.64), gives

$$q - CE = -CE\epsilon^{-\frac{t}{RC}}, \tag{12.66}$$

or $\qquad q = CE[1 - \epsilon^{-\frac{t}{RC}}]. \tag{12.67}$

expression for the charge on the plates of the capacitor at any time following the closing of the switch.   The solution is

$$q = CE[1 - \epsilon^{-\frac{t}{RC}}]. \tag{12.67}$$

Study of this equation shows that the charge does not increase instantaneously to its final value CE, but increases exponentially, as shown in Fig. 12.21, at a rate depending upon the capacitance and resistance of the circuit.   In a time t equal to RC seconds, called the **time constant** of the circuit, the charge will have reached 63.2 per

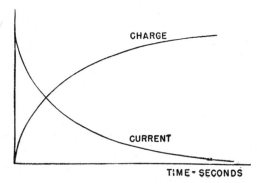

CHARGE

CURRENT

TIME - SECONDS

Fig. 12.21.   Graphs showing charge and current as functions of time-capacitor being charged through a resistance.

cent of its final value.   That this is so can be readily seen by putting $t = RC$ in Equation (12.67), which then becomes

$$q = CE[1 - \epsilon^{-1}] = 0.632CE. \tag{12.68}$$

Multiples of the time constant are always convenient instants at which to calculate the charge because they result in integers (1, 2, 3, 4, and so forth) for the exponent in Equation (12.67).

We can readily find the current, which is the rate at which charge is being transferred from one plate to the other, by going back to Equation (12.60).   Since

$$i = \frac{dq}{dt},$$

we may substitute for q the expression obtained above to obtain

$$i = \frac{d(CE[1 - \epsilon^{-\frac{t}{RC}}])}{dt}. \tag{12.69}$$

Upon carrying out the differentiation, we obtain

$$i = \frac{E}{R} \epsilon^{-\frac{t}{RC}}. \tag{12.70}$$

Study of this equation shows the current to be limited only by resistance at the instant the circuit is closed, and to decrease exponentially, as shown in Fig. 12.21, becoming less as the charge on the plates increases. The time constant $T = RC$ is a convenient value to use here also, since it gives integer values of the exponent.

EXAMPLE: A capacitor rated 0.1 μf is charged from a 100-v battery through a series resistance of 1000 ohms. Find (a) the time for the condenser to receive 63.2 per cent of its final charge, (b) the charge received in this time, (c) the initial rate of charging, and (d) the rate of charging when the charge is 63.2 per cent completed.

SOLUTION: (a) The time to receive 63.2 per cent of the final charge is the time constant

$$T = RC$$
$$= (1000)10^{-7} = 10^{-4} \text{ sec.}$$

(b) The charge is found from Equation (12.67).

$$q = EC[1 - \epsilon^{-\frac{t}{RC}}]$$
$$= (100)(10^{-7})[1 - \epsilon^{-1}] = 0.632 \times 10^{-5} \text{ coulomb.}$$

(c) The initial rate of charging is found from Equation (12.70):

$$i = \frac{E}{R} \epsilon^{-\frac{t}{RC}}.$$

When $t = 0$, $\epsilon^{-\frac{t}{RC}} = 1$ and

$$i = \frac{E}{R} = \frac{100}{1000} = 0.1 \text{ amp.}$$

(d) The rate of charging when the charge is 63.2 per cent is

$$i = \frac{E}{R} \epsilon^{-1} = \frac{100}{1000} 0.368 = 0.0368 \text{ amp.}$$

Problems

(**48-XII**) A 1-μf capacitor is connected in series with a 1-megohm resistor and charged from a 100-v battery. (a) Find the time constant of the circuit. (b) Find the charge on the capacitor at times equal to 1, 2, 3, 4, and 5 times the time constant, and plot charge against time. (c) Find the initial rate of charging and rate of charging for times equal to 1, 2, 3, 4, and 5 times the time constant, and plot rate of charge against time.

(**49-XII**) A 0.002-μf capacitor is connected in series with a 50-ohm resistor and charged from a 100-v battery. Calculate (a) initial rate of charging, (b) time constant, (c) charging rate at a time equal to the time constant, and (d) charge at a time equal to the time constant.

23. Capacitance in alternating current circuits—Reactance. If a capacitor is connected to a source of alternating potential difference, as shown in Fig. 12.22, the charge on its plates must be continually changing in order that it may be proportional at every instant to the potential difference. The relation

$$q = Ce \qquad (12.21)$$

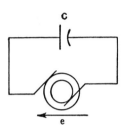

must be satisfied at all times. This requires that current flow through the connecting wires in order that electrons may be shifted from one plate to the other as required by the changing potential difference. Then, since

Fig. 12.22. Capacitor connected to a source of alternating emf.

$$i = \frac{dq}{dt}, \qquad (12.60)$$

substituting gives

$$i = C\frac{de}{dt}. \qquad (12.71)$$

The current at any instant is proportional to the rate of change of voltage at that instant.

Now, if e varies sinusoidally according to the equation

$$e = E_{max} \sin \omega t, \qquad (12.72)$$

the equation of the current can be found by substituting (12.72) in (12.71) and performing the differentiation as indicated:

$$i = C\frac{d[E_{max} \sin \omega t]}{dt} \qquad (12.73)$$

$$= \omega C E_{max} \cos \omega t. \qquad (12.74)$$

The maximum value of current will occur when $\cos \omega t = 1$, and its value will be

$$I_{max} = \omega C E_{max}. \qquad (12.75)$$

From this expression, it can be seen that

$$\frac{E_{effective}}{I_{effective}} = \frac{E_{max}}{I_{max}} = \frac{1}{\omega C}. \qquad (12.76)$$

The quantity $1/\omega C$ is thus seen to be dimensionally the same as resistance, since it is the ratio of voltage to current. It is called **capacitive reactance.**

The symbol for capacitive reactance is X_c, and it is defined by the equation

$$X_c = \frac{1}{\omega C} = \frac{1}{2\pi f C},$$
(12.77)

where X_c is capacitive reactance in ohms.

f is frequency in cycles per second.

C is capacitance in farads.

The student should carefully compare Equation (12.77) with Equation (11.56) in Chapter XI. He will see at once that whereas inductive reactance increases with frequency, capacitive reactance becomes *less* as frequency is increased. The reactance of a capacitor is infinity for direct current and decreases with increasing frequency to very small values at high frequency. This suggests one purpose for which a capacitor can be used: if it is desired to prevent the flow of direct current in a certain branch of a network, and at the same time allow alternating current to flow, a capacitor should be inserted in the branch. A capacitor so used is called a **blocking condenser.**

The fact that capacitive reactance and inductive reactance behave in inverse manner with change of frequency is the basis of the phenomena of resonance and tuned circuits, upon which depend the arts of radio and communication engineering generally. These phenomena form an important part of any course in alternating current circuits.

Example: What is the reactance of a 1-μf capacitor at a frequency of 60 cycles per sec?

Solution:

$$X_c = \frac{1}{2\pi f C} = \frac{1}{2\pi \times 60 \times 10^{-6}} = 2660 \text{ ohms.}$$

24. Displacement current. The idea introduced in this chapter of current flowing in a circuit that is apparently incomplete will seem at first to be contradictory to what was said in the beginning chapters of this book. We have learned to think of current as flowing only in complete circuits, and as being the same in all parts of a series circuit. This is fundamentally correct, and instead of having to change our ideas about the continuity of current, what we need to do is to form a somewhat broader conception of what current is. Thus far, we have thought of current strictly in terms of moving electrons. From this limited viewpoint, we would be forced to say that, in the circuit in Fig. 12.1, current flows only as far as plate A; then there is a space between plate A and plate B where no current flows; and then from plate B the flow of current commences again.   This is correct if we restrict ourselves to conduction current—the current accounted for by the motion of electrons.   But if we define current as that which produces a magnetic field, then we may say that current flows in every part of the circuit in Fig. 12.1, because experiment shows that the part between plate A and plate B is as effective in producing a magnetic field as any other.

Although we have no free charges moving between the plates, we have or may have a changing electric field that is magnetically the equivalent of current.   It is termed **displacement current** and may readily be expressed by Equation (12.60):

$$i = \frac{dq}{dt} = \frac{d\psi}{dt}$$

or by Equation (12.71):

$$i = C\frac{de}{dt}$$

or in the alternating current case, by Equation (12.75):

$$I_{max} = \omega C E_{max}$$

or
$$I_{effective} = \omega C E_{effective}.$$

EXAMPLE 1: What is the displacement current in a 1-μf capacitor when the voltage is changing at the rate of 10,000 v per sec?
SOLUTION: From Equation (12.71),

$$I = (10^{-6})(10,000) = 10^{-2} \text{ amp.}$$

EXAMPLE 2: What is the effective value of the displacement current when an alternating voltage of 100 v at a frequency of 60 cycles per sec is applied to a 1-μf capacitor?
SOLUTION: From Equation (12.75),

$$I_{eff} = (2\pi \times 60)(10^{-6})(100) = 0.0377 \text{ amp.}$$

Problems

(50-XII) What is the reactance of a 0.001-μf capacitor at a frequency of (a) 0 cycles per sec (direct current)? (b) 1000 cycles per sec? (c) 10^6 cycles per sec? (d) 10^9 cycles per sec?

(51-XII) What is the effective value of the displacement current from one wire to the other when the two wires of the line described in Problem 25-XII are operated at an alternating voltage of 2300 v and a frequency of 60 cycles per sec?

Study Questions

1. What limits the quantity of electricity that can be transferred from one body to another?

2. Sketch the electric field in the vicinity of two parallel wires both positively charged.

3. It is a well-established fact that there is no electric field inside a charged hollow conductor, such as a sphere. Explain.

4. The definition of unit electric field intensity mentions a "1-coulomb test charge." Is such a charge practical? Why?

5. In Fig. 12.3, the work done in moving a test charge from the negative plate to the positive plate is independent of the path taken. Why is this so?

6. In Fig. 12.3, how much work would be done in moving a test charge of 10^{-8} coulomb once around a 5 cm by 5 cm square which lies entirely within the field and in a plane perpendicular to the plates, and which has two of its sides parallel to the plates. Take the electric field intensity as 10^{-4} newtons per coulomb.

7. In Fig. 12.3, how much work would be done in moving a test charge of 10^{-8} coulomb once around a 5 cm by 5 cm square which lies entirely within the field and in a plane parallel to the plates. Take the electric field intensity as 10^{-4} newtons per coulomb.

8. Are the algebraic signs in equations (12.5) and (12.30) consistent with our definitions of E and V? Would it be correct to write $\mathcal{E} = E/S$?

9. In an arrangement like that shown in Fig. 12.5 what would happen if the metal rod were removed (still insulated) from between the plates? What would happen if the metal rod were allowed to touch the positive plate momentarily and then were removed (still insulated) from between the plates?

10. The lines of the electric field in the vicinity of a 2-wire line carrying current are ordinarily thought of as originating on the positive wire, terminating on the negative wire, and lying in planes perpendicular to the line. Is this strictly correct? Why?

11. A capacitor with solid dielectric is charged to rated voltage and then discharged by short-circuiting its terminal momentarily. After a few seconds, the terminals are again short-circuited and a second discharge occurs. Explain.

12. Oil-insulated power cables, utilizing oil under pressure, are being specified for some purposes in preference to cables using solid insulation. What advantages can be claimed for the oil-insulated cable?

13. In what ways do lines of electric flux differ from lines of magnetic flux?

14. In Art 10, certain experiments designed to bring out the distinction between electric flux density and electric field intensity are described. Can you suggest parallel experiments to bring out the distinction between magnetic flux density and magnetic field intensity?

15. By means of dimensional analysis show that

$$D = M^{1/2}L^{-3/2}\mu^{-1/2}.$$

16. By means of dimensional analysis show that

$$\mathcal{E} = M^{1/2}L^{1/2}\mu^{1/2}T^{-2}.$$

17. By means of dimensional analysis show that

$$\frac{1}{\sqrt{\mu\epsilon}} = \text{velocity.}$$

18. An electrical worker, thinking to insulate better a part of an electrical machine, adds a layer of a different insulating material to that called for in the specifications. Is there any possibility that by doing this he may make breakdown of the insulation more likely? Explain.

19. An average electric field intensity of about 100 v per m is found to exist at the earth's surface, presumably because the earth itself carries a negative charge. What charge uniformly distributed over the earth's surface would give rise to this value of electric field intensity?

20. In the telephone industry, many long-distance circuits which were originally open-wire lines have been replaced by cables. What effect has this had upon the capacitance of such circuits?

21. Derive the expression for the capacitance per unit length of a coaxial conductor, the inner conductor of which has a diameter of d m, and the outer conductor an inside diameter of D m.

22. Discuss the practicability of storing in capacitors sufficient amounts of electrical energy to operate a lamp or lamps during an emergency. Make calculations to show the proposition is or is not feasible.

23. In one particular catalog, a capacitor rated 100 μf, 25 v direct current is listed for $0.74. However, a capacitor rated 1 μf, 2500 v direct current is listed for $7.06. Explain this apparent discrepancy in prices.

24. In designing a certain control circuit it is desired to have a certain 0.01-μf capacitor take 95 per cent of its final charge in 1/500 sec, following the application of a direct current voltage to its terminals. How can this be accomplished?

25. For what frequency is the reactance of a 1-μf capacitor numerically equal to the reactance of a coil having a self-inductance of 1 henry?

CHAPTER XIII

ELECTROCHEMISTRY

1. Conduction of electricity in liquids. Pure liquids, as a rule, are not conductors of electricity. Some liquids, such as mineral oils, are excellent nonconductors, or **insulators,** having resistivities as high as 10^{11} ohm-meters. Pure water is an extremely poor conductor, the conductivity of tap water being due to impurities which are always present. Mercury is, of course, a good conductor, as are all metals, even when melted. The most important liquid conductors,

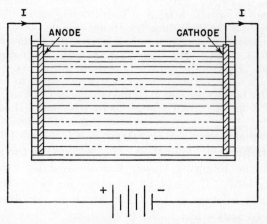

Fig. 13.1. Conduction of electricity through a liquid.

however, are solutions of substances known as **electrolytes.** If a salt, such as copper sulphate, be dissolved in water, it becomes possible to pass a current through the solution from one metal plate to another, as shown in Fig. 13.1. The plates are known as **electrodes;** the one by which the current enters the solution being called the **anode** and the one by which the current leaves the solution, the **cathode.** If these plates are copper and the electrolyte is copper sulphate, it is found that as conduction proceeds, the cathode gains weight but that the anode loses weight in equal amount. The gain in weight at the cathode is found to be due to the deposition on it of pure copper, and to be proportional to the quantity of electricity that has been passed through the solution. From these facts, it appears that particles of copper are, in effect, traveling through the solution, and that these same particles are the carriers of the electric current. Conduction of electricity in an electrolyte, with the attendant results, is called **electrolysis.**

If we use silver nitrate in the solution and silver plates as the electrodes, we again find a transfer of metal from one plate to the other that is proportional to the quantity of electricity. We also find (1) in both instances the plate that gains is the cathode, or the one by which the current leaves the solution and (2) if equal quantities of electricity are passed through the two cells, the mass of the metal deposited is directly proportional to its atomic weight and inversely proportional to its valence.

If we use a dilute solution of sulphuric acid and platinum electrodes, we find that at the cathode, hydrogen gas is liberated but that at the electrode by which the current enters, oxygen is set free. In this case, there is no gain or loss of mass of the electrodes, and we are apparently decomposing the water into its constituents. The same quantitative relations observed above, however, are found to hold in this case also. They are **Faraday's laws of electrolysis** and are here restated for reference:

1. *The mass of a substance liberated or deposited varies directly as the quantity of electricity.*

2. *The mass of substance liberated or deposited varies directly as its atomic weight and inversely as its valence.*

2. Dissociation and conduction. To account for the conductivity of solutions, the following theory was devised by Svante August Arrhenius in 1887. If a salt be dissolved in water, the molecules do not go into solution as such, but break up, or **dissociate,** into particles called **ions** which differ from atoms in that they are electrically charged.

It will be remembered from chemistry that a stable chemical compound is formed when an element such as sodium, which has one or more readily detached orbital electrons, or **valence** electrons, is combined with an element such as chlorine that needs one or more electrons to fill its orbits. When such a compound is put into solution, the electric forces which hold its parts together are weakened owing to the high permittivity of the water, and it breaks up. The chlorine takes with it the electron which normally belonged to the univalent sodium atom:

$$NaCl \rightarrow Na^+ + Cl^-. \qquad (13.1)$$

Atomic groups or radicals, such as SO_4 and NO_3, dissociate as negatively charged ions, as

$$CuSO_4 \rightarrow Cu^{++} + SO_4^{--}. \tag{13.2}$$

In general any acid, base, or salt is an electrolyte. The metals and hydrogen dissociate as positive ions, and the nonmetals and radicals, as negative ions.

$$H_2SO_4 \rightarrow H^+ + H^+ + SO_4^{--}. \tag{13.3}$$
$$NaOH \rightarrow Na^+ + OH^-. \tag{13.4}$$

There is considerable difference in the extent to which dissociation takes place in different compounds. In some, such as HCl, KOH and KCl, ionization in 0.1 normal solutions is practically 100 per cent. In others, such as acetic acid and boric acid, ionization at this concentration is a fraction of 1 per cent. Dissociation is always greatest at small concentrations, the percentage of molecules which are dissociated becoming less as concentration is increased. Even pure water ionizes very slightly,

$$H_2O \rightarrow H^+ + OH^-, \tag{13.5}$$

and thus becomes a conductor to a small extent.

The phenomenon of dissociation is also encountered in melted salts. Thus, melted NaCl is a conductor, as is melted Al_2O_3, and several important electrochemical processes depend upon sending current through salts or ores in the molten state.

When an electric field of intensity ε volts per meter is established between two electrodes in a solution of an electrolyte or in an electrolyte in the molten state, the ions of both signs are acted upon by electric forces, according to the equation

$$F = \varepsilon Q, \tag{12.1}$$

where F is the force in newtons.

Q is the charge on an ion in coulombs.
The ions are caused to drift through the liquid—the positive ions toward the cathode and the negative ions toward the anode as shown in Fig. 13.2.

The positive ions, upon arrival at the cathode, take up sufficient electrons from the cathode to become neutral atoms which may stick to the cathode, pass off as a gas, fall to the bottom of the container as sludge, or enter into secondary chemical reactions, depending upon the particular conditions that exist in the cell. The negative ions, upon arrival at the anode, give up their excess electrons, becoming neutral atoms or atom groups. The electrons given up at the anode move through the external circuit to the cathode where they are available to neutralize the positive ions arriving there.

The current is thus seen to be carried within the electrolyte by ions, and in the external circuit, by electrons.   The rate of transfer of charge across any boundary in the circuit must be the same; the net charge carried by positive ions and negative ions across a boundary surface set up midway between the electrodes must equal the net charge carried by electrons past a point on the external circuit in the same time.

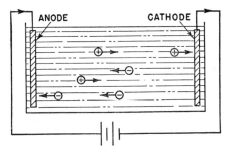

Fig. 13.2.   Moving ions in a solution conducting electricity.

3. Deduction of Faraday's laws.   The theory of dissociation and conduction stated above leads logically to **Faraday's laws.**   This may be shown as follows:

Let n = number of ions arriving at an electrode per second.

w = atomic weight of the substance liberated or deposited.

a = mass in grams of an atom having unit atomic weight.

m = mass of substance liberated or deposited (grams per sec).

Then

$$m = awn. \qquad (13.6)$$

Let q = quantity of electricity in coulombs that passes through the cell per sec.

v = valence = number of electrons each ion has in excess or deficiency of normal atom.

e = charge in coulombs of an electron.

Then,

$$q = nve. \qquad (13.7)$$

Solving (13.7) for n and substituting in (13.6),

$$m = \frac{awq}{ve}. \qquad (13.8)$$

From (13.8), it is obvious that m is proportional to q (**Faraday's first law**) and that m is proportional to w/v (**Faraday's second law**).

The quantity a/e is a constant, which repeated experiments have shown to be equal to $1/96{,}485$. Thus, we may write

$$m = \frac{1}{96{,}485} \frac{wq}{v}. \tag{13.9}$$

From this it can be seen that a quantity of electricity equal to 96,485 coulombs would liberate or deposit a number of grams of a substance equal to its atomic weight divided by its valence. This quantity of electricity is called **1 faraday**. For practical calculations, Equation (13.9) is a most useful relationship. It enables us to determine the mass of a certain substance that will be liberated, deposited, or consumed in a given electrochemical process by the passage of a given quantity of electricity.

EXAMPLE: Copper is being deposited upon the cathode of a Cu-$CuSO_4$-Cu cell by a current of 1000 amp. How much copper is deposited in 24 hr?

SOLUTION: The ion in which we are interested here is Cu^{++}, with an atomic weight of 63.57 and a valence of 2. Hence,

$$m = \frac{1}{96{,}485} \frac{63.57}{2} (1000 \times 24 \times 3600)$$
$$= 28{,}450 \text{ g.}$$

Problems

(**1-XIII**) If the potential difference at the terminals of the cell in the foregoing example is 0.25 v, and electrical energy costs 1 cent per kwhr, what is the cost per pound of depositing copper?

(**2-XIII**) How much silver would be deposited in 24 hr by a current of 1000 amp from an $AgNO_3$ solution? (Atomic weight of silver is 107.88, valence 1.)

(**3-XIII**) If the potential difference at the terminals of the cell in Problem 2-XIII is 3 v and the cost of electrical energy is 1 cent per kwhr, what is the cost per pound of depositing silver?

4. Digression upon the ratio a/e. Not only is Equation (13.9) useful for practical electrochemical calculations, but the fact that a/e is found to be a constant equal to $1/96{,}485$ suggests an interesting possibility. If we know e, the charge on an electron in coulombs, we may find a, the mass in grams of an atom having unit atomic weight. Millikan's experiments showed e to be 1.60×10^{-19}; consequently,

$$a = \frac{1.60 \times 10^{-19}}{96{,}485} = 1.66 \times 10^{-24} \text{ g.} \tag{13.10}$$

Since the atomic weight of hydrogen is 1.008, the above calculation gives approximately the mass in grams of the hydrogen atom. The mass in grams of any atom could be found by multiplying its atomic weight by 1.66×10^{-24}. Furthermore, $1/a$ gives the number of atoms in 1 gram of a substance having unit atomic weight, or the number of atoms in 1 g-atom of a substance of any atomic weight, or the number of molecules in 1 g-molecule of a compound of any molecular weight. This number, which comes out 6.02×10^{23}, is **Avogadro's number.** If, instead of taking the electronic charge as known, we had begun with Avogadro's number, we could have used our experimentally determined value of a/e to find the charge on an electron.

EXAMPLE: What is the mass of an atom of chlorine? Of a molecule of KCl? How many molecules of KCl in 74.55 g?

SOLUTION: The mass of an atom of Cl is its atomic weight multiplied by a, the mass of an atom of unit atomic weight:

$$m = 35.46 \times 1.66 \times 10^{-24} = 58.8 \times 10^{-24} \text{ g.}$$

The mass of a molecule of KCl is its molecular weight multiplied by a:

$$m = (39.09 + 35.46)1.66 \times 10^{-24} = 124 \times 10^{-24} \text{ g.}$$

Since 74.55 is the molecular weight of KCl, this number of grams will contain 6.02×10^{23} molecules (Avogadro's number).

Problems

(**4-XIII**) What is the mass in grams of a copper atom? How many atoms are there in a cubic centimeter of copper? Atomic weight of copper is 63.57, valence 2, and density 8.89 g per cu cm.

(**5-XIII**) Using the results of Problem 4-XIII, determine the number of atoms per centimeter in No. 10 copper wire. On the assumption that there is 1 free electron per atom, determine the electron velocity in No. 10 copper wire carrying a current of 25 amp.

5. Velocity of the ions in electrolytes. Since we are able to determine the number of molecules in a given quantity of any salt and since we are also able to determine what percentage of the molecules ionize when the salt is put into solution at a given concentration, we can find the number of ions present in a given solution. Then, assuming that all the ions are active in carrying charge, we can find the velocity with which they move.

Consider a box-like container, as shown in Fig. 13.3, L meters long and with the ends formed by the two electrodes. Let this container be filled with a solution that, to begin with, contains Z pairs of ions, and suppose that both positive ions and negative ions move with a velocity of u meters per second. Let the charge on each ion be *ve* coulombs. In a time

$$t = \frac{L}{u} \tag{13.11}$$

every ion present in the solution to begin with will have reached one electrode or the other. The quantity of electricity passed through the cell will be

$$q = it = Zve, \tag{13.12}$$

from which

$$t = \frac{Zve}{i}. \tag{13.13}$$

Equating (13.11) and (13.13) and solving for *u*, we obtain

$$u = \frac{Li}{Zve}. \tag{13.14}$$

In cases where the velocity of the positive ion is not equal to the velocity of the negative ion, as assumed here, the derivation is more complicated.

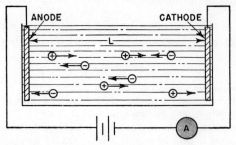

Fig. 13.3. Determination of the velocity of the ions.

The velocity determined by Equation (13.14) corresponds to a certain electric field intensity ε volts per meter in the solution. If we assume the velocity to be directly proportional to field intensity, we can, in any particular case, find what the velocity would have been if the field intensity had been 100 v per m (1 v per cm). This velocity, expressed in centimeters per second, is called the **mobility** of the ions.

$$\text{Mobility} = \frac{u}{\varepsilon} \, 10^4, \tag{13.15}$$

where *u* is velocity of the ions in meters per second as determined from Equation (13.14).

ε is electric field intensity in volts per meter, corresponding to calculated *u*.

EXAMPLE: A liter of 0.1-normal KCl solution is contained in a glass trough 5 by 10 by 40 cm. At each end is an electrode in the form of a flat, silver plate 5 by 10 cm. When a potential difference of 100 v is established between the electrodes, a current of 0.347 amp flows. Calculate the velocity of the ions on the assumption that the positive ions and the negative ions have equal velocities (substantially correct in this case). Calculate the mobility of the ions.

SOLUTION: A liter of 0.1-normal KCl solution will contain 0.1 g-molecule of KCl. This is 7.455 g, and the number of molecules is

$$0.1 \times 6.02 \times 10^{23} = 6.02 \times 10^{22}.$$

Assuming that ionization is 100 per cent, Z, the number of ion pairs present to begin with, is 6.02×10^{22}. The charge ve on each ion is 1.6×10^{-19} coulomb. The velocity is then found as

$$u = \frac{0.4 \times 0.347}{(6.02 \times 10^{22})(1.60 \times 10^{-19})} = 1.44 \times 10^{-5} \text{ m per sec}$$
$$= 0.00144 \text{ cm per sec.}$$

The mobility of the ions is

$$m = \frac{1.44 \times 10^{-5}}{\dfrac{100}{0.4}} \times 10^4 = 0.576 \times 10^{-3}.$$

6. Conductivity of solutions. The resistance of a conducting path through a solution may be measured between two electrodes immersed in it. Such measurements are most often made by a Wheatstone bridge method. Two difficulties present themselves: (1) The shape of the container and of the electrodes may be such as to make it difficult to determine the length and cross-sectional area of the conducting path used. (2) Chemical reactions at the electrodes cause emf's to be set up within the cell (Section 7) which obscure the effect of resistance. The first difficulty is obviated by using an apparatus especially designed for the purpose. Such an apparatus, known as a **conductivity cell,** is shown in Fig. 13.4. The effect of emf's set up at the electrodes is eliminated by using an alternating emf in place of a battery. The galvanometer is replaced by a telephone receiver, and balance is achieved by adjusting the bridge arms until no tone is heard in the receiver.

The measurements must usually be reduced to resistivity or conductivity for purposes of comparison. Several conclusions may be drawn from a study of the data. First, the resistivities of electrolytes are always many thousand times as great as the resistivity of metal conductors. Resistivities of electrolytes are of the order of 1 to 1000 *ohms* per cu cm where metals show resistivities of 1 to 100 *microhms* per cu cm. For a given temperature and concentration, the current through an electrolyte is found to be proportional to the potential difference applied to the electrodes. In other words, Ohm's law applies to electrolytes.

The resistance is found to decrease rapidly with increasing temperature, which is directly opposite to the behavior of metal conductors. The resistance may change by as much as 2 per cent for a temperature change of 1° C.

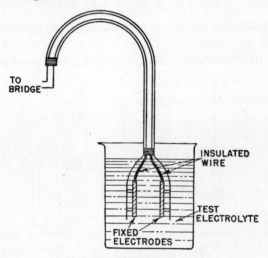

Fig. 13.4. Conductivity cell.

In very dilute solutions, it is found that the conductivity increases directly as the concentration. As the concentration is increased, the rate of increase of conductivity becomes less, and at very high concentrations, the conductivity decreases.

Problems

(**6-XIII**) What is the conductivity of the 0.1-normal KCl solution in the example at the end of Section 5?

(**7-XIII**) The mobility of the ions in 3-normal KCl solution may be taken as 0.45×10^{-3}. Using this value, calculate the current that would have flowed in the trough in the example at the end of Section 5 had it contained a liter of 3-normal KCl solution.

(**8-XIII**) Derive an expression for the conductivity of a solution in terms of number of ion pairs per cubic centimeter, mobility of the ions, and charge on each ion. (Assume the same mobility for positive ions and negative ions.) Explain the variation of conductivity with concentration on the basis of the expression obtained.

7. Potential difference between an electrode immersed in a solution and the solution. Whenever a metal electrode is immersed in a solution of an electrolyte, a potential difference is established between the electrode and the solution. This potential difference is explainable in terms of certain forces, or pressures, that are not electrical in nature. The molecules of any metal tend to go into solution as positive ions, this tendency being known as **solution pressure.** On the other hand, the positive ions in the solution tend to be forced into the metal by **osmotic pressure.** The relative values of solution and osmotic pressure vary from one metal to another. In the case of zinc, for example, the solution pressure is the greater, and positive ions are forced into the solution. As positive ions leave

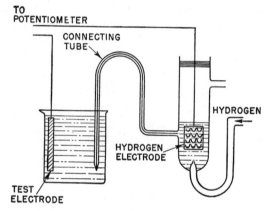

Fig. 13.5.   Standard hydrogen electrode.

the zinc, it acquires a negative charge, but the layer of solution immediately surrounding the zinc is positively charged. Thus, there is a difference of potential existing between the two surfaces, which may be regarded as separated by a distance of the order of one molecular diameter. Ions continue to be forced into the solution until the potential difference reaches such a value that equilibrium is brought about between the solution pressure, on the one hand, and the osmotic pressure plus the forces of electrical attraction, on the other hand.

If the immersed substance be a metal such as copper, the osmotic pressure exceeds the solution pressure, and positive ions are forced from the solution into the electrode, charging it positive and leaving the solution immediately around the electrode with a negative charge. Equilibrium is established when enough ions have been forced in to make the sum of the solution pressure and the electrical forces of attraction equal to osmotic pressure.

In order to measure the potential difference between the solution and an electrode, it is necessary to make contact with the solution with some sort of auxiliary electrode. But there must necessarily be a potential difference developed between the solution and the auxiliary electrode, and what is measured is, therefore, the algebraic sum of the two individual potential differences. For purposes of standardization, an electrode of hydrogen (formed by occluded hydrogen in a layer of platinum black deposited on platinum) shown in Fig. 13.5 is often used as the auxiliary electrode. By measuring the potential differences between a hydrogen electrode and electrodes of various metals, it is possible to make up a useful table from which the potential difference for any given combination may be found. The potential difference between the hydrogen electrode and the solution is arbitrarily taken as zero, and the table is based on each electrode being immersed in a normal solution of one of its own salts in which the valence of the elements is as shown in the table.

TABLE VII

ELECTRODE POTENTIAL DIFFERENCES

Sodium	−2.70	Lead (2)	−0.13
Magnesium	−1.86	Hydrogen	0.00
Aluminum	−1.34	Bismuth	+0.20
Zinc	−0.76	Copper (2)	+0.34
Iron (2)	−0.43	Mercury (1)	+0.80
Nickel (2)	−0.23	Silver	+0.80
Tin (2)	−0.14	Gold (1)	+1.5

For instance, if we make up a cell in which a zinc electrode is immersed in $ZnSO_4$ solution and a copper electrode is immersed in $CuSO_4$ solution, the two solutions being separated and prevented from mixing by a porous wall, the emf of such a cell would be $0.34 - (-0.76) = 1.1$ v.

A study of Table VII will show that the elements are arranged in the same order as in a chemical-displacement series, or activity series, with the most active element first. Much valuable information is contained in the series. If any element which precedes hydrogen in the series is immersed in an acid electrolyte, ions of the metal will replace hydrogen ions in the solution. Thus, zinc immersed in H_2SO_4 will replace H^+ ions in the solution with the formation of $ZnSO_4$. Furthermore, if any element in the series is immersed in a solution of a salt of a metal which follows it, its ions will replace those of the metal in solution. Iron immersed in $CuSO_4$ will be instantly covered with a layer of displaced copper ions.

If it were desired to deposit iron upon copper, however, it would be necessary to establish a potential difference of $0.34 - (-0.43)$ $= 0.77$ v between the copper surface and the Fe^{++} ions in the solution in order that they might move against the solution pressure. If there were also present in the solution ions of another metal such as nickel, they would be deposited when a potential difference of only $0.34 - (-0.23) = 0.57$ v existed between the copper surface and the solution. The Ni^{++} ions are, therefore, deposited more easily than the Fe^{++} ions, and it would not be possible to deposit iron without depositing nickel also. On the other hand, if it were desired to deposit nickel, not iron, from a solution containing both ions, this could be done by properly adjusting the applied potential difference. Since hydrogen ions are always present in an acid solution, it will be impossible to deposit a metal standing before hydrogen in the series, without depositing hydrogen also.

Problems

(**9-XIII**) What metals from Table VII should be used as the electrodes of a primary cell to obtain the greatest possible emf? Would such a cell be practicable? Why?

(**10-XIII**) Electrochemical cells are set up using (a) zinc and lead electrodes, (b) copper and silver electrodes, and (c) tin and bismuth electrodes. Each electrode is immersed in a solution of one of its own salts. The solutions are separated by porous cups. What is the emf of each cell? Which is the positive electrode?

(**11-XIII**) The electrodes of a certain cell are copper and iron, respectively, and the electrolyte contains both Cu^{++} and Fe^{++} ions. What action would take place with (a) no connections to the electrodes, (b) the electrodes connected externally by a short piece of wire, (c) a battery with an emf of 0.77 v connected to the electrodes, positive to copper, and (d) a battery with an emf of 0.77 v connected to the electrodes, positive to iron?

8. Theory of a simple cell. Let us consider the Zn-HCl-Cu cell shown in Fig. 13.6. As explained in the preceding section, solution pressure forces Zn^{++} ions out of the zinc electrode into the surrounding solution until equilibrium is attained between solution pressure on the one hand and osmotic pressure plus electric forces of attraction on the other hand.[1] At the copper electrode, osmotic pressure forces H^{+} ions onto the surface until equilibrium is reached between osmotic pressure on the one hand and solution pressure plus electric forces of repulsion on the other hand. The equilibrium difference of potential between the electrodes will be approximately 1.1 v, as determined from Table VII.

---

[1] This equilibrium is not readily attained in practice because of local action due to impure zinc and agitation of the solution by displaced hydrogen ions.

Now, suppose the switch is closed to complete the external circuit between the electrodes. Electrons move through this circuit from the zinc electrode to the copper, seeking to equalize the potential difference. But this loss of negative charge by the zinc electrode upsets the equilibrium which existed there, and permits the solution pressure to force more Zn^{++} ions into solution. Likewise, the equilibrium at the copper electrode is upset by the arrival of electrons through the external circuit, and the osmotic pressure is able to force more H^+ ions onto the electrode. Within the cell, there are thus two streams of ions: Z^{++} and H^+ ions toward the cathode (copper), and Cl^- ions toward the anode (zinc). These streams of ions must transfer charge from one electrode to the other within the cell at exactly the same rate as it is transferred through the external circuit by free electrons.

Obviously, the flow of current through the resistance of the external circuit involves the expenditure of energy at a rate equal to I^2R joules per second. This energy must come from the chemical reaction within the cell—the reaction whereby zinc is converted into zinc chloride. If this reaction took place in a test tube, all of the energy involved would appear as heat. By having it take place in an electrochemical cell, a substantial part of it becomes available as electrical energy.

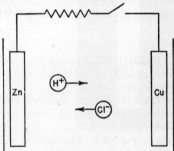

Fig. 13.6. Simple Zn-HCl-Cu primary cell.

Faraday's laws of electrolysis apply to cells of this kind and Equation (13.9) may be used to determine the quantity of electricity available from the conversion of a given quantity of zinc. The product of this quantity of electricity by the terminal voltage of the cell can then be taken to find the energy available from the given quantity of zinc.

EXAMPLE: The terminal voltage of a Zn-HCl-Cu cell when delivering a current of 0.1 amp is found to be 0.7 v. How much electrical energy is available from such a cell per gram of zinc consumed?

SOLUTION: Ey Equation (13.9), the quantity of electricity per gram of zinc is

$$q = \frac{(1)(96500)(2)}{65.38} = 2950 \text{ coulombs.}$$

The energy is, therefore,

$$W = 2950 \times 0.7 = 2060 \text{ joules per g of zinc.}$$

9. Practical primary cells. The simple Zn-HCl-Cu cell just described is not suitable for practical use. The reason is brought out in the example at the end of the preceding section: the figures quoted there are typical of such cells. When delivering a rather small current (0.1 amp), the terminal voltage falls from the open-circuit value of 1.1 v to 0.7 v. This decrease in voltage is due to **polarization** and high internal resistance. Polarization, as used in connection with primary cells, refers to the effective coating of the cathode with hydrogen ions, thereby making it virtually a hydrogen electrode. Thus, our cell becomes in effect a Zn-HCl-H cell. The gas coating of the cathode also has the effect of so raising the internal resistance of the cell that it becomes incapable of delivering any considerable current, even if short-circuited. Obviously, in a practical cell, means must be found to minimize the effect of polarization and to limit internal resistance to a small value. Also, the cell must be portable and must not be subject to evaporation.

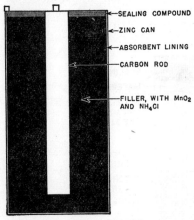

SEALING COMPOUND
ZINC CAN
ABSORBENT LINING
CARBON ROD
FILLER, WITH MnO_2 AND NH_4Cl

Fig. 13.7.   Dry cell.

At present, only two primary cells are of any practical importance. One of these is the familiar "dry cell" shown in Fig. 13.7. The container, which also serves as the anode, is a zinc can lined with absorbent material which is saturated with the electrolyte, ammonium chloride. The cathode is a central rod of carbon, and the space between the cathode and the can is packed with a mixture of powdered coke, graphite, and manganese dioxide (MnO_2). The mixture is also saturated with the electrolyte and the can is sealed to prevent evaporation and facilitate handling.

The main chemical reaction in a dry cell is represented by the equation

$$Zn + 2NH_4Cl \rightarrow ZnCl_2 + 2NH_4. \qquad (13.16)$$

The energy supplied to the circuit comes from this reaction. The purpose of the manganese dioxide in the cell is to combine with NH_4 according to the equation

$$MnO_2 + NH_4 + 2H_2O \rightarrow NH_4OH + Mn(OH)_3. \qquad (13.17)$$

Otherwise, the NH_4 would combine with water to form NH_3OH and hydrogen, with consequent polarization at the carbon electrode. The MnO_2 is, therefore, a depolarizing agent. If the cell is made to deliver considerable current for a time, the depolarizing reaction may not occur fast enough to prevent the formation of hydrogen. This causes a sharp rise in the internal resistance of the cell. If the current is discontinued, however, and the cell is allowed a recuperation period, the internal resistance returns to its normal value.

The useful life of a dry cell is usually ended either by the zinc container being consumed (partly by local action which goes on regardless of the use of the cell) or by evaporation and consequent rise of internal resistance. Even a "dead" dry cell may show normal

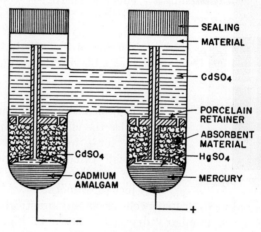

Fig. 13.8. Standard cell.

emf at open circuit; consequently, the best test of condition is to measure the current the cell will deliver at short circuit. A new No. 6 dry cell (the usual size) has a normal emf of about 1.5 v and an internal resistance of about 0.05 ohm.

The only other primary cell of importance is the Weston standard cell. This cell is used solely as a reference standard of potential difference. Carefully made of chemically pure materials and sealed into an H-shaped glass container, as shown in Fig. 13.8, it maintains its emf of 1.0183 v indefinitely, provided it is properly used. It is intended to be used only in connection with a potentiometer, and with a protective resistance in series, so that no current exceeding a few microamperes ever flows through it. To attempt to check the emf of such a cell with a voltmeter, for instance, would render it useless as a standard.

Problems

(**12-XIII**) The zinc can of a certain dry cell weighs 4 oz. How long will this cell deliver a current of 1 amp before the zinc is 75 per cent consumed?

(**13-XIII**) If zinc costs 20 cents per lb, what is the cost per kwhr of supplying electrical energy from dry cells? Assume the zinc is the only cost and that a cell may be used until the zinc is 75 per cent consumed.

10. Storage cells. A storage cell is one in which the chemical reactions are reversible, so that a depleted cell may be restored to its original condition by passing current through it in the reverse direction. The reactions of many cells are reversible to some extent, but there are only two cells which are efficient enough to be of practical importance. These are the lead-sulphuric acid cell, familiar to everyone as the commonly used automobile battery, and the Edison nickel-iron cell.

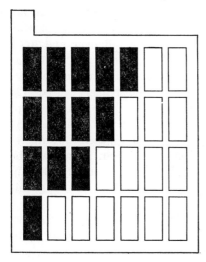

The lead-acid cell, as usually built, consists of two sets of plates, alternately positive and negative, held apart by separators of porous insulating material in a very compact assembly, and immersed in a solution of sulphuric acid (H_2SO_4) in water. The plates are grids, or frames, cast of a lead-antimony alloy, into which the active material is pressed in the form of a stiff paste, as shown in Fig. 13.9. The active material of the positive plates is lead peroxide (PbO_2), and of the negative plates, spongy lead (Pb).

Fig. 13.9. Pasted type plate for lead-acid storage cell.

The principal chemical reactions are stated by the equations

$$PbO_2 + H_2SO_4 \leftrightarrows PbSO_4 + H_2O + O. \qquad (13.18)$$
$$Pb + H_2SO_4 \leftrightarrows PbSO_4 + 2H. \qquad (13.19)$$

The first equation represents the reaction at the positive plate, and the second equation, the reaction at the negative plate. Both equations are read from left to right for discharge, and from right to left for charge. The energy available on discharge is seen to come from the conversion of lead peroxide and lead to lead sulphate, and the storage of energy is accomplished through the conversion of lead sulphate back to lead peroxide and lead.

The normal open-circuit emf of a lead cell is about 2 v, and the internal resistance is extremely low. In a typical three-cell battery as used in automobiles, the internal resistance is low enough to permit the battery to deliver several hundred amperes on short circuit. It is this ability to deliver very large currents for short periods of time that makes the lead cell superior for automobile starters.

The conversion of the electrolyte to water on discharge and back to H_2SO_4 on charge makes the specific gravity of the solution a good criterion of the state of charge of a cell. Of course, the conversion is not carried to extremes in practice. The specific gravity of the electrolyte in a fully charged automobile battery is about 1.280 (for concentrated H_2SO_4 it is 1.84), and should not be permitted to fall below 1.15 before recharging. The normal use of any storage battery involves a cycle of charge and discharge, repeated over and over, avoiding both overcharging and complete discharging. Storage batteries are customarily rated in ampere-hours, based upon an eight-hour discharge. For example, an automobile battery rated 120 amp-hr could be expected to deliver a current of $^{120}\!/_8 = 15$ amp for 8 hr. This is the normal charge and discharge rate for the battery. If it is discharged at a higher rate, say 30 or 300 amp, then the ampere-hours which can be taken from the battery without injury will be less than the rated 120. Thus, instead of being able to supply 300 amp for $^{120}\!/_{300} = 0.4$ hr (24 min), the battery might be able to supply this current for only 4 min without injury.

The useful life of a lead battery is usually ended by loss of active material from the plates, by failure of the separators, or by "sulphating." Some loss of active material goes on in normal use, and the loss is increased by overcharging and charging at an excess rate. Collecting in the bottom of the cell, the loose material may eventually short-circuit the plates. Failure of separators may result from buckling of the plates, owing to prolonged discharge at an excessive rate. Sulphating is a consequence of allowing the battery to remain in completely discharged condition. The lead sulphate becomes insoluble, and charging cannot convert it back to lead peroxide, as in normal use.

The plates of the Edison nickel-iron cell are steel grids, into the spaces of which are fitted perforated steel tubes, or pockets, containing the active material, as shown in Fig. 13.10. The active material of the positive plates is nickel peroxide, and of the negative plates, powdered iron. The electrolyte is a solution of potassium hydroxide with added lithium hydroxide. The principal reactions at the electrodes are the conversion of iron to iron oxide (FeO) at the negative plate, and nickel peroxide (NiO_2) to nickel oxide (NiO) at the positive plate on discharge, the reactions being reversible and taking place in the opposite order when the cell is charged.

The open-circuit emf of an Edison cell is about 1.4 v. Its internal resistance is considerably higher than that of the lead-acid cell, making the nickel-iron cell unsuited to use as an automobile battery. More costly than lead-acid batteries, nickel-iron batteries have the advantage of less weight for a given energy output; longer life; and exceptional ability to stand undercharge, excess charge, and other misuse without damage.

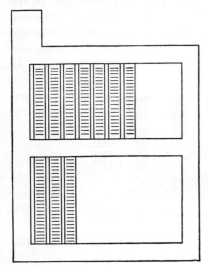

Fig. 13.10.   Plate for Edison nickel-iron storage cell.

The use of storage batteries is by no means confined to the small portable batteries seen in everyday life. They are used extensively in isolated power plants, where central-station service is not available; for stand-by or emergency service, where central-station service is available but risk of failure of service cannot be assumed, as in telegraph and telephone offices; for the operation of vehicles such as industrial trucks and small locomotives in factories and mines; for the complete operation of submarines while submerged; and for numerous other industrial and commercial applications. Some of these batteries, as those used for stand-by service, may weigh as much as 3000 lb per cell and may consist of 100 or more cells.

Problems

(**14-XIII**) How much lead is converted to lead sulphate in the negative plates of a lead-acid cell during the delivery of 100 amp-hr by the cell?

(**15-XIII**) A certain type of Edison nickel-iron battery has an emf of 4 v and an internal resistance of 0.05 ohm. How many such batteries would have to be connected in series to operate an automobile starter which requires 100 amp and has a resistance of 0.01 ohm? How many would have to be put in parallel?

11. Practical applications of electrochemistry. A great many operations in industry involve electrochemical processes. One of the most important is the refining of copper. Anodes of crude copper

(99 to 99.5 per cent pure) weighing 500 to 700 lb are suspended in tanks containing the solution ($CuSO_4$ and H_2SO_4). Thin sheets of pure copper (about 99.93 per cent) are used as cathodes. Currents of about 10,000 amp are used, but since there is no net emf developed by the cell, the voltage across a cell need only be equal to the IR drop (about 0.25 v). The impurities, such as gold and silver, present in the crude copper are not dissolved in the solution and are recovered in the sludge that settles in the cells. Impurities, such as lead and nickel, which are electronegative with respect to copper, are not deposited because there is not sufficient potential difference at the cathode to permit these ions to move against the solution pressure. The deposition of Pb^{++} ions, for example, would require a potential difference of not less than $(0.34) - (-0.12) = 0.46$ v. Since the high purity attainable by the electrolytic process is necessary in

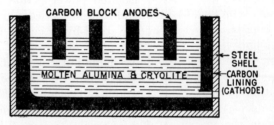

Fig. 13.11. Electric furnace for refining of aluminum.

copper used for electrical conductors, most of the copper produced in the United States is refined by this method.

Practically all aluminum is produced electrolytically. The solution in aluminum refining is not aqueous, but consists of alumina (Al_2O_3) dissolved in molten cryolite ($AlF_3 3NaF$). The cathode is the carbon-lined steel furnace shown in Fig. 13.11, in which the process takes place, and the anodes are carbon blocks. The current used is from 10,000 to 20,000 amp, which serves not only to deposit the metal, but to maintain the solution in a molten state. Pure (99 per cent) aluminum is periodically tapped off from the cathode and fresh material added, this process running continuously.

Magnesium is produced by the electrolysis of molten magnesium chloride. The source of the magnesium chloride is sea water. It might seem, at first thought, that magnesium could be deposited directly by electrolysis of the sea water itself. Inspection of the electromotive series in Table VII shows why this is not possible. Magnesium is electronegative with respect to hydrogen (1.55 v) and could be deposited only if that potential difference were established between the cathode and the solution. Before this value could be reached, however, hydrogen ions would be deposited rapidly enough to conduct whatever current was being sent through the cell, and no magnesium ions would ever reach the cathode.

The production of hydrogen and oxygen on a commercial scale is carried out by the electrolysis of water. Chlorine and sodium hydroxide are produced by the electrolysis of sodium chloride solution.

The rate of deposition of silver from a solution of $AgNO_3$ has served for many years as the legal standard of current, an **international ampere** being that current which would deposit 0.001118 g per sec. The precision of the absolute current balance has now advanced to the stage where an arbitrary standard is no longer necessary, and the absolute ampere, as defined in Chapter II, has replaced the international ampere as the standard.

The deposition of one metal upon another, known as **electroplating,** is another important application of electrochemistry. Objects may be electroplated either to improve their appearance or to protect them against corrosion. The metals commonly deposited are gold, silver, copper, tin, nickel, chromium, and zinc.

The technique of successful electroplating includes proper cleaning and preparation of the articles to be plated; choice of a suitable electrolyte, and of the best concentration and temperature; adjustment to obtain the proper current density over the surface to be plated; and so forth. In addition, there are many practical "kinks," such as adding organic substances to the solution to obtain smoother deposits, which are not readily explainable by electrochemical theory. In general, the electrolyte contains a salt of the metal to be deposited, and also an acid or alkali for increasing the conductivity of the solution. The anode is usually the metal to be deposited, though it may sometimes be a neutral metal with which no chemical reaction takes place, and all of the metal deposited is supplied in the form of a salt to the solution. Because of the fact that the cathode and anode are different metals, the electroplating cell develops an emf of its own, which must be taken into account when estimating the external voltage required to obtain the desired current.

Electrolysis sometimes occurs under circumstances that lead to harmful results. Suppose current enters a pipe line from the moist surrounding earth, flows along the pipe for a distance, and then leaves it to flow into the surrounding earth. Such a current may be a consequence of the earth being part of an electric circuit, as in the vicinity of an electric railway, but investigation shows that currents enter and leave pipe lines miles away from any sort of electrical installation and, therefore, are quite independent of any generator or battery. The origin and nature of these earth currents is not understood. At the point where the current enters the pipe, no harm is done, but at the point where the current leaves the pipe to reenter the earth, metal is lost, as at the anode of an electrochemical cell. The mineral salts dissolved in the moisture of the surrounding soil constitute the electrolyte, and Fe^{++} ions move from the pipe into the earth. This corrosion may eventually cause the pipe to fail.

Similar instances of corrosion are sometimes found in bearings, in pump rods, and in the reinforcing steel in concrete. One remedy

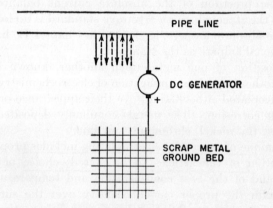

PIPE LINE

DC GENERATOR

SCRAP METAL
GROUND BED

Fig. 13.12. Cathodic protection of pipe lines against corrosion due to earth currents.

would be to insulate the metal completely from its surroundings, but this is not always practicable. A method called **cathodic protection,** which is often applied to pipe lines, depends upon artificially establishing countervoltages to prevent the flow of earth currents. At the point at which current is leaving the pipe, a generator is connected from the pipe to a mass of metal buried in the earth, as shown in Fig. 13.12. The polarity of the generator and its emf are then adjusted to stop the flow of current away from the pipe.

Problems

(**16-XIII**) Each cell in an electrolytic copper refinery is to deposit 200 lb of copper in 24 hr. What current must be used? Copper has an atomic weight of 63.57 , and a valence of 2 in $CuSO_4$.

(**17-XIII**) A plating of chromium 0.005 in. thick is to be put on a surface having a total area of 190 sq in. If the current used is 5 amp, how long should it take? Chromium has a valence of 3 in the solution used, its atomic weight is 52, and its density 6.93 g per cu cm.

(**18-XIII**) A current of 0.30 amp enters an iron pipe line, 12 in. in diam, along a section of 100 ft long. The pipe has a protective coating (which was faultily applied) and $\frac{1}{10}$ of 1 per cent of the area is exposed. If the walls of the pipe are 0.375 in. thick and failure occurs when this is reduced to 0.075 in., how long will the pipe last? The atomic weight of iron is 55.84, valence is 2. and density is 7.87.

(**19-XIII**) A hundred cubic meters of hydrogen at 760-mm pressure and 0° C is to be produced by the electrolysis of water. (a) What current would have to be used to accomplish this in 24 hr? (b) How much oxygen would be produced at the same time? Hydrogen has an atomic weight of 1.008, a valence of 1, and a density of 0.0898 g per l. Oxygen has an atomic weight of 16, a valence of 2, and a density of 1.429 g per l.

(**20-XIII**) It is suggested that perpetual motion might be realized by using electricity to decompose water into hydrogen and oxygen, burning the hydrogen in an internal-combustion engine which would drive a generator to produce the electricity to decompose more water. Obtain data and make calculations to prove the scheme to be possible or impossible. Show plainly all assumptions that are made and show source of data.

12. Thermoelectric effects. If two dissimilar metals are in contact, electrons from one diffuse into the other, as though the electron gas pressures in the two metals were different. This continues until

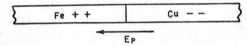

Fig. 13.13.   Peltier electromotive force.

the difference in potential across the boundary surface becomes high enough to establish equilibrium. Thus, there is established an emf known as the **Peltier electromotive force.** The direction and magnitude of the Peltier emf depend upon what metals are used and on the temperature of the junction. In the case of iron and copper at room temperature, electrons will move from the iron into the copper, and thus cause an emf to act in the direction shown in Fig. 13.13.

If a current is now sent through the junction in the direction indicated (using an external battery), heat energy is converted to electrical energy at a rate equal to $E_P \times I$ watts, and the junction will be cooled accordingly. Current in the other direction would heat the junction. This is known as the **Peltier effect.** At 0° C, the Peltier electromotive force for an iron-copper junction is 0.00432 v, with iron positive. It decreases to zero at 274.5° C, then increases to 0.0163 v at 600° C, with copper positive. It is evident that the amount of heating or cooling due to the Peltier effect is small, and it is masked by the much larger heating due to I^2R loss of the metals.

If one section of a wire is maintained at a higher temperature than another, the difference in electron gas pressures in the hot and cold parts causes a migration of free electrons from one part to the other until the potential difference, due to transfer of electrons, brings about equilibrium. The emf thus established is known as the **Thomson electromotive force.** The direction of the Thomson electromotive force depends upon the metal. In copper, the electrons are urged from hot to cold; in iron, the reverse is true. The magnitude of the Thomson electromotive force depends upon the temperatures of the sections. For copper with one section at 0° C and another section at 600° C,

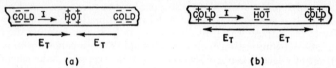

(a)   (b)

Fig. 13.14.   Thomson electromotive forces: (a) in copper; (b) in iron.

it is 0.00323 v with the hot parts positive. For iron with the same temperatures it is 0.0165 v with the cold part positive. If, by means of an external battery, current is sent through a wire in which Thomson electromotive forces are present, as in Fig. 13.14a, heat energy will be converted into electrical energy in the left end (thereby lowering its temperature), while electrical energy will be converted into heat energy in the right end (thereby raising its temperature). This is called the **Thomson effect.**

If two pieces of wire of dissimilar metals are joined at both ends to form a closed circuit, as shown in Fig. 13.15, and one junction is maintained at a higher temperature than the other, both Peltier and

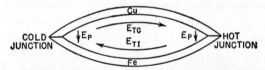

Fig. 13.15.   Thermocouple circuit, showing Peltier and Thomson electromotive forces.

Thomson electromotive forces will be present. For copper and iron with one junction, say, at 0° C and the other at 100° C, the directions of the electromotive forces would be as shown. If the hot junction temperature exceeded 274.5° C, the direction of E_p at that junction would be reversed. The resultant of the Peltier and Thomson electromotive forces in a closed circuit is known as the **Seebeck electromotive force,** and the flow of current in the circuit is called the **Seebeck effect.**

The three thermoelectric effects are of great significance in forming a theory of the conduction of electricity in metals. Any complete theory must explain them, and the data that can be obtained experimentally furnish a valuable check on the validity of any theory.

Apart from the theoretical significance, the Seebeck effect has a practical application in the **thermocouple.** We may cut into one of the wires which make up a circuit like that shown in Fig. 13.15 and insert a galvanometer to measure the current or a potentiometer to measure the Seebeck electromotive force, and as long as all parts inserted in the circuit remain at uniform temperature, the Seebeck electromotive force is unchanged. If we maintain one junction at a fixed temperature (usually done by inserting it in melting ice) and calibrate the other junction by observing electromotive forces for various temperatures, we have an excellent temperature-measuring device. Thermocouples may be inserted and read in inaccessible places or at temperatures that are too high for thermometers. They are very widely used in industry.

Problem

(**21-XIII**) What is the Seebeck electromotive force in a copper-iron circuit if one junction is maintained at 0° C and the other at 600° C? What is the direction of this emf?

13. Piezoelectric effect. Certain crystalline solids, particularly quartz and Rochelle salt, have the unique property of becoming

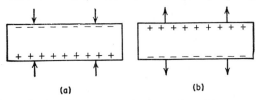

(a)   (b)

Fig. 13.16. Piezoelectric effects in crystal subjected to: (a) compression; (b) tension.

electrically charged between opposite faces when subjected to mechanical forces. This is known as the **piezoelectric effect.** Thus, if a piece of quartz is subjected to pressure, as in Fig. 13.16a, the surface becomes charged as indicated. If the same specimen is subjected to tension, as in Fig. 13.16b, the sign of the charge is reversed. The charge per unit area is small (about 2×10^{-12} coulomb per sq m per newton) and is proportional to the force.

If a quartz crystal is placed in an electric field, the inverse effect is observed: the crystal expands or contracts, depending upon the direction of the field. Thus, in an alternating electric field, the crystal would expand and contract cyclically, and if the frequency of the field were made equal to a natural frequency of vibration of the crystal, the amplitude of motion might become considerable. Circuits have been devised whereby the vibrations of the crystal can in turn be made to control the frequency of the applied field, and the vibrations thus made continue at the natural frequency of the crystal. Such devices, known as **crystal oscillators,** provide the most reliable sources of constant-frequency alternating current available, and are widely used in controlling the frequency of radio transmitters. Since the natural frequency of a particular crystal depends upon its thickness and upon the orientation of the applied field relative to the axes of the crystal, it is possible to cut and finish a crystal so that it will have the desired natural frequency.

The amplitude of the piezoelectric effect in Rochelle salt is many times as great as in quartz, but its mechanical properties make it less satisfactory as a material for oscillator crystals.

Study Questions

1. Criticize the statement "The cathode is the negative electrode." Under what conditions will the statement not be true?

2. What is the essential difference between the conduction of electricity in solutions and in metals?

3. Does ionization depend upon the passage of a current through the solution, or vice versa?

4. May a substance go into solution without forming ions? Explain.

5. Why is a smaller quantity of electricity required to deposit 100 g of lead (valence 2, atomic weight 207.2) than is required to deposit 100 g of copper (valence 2, atomic weight 63.57)?

6. Why is a smaller quantity of electricity required to deposit 100 g of silver (valence 1, atomic weight 107.88) than is required to deposit 100 g of cadmium (valence 2, atomic weight 112.41)?

7. How could electrochemical data be useful in determining the electronic charge? What other data would be necessary?

8. Would rubber tubes filled with an electrolyte solution make satisfactory electrical conductors for general purposes? Why?

9. Does it seem logical that the conductivity of a solution should increase with concentration? Why? Why should the conductivity decrease if the concentration is increased beyond a certain point?

10. Is it possible to measure the potential difference established when a metal electrode is immersed in a solution? Why? How are the potential differences shown in Table VII obtained?

11. Theoretically a primary cell might be constructed with any two metals that stand far enough apart in Table VII to yield a substantial potential difference. Most such cells would be impractical. What characteristics, besides potential differences, should a cell for general use possess?

12. Can you suggest a method for determining the current in a pipe line without interfering in any way with its operation?

13. When a measuring instrument is inserted into a thermocouple circuit, at least two additional thermal junctions are introduced. Why is the Seebeck electromotive force not modified by the electromotive forces at these junctions?

CHAPTER XIV

ELECTRONICS

1. The nature of a gas. Electronics is that part of electrical engineering which pertains to the conduction of electricity in gases and in vacuums, and to the various devices and circuits for utilizing these phenomena. We shall, therefore, begin by considering the nature of a gas and of a vacuum.

According to the kinetic theory of gases, molecules are continually in motion in all conceivable directions. The individual molecules dart about, colliding with one another and with the walls of the container in a perfectly random manner. Their speeds and the violence of their collisions depend upon the absolute temperature. The pressure on the inner walls of the container may be regarded as due entirely to the impacts of the molecules that strike it. If the behavior of an individual molecule could be followed, it might be found now moving in one direction with speed m, now colliding with another molecule, now moving in another direction with speed n, and so forth. It may move a distance d between the scene of its first collision and its second, a distance e between its second and its third. The distance a molecule travels between two collisions is known as its **free path.** The average distance, taking into account all the molecules in a given volume of gas and all the collisions of each molecule, is the **mean free path.**

Obviously, the mean free path depends upon the pressure. If we remove molecules of gas from a given vessel, we reduce the pressure and at the same time increase the average distance that a molecule can move without colliding with another. An individual molecule at a given instant may be moving in any direction at any velocity, and may move for any distance up to the largest permitted by the container without a collision. As regards an individual molecule, these things are matters of chance. When we come to consider a certain volume of a particular gas at definite pressure and temperature, however, we know that, on the average, equal numbers of molecules are moving in each direction, that there is a definite average speed, that the number of molecules moving at this speed or any other speed can be calculated, and that, on the average, the molecules move a certain distance (also calculable) between collisions. For example, in air at normal pressure and temperature, there will be 2.7×10^{19} molecules per cu cm (also true for any other gas under the same conditions). The average velocity will be around 500 m per sec, and the mean free path will be about 6×10^{-5} cm. Consequently, a molecule will, on the average, experience over 5×10^{9} collisions per sec.

As gas molecules are removed from a container by pumping, the pressure is reduced in direct proportion to the number of molecules still present. The number of collisions per second is reduced, and the mean free path is increased—both in proportion to the decrease in pressure. The lowest pressure obtainable with a rotary-type vacuum pump is about 0.001 mm of mercury, or about 1/760,000 of atmospheric pressure. By use of a diffusion pump, the pressure may be lowered still further to about $1/7.6 \times 10^{10}$ of atmospheric pressure, or about 10^{-8} mm of mercury. The achievement of extremely low pressures such as this involves heating the container to drive off gas absorbed in its pores, and other special techniques. It can be seen that the number of molecules per cubic centimeter is large, even in the best vacuum attainable. Starting with 2.7×10^{19} molecules per cu cm at atmospheric pressure, the best we have been able to do is to reduce this to 3.56×10^{8} molecules per cu cm. More important, however, is the fact that by thus reducing the pressure, we have increased the length of the mean free path until collisions between molecules are now comparatively rare events. Molecules can now travel the length of the container with relatively few collisions.

Problems

(1-XIV) How many molecules would be present in 1 cu cm of air at a pressure of 0.1 mm of mercury? What would be the mean free path? How many collisions would a molecule experience per second (on the average) assuming the effective velocity remains 500 m per sec?

(2-XIV) The effective velocity of the gas molecules can be shown to be proportional to $1/d$, where d is the density of the gas at normal pressure and temperature. Using this relationship, calculate the effective velocity, collisions per second, and mean free path in hydrogen at normal pressure and temperature. (Density of air is 1.2929 g per l, and of hydrogen, 0.0899 g per l.)

(3-XIV) What is the mean free path in the most perfect vacuum attainable?

2. Behavior of electrons in electric fields in vacuums. Let us now consider an electron at rest in an electric field established between two parallel plates in a vacuum. By Equation (12.1), the force

acting upon the electron is

$$F = \mathcal{E}e,$$

where F is the force in newtons.

$\mathcal{E}$ is the electric field intensity in volts per meter.

e is the charge on the electron in coulombs.

This is a continuous force which will continue to act as long as the electron is in the field. Since the electron is in vacuum and nothing is in its way, it will gain velocity in the direction opposite to the field according to the equation

$$a = \frac{F}{m} = \frac{\mathcal{E}e}{m}, \tag{14.1}$$

where a is acceleration in meters per second per second.

m is mass of the electron in kilograms.

In t seconds the velocity acquired will be

$$V_f = at = \frac{\mathcal{E}et}{m} \text{ m per sec.} \tag{14.2}$$

The average velocity during this time (since there is uniform acceleration) is

$$V_a = \frac{0 + V_f}{2} = \frac{at}{2} = \frac{\mathcal{E}et}{2m} \text{ m per sec.} \tag{14.3}$$

The distance traveled during the time t will be

$$S = V_a t = \frac{\mathcal{E}et^2}{2m} \text{ m.} \tag{14.4}$$

We may solve (14.4) for time to obtain

$$t = \sqrt{\frac{2mS}{\mathcal{E}e}}. \tag{14.5}$$

Substituting (14.5) back in (14.2) to get an expression for final velocity which is independent of t, we have

$$V_f = \frac{\mathcal{E}e}{m} \sqrt{\frac{2mS}{\mathcal{E}e}} = \sqrt{\frac{2\mathcal{E}eS}{m}}. \tag{14.6}$$

Since $\mathcal{E}S$ is the potential difference E through which the electron has moved,

$$V_f = \sqrt{\frac{2e}{m}} \sqrt{E}, \tag{14.7}$$

and putting in the numerical values for e and m, we have, finally,

$$V_f = \sqrt{\frac{2 \times 1.60 \times 10^{-19}}{9.1 \times 10^{-31}}} \sqrt{E} = 5.93 \times 10^5 \sqrt{E} \text{ m per sec.} \tag{14.8}$$

EXAMPLE: What force acts on an electron in an electric field in which the intensity is 10^4 v per m? What velocity does the electron acquire in moving 1 cm?

SOLUTION: The force by Equation (12.1) is

$$F = (10^4)(1.60 \times 10^{-19}) = 1.60 \times 10^{-15} \text{ newton.}$$

The potential difference through which the electron moves is 100 v. By Equation (14.8), the velocity is, therefore,

$$V_f = 5.93 \times 10^5 \sqrt{100} = 5.93 \times 10^6 \text{ m per sec.}$$

The theory of relativity requires that the mass of a moving body increase with velocity, according to the equation

$$m = \frac{m_r}{\sqrt{1 - \left(\frac{V}{c}\right)^2}}, \tag{14.9}$$

where m is the mass of the body at velocity V.

m_r is the mass of the body at rest.

c is the velocity of light.

In mechanics, no velocity approaching the velocity of light is ever encountered, and the correction to be applied to the mass of a body on account of its velocity always turns out to be insignificant. This is usually the case in electronics also, but not always. In large X-ray tubes, for example, electrons may fall through potential differences of the order of 10^6 v, and if the mass remained constant, the electrons would, according to Equation (14.8), reach velocities *exceeding* the velocity of light. The actual velocities, however, are found to be *less* than the velocity of light, and to agree with the velocities calculated by making the correction for change of mass.[1] The correction usually may be neglected and Equations (14.1) to (14.8) taken as correct if the final velocity as given by Equation (14.8) is not greater than 3×10^7 m per sec ($\frac{1}{10}$ of the velocity of light).

The kinetic energy possessed by an electron moving at velocity V is

$$W = \frac{mV^2}{2}. \tag{14.11}$$

[1] In making the correction, it is necessary to start with Equation (14.1) and carry the derivation through again to obtain

$$V_f = C \sqrt{1 - \frac{1}{(1 + 1.97 + 10^{-6}E)^2}}. \tag{14.10}$$

Substituting the expression for velocity of (14.7) in (14.11), we obtain

$$W = \frac{m\left(\sqrt{\frac{2e}{m}} \sqrt{E}\right)^2}{2} = Ee. \qquad (14.12)$$

This result could have been foreseen from the defining equation for potential difference,

$$W = EQ. \qquad (2.16)$$

The energy of the moving electron in joules is simply the potential difference through which it has fallen (in volts) multiplied by its charge in coulombs. Instead of expressing the energy in joules, it is frequently expressed in **electron volts,** defined as follows: *One electron volt is the energy gained by an electron in falling through a potential difference of 1 v.*

Since the charge on an electron is 1.60×10^{-19} coulomb, it is seen that

$$1 \text{ electron volt (ev)} \equiv 1.60 \times 10^{-19} \text{ joule.}$$

In the literature of electronics, energy is often expressed simply as so many "volts." By this is meant the energy gained by the electron or by any other charged particle in falling through that many volts. All of the equations in this section may be taken to apply to any charged particle, provided the proper values are substituted for its charge and mass.

Problems

(4-XIV) What force acts upon an electron in the field between parallel-plate electrodes 0.2 cm apart in a vacuum if the potential difference is 90 v? How much time would be required for an electron starting at rest from one electrode to reach the other electrode? With what velocity would it reach the other electrode? How much kinetic energy would it possess?

(5-XIV) How far would an electron have to move without collision in a uniform electric field intensity of 10^5 v per m in order to acquire energy equal to 10^3 ev? What is the velocity corresponding to this energy?

(6-XIV) At what velocity would the mass of an electron be increased by 1 per cent above its mass at rest? Through how many volts difference in potential must the electron fall to gain this velocity?

(7-XIV) If the mass of an electron did not change with velocity, through how many volts would it have to fall in order to acquire the velocity of light $(3 \times 10^8$ m per sec)?

3. Thermionic emission.

The free electrons within a metal may be likened to the molecules of a gas, being continually in motion in all conceivable directions in a perfectly random manner. At room temperature and even considerably above, this random motion of the electrons is practically confined within the metal itself. Very few electrons possess enough kinetic energy to carry them through the surface against the forces of attraction exerted by the nuclei that make up the space lattice of the metal. As the temperature of the metal is raised, however, part of the energy it absorbs is represented by increased thermal agitation in the "electron gas" within the metal, and more and more electrons acquire enough energy to carry them clear of the surface and into the surrounding space. This is called **thermionic emission.** As electrons leave the surface, the metal itself is left with a positive charge, and the forces of attraction between it and the emitted electrons increase until equilibrium is established, with electrons falling back as fast as they are emitted. It seems obvious, then, that the rate of emission of electrons must be a function of the kinetic energy of the electrons and, therefore, of the absolute temperature. The relationship was first worked out by Owen Williams Richardson in 1901 and has since been modified by Saul Dushman. It may be written in equation form as

$$I = AT^2\epsilon^{-\phi/KT}, \tag{14.13}$$

where I is the current equivalent of the emission, expressed in amperes per square meter of emitting surface.

     A is a constant which for pure metals is about 6×10^5.

     T is the absolute temperature of the emitting surface.

     ϵ is the natural base.

     ϕ is the **work function** in volts (varies from 1 to 7 volts).

     K is a constant the value of which is 0.863×10^{-4}.

The work function expresses in volts the potential difference through which an electron would have to fall in order to acquire enough kinetic energy to carry it through the surface. The electron, of course, actually receives its energy from the thermal source used to raise the temperature of the metal. It is merely convenient to measure the work function in volts, and to express it thus for purposes of calculation.

Although any metal will serve as an emitter at high enough temperature, it has been found that only a few metals are practicable. An emitter must be capable of withstanding the required temperature without melting or otherwise deteriorating. Furthermore, it must not require too much energy for heating in proportion to its emission. Tungsten, which has a work function of 4.52 v, has been found to meet the requirements best, and is used practically altogether. Barium and strontium have work functions much lower than tungsten but are not available in suitable forms. A practical barium-strontium emittor is obtained by coating tungsten with a mixture of the oxides of these metals. The resultant emittor has a work function of 1.05 v and, consequently, gives equivalent emission at much lower temperatures. Such emittors are not satisfactory, however, where large potential differences are to exist between the emittor and other near-by electrodes, as in high-voltage vacuum tubes.

It is not essential that the emittor be heated electrically by passing a current through it. In some instances, the emittor consists of a layer of barium-strontium oxides on the surface of a small metal cylinder, which is heated indirectly by a tungsten wire inside the

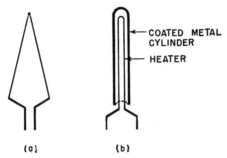

Fig. 14.1. Typical emittors: (a) directly heated; (b) indirectly heated.

cylinder, but electrically insulated from it. Some typical emittors are shown in Fig. 14.1.

Problems

(8-XIV) What is the emission from a tungsten wire 10 cm long and 5 mils in diameter at a temperature of 2200° C? At 2200° K?

(9-XIV) At what temperature would a barium-strontium oxide-coated wire ($\phi = 1.05$, $A = 100$) 5 cm long and 5 mils in diameter have to operate to give a total electron emission equivalent to 40 ma?

4. The diode. Probably the simplest electronic device consists of an evacuated bulb, within which are (1) an emittor, or cathode, which may be heated by passing a current through it and (2) a plate, or anode. Such a device is called a **diode,** or two-element vacuum tube. A typical arrangement is with the emittor placed vertically in the center of the bulb, and surrounded by the plate, as in Fig. 14.2. In operation, a battery or small transformer heats the emittor to the required temperature, while a second battery or transformer maintains a potential difference between the emittor and the plate, as shown schematically in Fig. 14.3. If the plate is made positive with respect to the emittor, the emitted electrons pass into an electric field which is directed from the plate toward the emittor. In this field, they are urged toward the plate, and a current is thus established

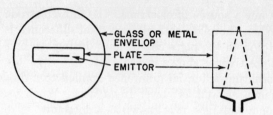

Fig. 14.2.   Arrangement of elements in a diode.

across the interelectrode space.   The conventional direction of the current, of course, is from plate to emittor within the tube—opposite to the direction of electron motion—and it completes its circuit through the plate battery or transformer.   The possibility of current flow in an evacuated bulb was discovered by Edison in the course of his experiments with the incandescent lamp in 1884, but no practical use was made of the discovery until years later, when John Ambrose Fleming applied it in the detection of radio-telegraph signals in about 1896.

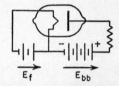

Fig. 14.3.   Basic circuit of a diode.

The principal use of the diode is as a rectifier of alternating current. If the plate is made negative with respect to the emittor, the direction of the electric field is such that the emitted electrons, instead of being urged toward the plate, are forced back upon the emittor.   Since

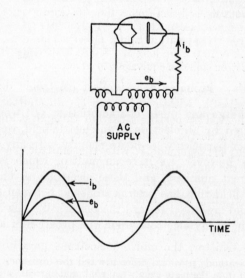

Fig. 14.4.   Diode used as a rectifier.

the plate is not a source of electrons,[1] the interelectrode current will be zero.   When the plate-cathode potential difference is alternating, current will flow in the plate circuit only during the half cycles when the plate is positive, as shown in Fig. 14.4.

The alternating-potential difference applied to a diode may be of radio frequency as well as power frequency.   When used to rectify radio-frequency voltages, it is known as a **detector.**   A diode-detector circuit with graphs of applied signal voltage and rectified output voltage are shown in Fig. 14.5.

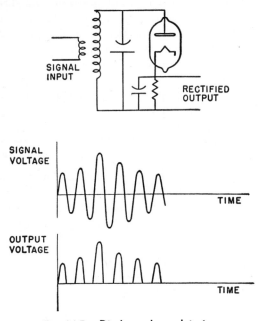

Fig. 14.5.   Diode used as a detector.

5. **Space charge and diode characteristics.**   In working out the velocity acquired by an electron in an electric field, we proceeded as though no other particles were in its vicinity.   In any electron tube like the diode, however, we have an emittor which is pouring out electrons in great numbers, and these electrons all find themselves in the electric field that has been established between the plate and the cathode, and are urged toward the plate.   We now wish to study the effect of the many electrons upon the progress of any particular one.

[1] If the plate-cathode potential difference becomes extremely high, electrons may be extracted from the plate even when cold, and current can thus be established in the reverse direction.

In order to simplify the discussion, let us assume the electrodes
are parallel plates, as in Fig. 14.6, with the cathode at the left and the
anode at the right.   Let us also assume, to begin with, that the electric
field intensity is perfectly uniform, as we would expect it to be in the
space between charged parallel plates.   Any emitted electron, then,
would start from rest, or with whatever velocity it had when emitted,
and would gain velocity uniformly until it reached the anode.   The
velocity of the electrons would be lowest at the surface of the cathode
and highest at the surface of the anode.   But the rate at which
electrons pass through any parallel plane surface, such as a-a or b-b,
between the plates must be the same; otherwise, the current would
not be the same in all parts of the circuit.   Consequently, the number
of electrons per unit volume of space must be much greater in a

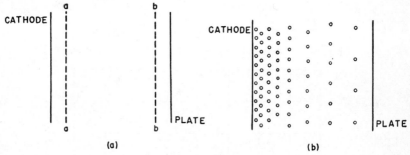

(a)   (b)

Fig. 14.6.   Distribution of space charge in a diode.

region like that between the cathode and plane a-a, where the electron
velocity is low, than in a region like that between plane b-b and the
anode, where the electron velocity is high.   Thus, the space between
the electrodes is filled with electrons on their way from cathode to
anode, known collectively as the **space charge.**   The relative density
of the space charge in various parts of the interelectrode space is
shown in Fig. 14.6b.

Now, the presence of the space charge has the effect of redistributing the electric field intensity in such a manner that the field
is no longer uniform.   The lines of electric flux, which originate on
the anode, now terminate largely upon the electrons of the space
charge, not upon the cathode.   Therefore, the electric flux density
and the electric field intensity are practically zero immediately in
front of the cathode.   The effect of the space charge in redistributing
the electric field intensity is shown in Fig. 14.7.   The low electric
field intensity in front of the cathode results in even slower velocities
for the electrons crossing planes, like a-a (Fig. 14.6a) and, consequently, in still greater space-charge densities in that region.

The practical consequence of space charge in most diodes (and other electron tubes as well) is that only a small part of the emitted electrons ever reach the plate. The remainder fall back into the cathode because the low electric field intensity in the region where they are is not able to accelerate them and get them away as fast as

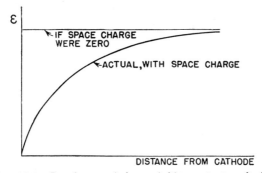

Fig. 14.7.   Distribution of electric field intensity in a diode.

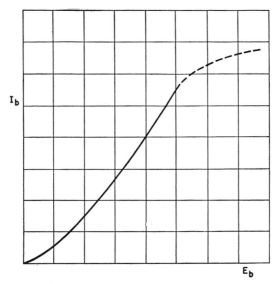

Fig. 14.8.   Typical plate-voltage-plate-current characteristic for a diode.

they are being emitted. The number of electrons reaching the plate can be increased by increasing the plate-cathode potential difference, and thus increasing the electric field intensity all along the path of the electrons. The relationship between potential difference and plate current is given by the Child-Langmuir $\frac{3}{2}$-power law as

$$I = KE^{\frac{3}{2}}, \tag{14.14}$$

where I is the plate current in amperes.

E is the potential difference between plate and cathode in volts.

K is a constant that depends upon the dimensions and geometrical arrangement of the electrodes.

A typical plate-voltage-plate-current curve for a diode is shown in Fig. 14.8. The lower part of the curve is seen to follow the $\frac{3}{2}$-power law rather closely. For larger values of plate voltage, particularly if the emission is low, it becomes possible to take all of the emitted electrons to the plate in spite of the space charge. Further increases in plate voltages then produce no further increase in plate current, and the curve flattens out. The plate current is then said to have reached **saturation**.

Problems

(10-XIV) The plate current in a certain diode is 100 ma when the plate-cathode potential difference is 135 v. What value will the plate current have when the potential difference is increased to 180 v?

(11-XIV) A certain diode has a tungsten filament, 15 cm in length and 0.0625 cm in diameter, which is maintained at a temperature of 2400° absolute. The plate current corresponding to a plate voltage of 500 is 250 ma. Calculate the saturation plate current and the plate voltage required to obtain it. Plot a few points on the e_b-i_b curve.

6. The triode. We have seen that the plate current corresponding to a certain plate-cathode voltage in a diode was essentially determined by the space charge. It seems logical, then, that if we were to place in the region next to the cathode, where the space charge is most dense, a third element so constructed that the electrons were able to pass through it, we could, by making this element negative or positive with respect to the cathode, control the plate current. If the third element were made negative, it would

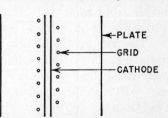

Fig. 14.9. Arrangement of elements in a triode.

have the effect of increasing the space charge and decreasing the plate current; if it were made positive, it would have the effect of neutralizing the space charge, thus permitting the plate current to increase. This third element, known as the **grid**, was first introduced into the electron tube by Lee De Forest about 1906. In practical triodes, the grid is ordinarily made of small wire, spirally wound on rigid supports, so that it envelops the cathode as shown schematically in Fig. 14.9. The spacing between wires is large compared with the diameter of the wire, so electrons may pass through virtually as if no electrode were there.

The triode is fundamentally an **amplifier**—that is, its basic purpose is to reproduce with increased magnitude small varying voltages which are impressed between its cathode and grid. As a consequence of its ability to amplify voltages, it is often made to serve other purposes as well, such as power amplification and the generation of alternating voltages. For the present, however, we will consider only its use for its basic purpose.

The essential connections of a triode are shown in Fig. 14.10. The battery E_{bb} maintains the plate positive with respect to the cathode, while the battery E_{cc} tends to maintain the grid negative with respect to the cathode. e_G represents the varying input, or **signal,** voltage which is to be amplified. In practice, E_{cc} is usually made large enough so that even when e_G has its largest positive value, the grid

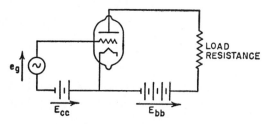

Fig. 14.10. Basic circuit of a triode.

will not become positive with respect to the cathode. If this is done, no electrons from the cathode will be attracted to the grid, and the current in the grid circuit can be considered zero.

The way in which the plate current of a triode varies with plate voltage and with grid voltage may be shown by plotting a family of curves like those shown in Fig. 14.11. For any particular grid voltage, say −10, the relationship of plate current to plate voltage may be read from the appropriate curve. These curves are seen to be approximately parallel straight lines (except at the lower extremities) which are spaced approximately equal distances apart.

The effectiveness of the grid in controlling the plate current can readily be seen from the characteristic curves. Suppose we adjust the grid voltage to −10 and the plate voltage to 250. The plate current is seen to be 4.7 ma. If we now decrease the grid voltage to −8, the plate current is increased to 8 ma, an increase of 3.3 ma. In order to obtain this same increase, we might have kept the grid voltage constant at −10 v and increased the plate voltage. The necessary plate voltage is seen to be 280, or an increase of 30 v. Thus, a change of 2 v on the grid brings about the same effect as a change of 30 v on the plate. The ratio of the change in plate voltage to the change in grid voltage to cause the same change in plate current is called the **amplification factor,** μ.

In equation form,

$$\mu = \frac{\Delta E_P}{\Delta E_{G(\text{for same }\Delta I_P)}}.$$ (14.15)

The amplification factor in the example above is thus $3\%_2 = 15$.

For any particular plate voltage, there is some negative value of grid voltage which will make the plate current zero. This condition is known as **cutoff.**

The ratio

$$R_P = \frac{\Delta E_P}{\Delta I_P}$$ (14.16)

is called **dynamic plate resistance.** Thus, in the example above, an increase of 30 v in plate voltage causes an increase of 0.0033 amp in

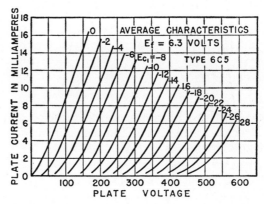

Fig. 14.11. Typical plate-current-plate-voltage characteristic for a triode.

plate current. The dynamic plate resistance is, therefore, $30/0.0033$ $= 9100$ ohms.

7. The triode as an amplifier. The operation of the triode as an amplifier can best be explained by carrying through an example. Suppose the triode described in the foregoing section is connected as in Fig. 14.12 and that the load resistance is adjusted to 20,000 ohms. Suppose the grid voltage is adjusted to -8 and the plate voltage to 250 to obtain a plate current of 8 ma, as before. Note that in order to have a plate voltage of 250, the voltage E_{BB} must be *greater* than 250 by an amount equal to the IR drop in the load resistance, so that $E_{BB} = 250 + (0.008 \times 20{,}000) = 410$ v. Since no current flows in the grid circuit, the voltage E_{cc} is equal to the actual grid-cathode voltage. Now, suppose an alternating signal voltage, $e_g = 2 \sin \omega t$, is connected into the grid circuit, so that the actual grid-cathode potential varies between -6 and -10 v. As the grid becomes less negative, the plate current increases, and as a first approximation, we might say that when the grid voltage was -6, the plate current (from the curve) would be 12 ma. This is not correct, however, because as the plate current increases, the IR drop in the load resist-

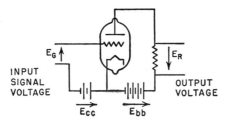

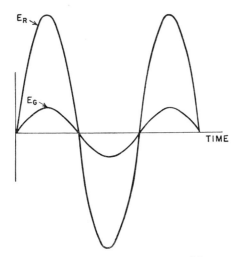

Fig. 14.12.   Triode used as an amplifier.

ance increases, and if E_{bb} is constant, then the actual plate-cathode voltage must be less.

Thus, we see that in order to make an accurate analysis of the amplifier we must have some way of taking into account the change in plate voltage due to the drop in the load resistance. One convenient way of doing this makes use of a **load line**, as shown in Fig. 14.13. The load line shows the actual plate-cathode voltage corresponding to any value of plate current. Its equation is

$$e_b = E_{bb} - i_b R. \tag{14.17}$$

Thus, for $i_b = 0$, $e_b = E_{bb} = 410$ v. When $i_b = 10$ ma, $e_b = 410 - (0.01 \times 20{,}000) = 210$ v. These two points fix the position of the load line in Fig. 14.13.

For any value of grid-cathode voltage, the operating point of the tube must be somewhere on the load line. We may take the intersections of the load line with the characteristics corresponding to various grid voltages and plot these against grid voltage to obtain a **dynamic transfer characteristic** as shown in Fig. 14.14. This curve shows how the plate current actually varies with grid voltage, taking into account the effect of the load resistance. If the plate-current-plate-voltage characteristics shown in Fig. 14.11 are equally spaced

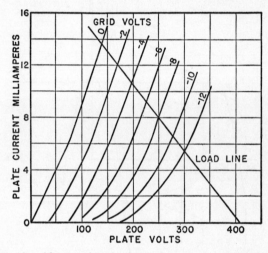

Fig. 14.13. Load line used to determine dynamic characteristic of a triode.

straight lines for a certain range of grid voltage, then the dynamic characteristic will be a straight line over this same range.

If we now study the effect of causing the grid voltage to vary sinusoidally between -6 and -10 (using Fig. 14.14), there is a corresponding variation in plate current from 9.25 to 6.75 ma. The voltage across the 20,000-ohm load resistance, therefore, varies from 185 to 135. Thus, a variation of 4 v in the signal voltage results in a 50-v variation in the output voltage of the amplifier. In other words, a signal voltage

$$e_g = 2 \sin \omega t$$

results in an alternating component in the output voltage

$$e_R = -25 \sin \omega t$$

With the particular value of load resistance selected in this example, we are able to realize an amplification factor of 12.5. The actual amplification factor obtained depends upon the values selected for the parameters.

Although amplifiers of this sort are not particularly efficient, it is not important that they should be. Their purpose is to amplify signal voltages without requiring any appreciable power from the source of the signal voltage, and the important thing is the voltage developed across the load resistance. In **power amplifiers,** the important thing is the variation in power that can be produced in

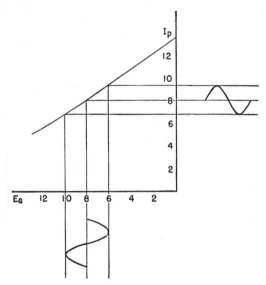

Fig. 14.14.   Dynamic transfer characteristic for a triode.

the load resistance (or load impedance) by a variation in grid voltage. Power-amplifier tubes are characterized by lower amplification factors and lower plate resistances than those intended for voltage amplification.

Problems

(12-XIV) Determine the dynamic transfer characteristic of the 6C5 triode using a load resistance of 50,000 ohms, E_{bb} = 300 v, and E_{cc} = -10 v. What voltage amplification is attained? What is the maximum alternating voltage that could be applied at E_g without distortion?

(13-XIV) Determine the dynamic transfer characteristic of the 6C5 triode using a load resistance of 100,000 ohms, E_{bb} = 180 v, and E_{cc} = -6 v. What voltage amplification is attained?

(14-XIV) Determine the amplification factor and plate resistance of a 2A3 triode, characteristic curves for which are shown in Fig. 14.15 for various operating points on the straight portions of the curve. Determine the dynamic transfer characteristic, using a load resistance of 2500 ohms, $E_{bb} =$ 400, and $E_{cc} = -43.5$. What voltage amplification is attained?

8. The tetrode and the pentode. The flow of electrons past the grid of a triode is controlled by the grid-cathode potential difference. However, the flow is not independent of the plate-cathode potential difference, nor of the variations in this voltage which occur when the tube acts as an amplifier. If the region in the vicinity of the grid could be screened from the electric field due to the plate voltage, the electrons in that region would be subject to the influence of the grid only, and the effects due to variation of the plate voltage would be avoided. This is accomplished by interposing between the grid and the plate another element known as a **screen grid**. The original grid

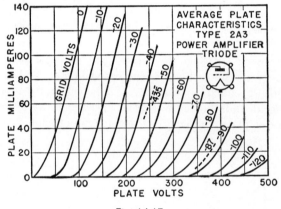

Fig. 14.15.

is referred to as the **control grid** and the resulting four-element tube is called a **tetrode**. The arrangement of the various elements is shown schematically in Fig. 14.16. The screen grid is usually maintained at a fixed potential difference and positive with respect to the cathode, as shown in Fig. 14.17. Since the plate voltage has little effect upon the electrons until they have passed the screen grid, a fairly low plate voltage will suffice to attract to the plate all electrons that come within its influence. Larger plate voltages produce little increase in plate current. A typical plate-current-plate-voltage characteristic curve for a tetrode is shown in Fig. 14.18.

The dip in the tetrode characteristic is due to a phenomenon known as **secondary emission**. When electrons strike the plate, they cause the emission of other electrons. In most tubes, the electrons emitted by the plate are in an electric field that carries them directly back into the plate. In the tetrode, however, if the plate voltage is less than the screen-grid voltage, these electrons are in a field which carries them in the other direction, and back to the screen grid. Therefore, for plate voltages high enough to cause secondary emission, but below the screen-grid voltage, plate current will actually decrease with plate voltage. To avoid this, a fifth element called a **suppressor**

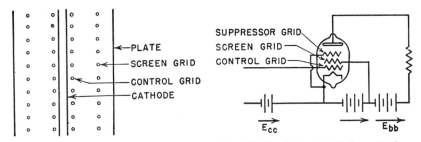

Fig. 14.16. Arrangement of the elements in a tetrode.

Fig. 14.17. Basic circuit of a pentode.

grid is introduced between the screen grid and the plate, and connected directly to the cathode as indicated in Fig. 14.17. This five-element tube is called a **pentode.** The electric field between the suppressor grid and the plate is thus directed away from the plate at all values of plate voltage, and secondary emission from the plate

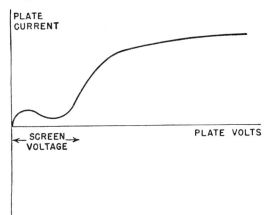

Fig. 14.18. Typical plate-current-plate-voltage characteristic for a tetrode.

returns directly back to the plate. A number of typical plate-current-plate-voltage curves for a pentode are shown in Fig. 14.19.

The tetrode and pentode, like the triode, are basically amplifier tubes. Their advantage over the triode is that higher amplification factors are possible. That this is so follows from the fact that, as compared with a triode, the change in grid voltage to cause a certain change in plate current is no greater, whereas the change in plate voltage to cause a certain change in plate current is much greater. The analysis of amplifier circuits using tetrodes and pentodes is not essentially different from the analysis of those using triodes. They may be treated as triodes with somewhat different characteristics.

Problem

(15-XIV) Determine the plate resistance and amplification factor for various operating points on the curves for the 6F6 pentode (Fig. 14.19).

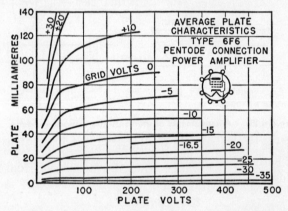

Fig. 14.19.　Typical plate-current-plate-voltage characteristic for a pentode.

9. Cathode-ray tube. A stream of moving electrons can be deflected by an electric field at right angles to the direction of motion and made to serve as an indicator of the intensity and mode of variation of the field. Tubes designed for this purpose are called **cathode-ray** tubes. The cathode-ray tube, besides being a very useful piece of laboratory equipment for analyzing the behavior of a-c circuits and apparatus of all sorts, is an important element in all television and radar equipment. The essential features of this tube are shown in Fig. 14.20. Electrons are emitted by a hot cathode K and are accelerated and focused by two anodes, A and A', to emerge as a narrow beam directed toward the end of the tube at the right. The velocity and beam width are controlled by the geometrical design of the anodes and by the voltages applied between the anodes and cathode. Another electrode, G, located between the cathode and the first anode is known as the *grid*, and has the effect, when it is made sufficiently negative with respect to the cathode, of interrupting the electron beam. This assembly of cathode, grid, and anodes is sometimes referred to as an **electron gun.** The electron beam emerging from the gun passes between two pairs of parallel **deflecting plates**

mounted at right angles one pair to the other. If no electric field exists between either pair of deflecting plates, the beam of electrons impinges at the center of the end of the tube and causes a luminous spot upon a coating of fluorescent salt. If a potential difference is now established between one pair of deflection plates, the spot will move parallel to the electric field between the plates a distance depending upon the potential difference.

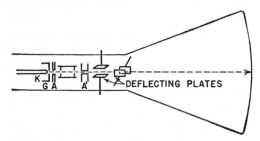

Fig. 14.20.   Arrangements of elements in a cathode-ray tube.

Suppose the dimensions of the tube are as shown in Fig. 14.21. An electron enters the deflecting plates at a velocity V_0 and is acted upon by a force at right angles to its motion,

$$F = \mathcal{E}e \text{ newtons,} \tag{12.1}$$

where $\mathcal{E}$ is the electric field intensity between the deflecting plates in volts per meter, and e is the charge on the electron in coulombs.

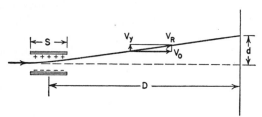

Fig. 14.21.   Electrostatic deflection of electrons in a cathode-ray tube.

The electron will experience an acceleration

$$a = \frac{F}{m} = \frac{\mathcal{E}e}{m} \text{ m per sec}^2, \tag{14.18}$$

where m is the mass of the electron in kilograms.

The electron is in the field of the deflecting plates for a time

$$t = \frac{S}{V_0} \text{ sec} \tag{14.19}$$

and, consequently, acquires a velocity

$$V_y = at = \frac{\mathcal{E}eS}{mV_0} \text{ m per sec} \tag{14.20}$$

in the direction opposite to the deflecting-plate field. As it emerges from the deflecting plates, the resultant velocity V_R makes an angle

$$\theta = \tan^{-1}\frac{V_y}{V_0} = \tan^{-1}\frac{\mathcal{E}eS}{mV_0{}^2} \tag{14.21}$$

with the original velocity V_0. After leaving the plates, the electron proceeds along a straight line to the screen. If the distance from the middle of the deflecting plates to the screen is D meters, the spot will be displaced on the screen by a distance

$$d_y = D\frac{\mathcal{E}eS}{mV_0{}^2} \text{ m.} \tag{14.22}$$

Since the velocity acquired by an electron in falling through a potential difference of E_a volts was shown to be

$$V = \sqrt{\frac{2e}{m}}\,\sqrt{E_a}, \tag{14.7}$$

we may substitute in (14.22) to obtain

$$d_y = \frac{D\mathcal{E}S}{2E_a}, \tag{14.23}$$

where E_a is the accelerating voltage applied between cathode and anode.

If the distance between the deflecting plates is C meters and their potential difference is E_y volts, then

$$\mathcal{E} = \frac{E_y}{C}. \tag{14.24}$$

Substituting (14.24) in (14.23), we obtain

$$^1 d_y = \frac{DE_yS}{2CE_a}. \tag{14.25}$$

The deflection of the spot is thus seen to be proportional to the voltage E_y applied to the deflection plates and to depend upon D, S, and C which are dimensions of the tube, and upon E_a, the accelerating voltage.

A similar analysis applies to the other set of deflecting plates. By applying voltages to both sets simultaneously, we can thus obtain a visual indication of the relation between the voltages. In some applications of the cathode-ray tube, an alternating voltage applied to the deflecting plates which deflect the spot horizontally is produced by an electron-tube circuit known as a **sweep oscillator,** and varies as shown graphically in Fig. 14.22. This voltage causes the spot to be swept in one direction, say left to right, at a uniform speed as desired; then it is swept back in the opposite direction so quickly that no trace is made upon the screen. We have thus a time base, the duration of which can be varied at will. If we now impress upon the other set of plates a voltage which we wish to investigate, the spot will trace out the second voltage as a function of time.

In other applications, such as television receivers, the voltage applied to the deflection plates causes the spot to **scan** the screen,

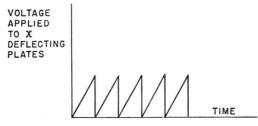

Fig. 14.22. **"Saw-tooth"** wave of voltage for obtaining linear time base for a cathode-ray tube.

appearing successively at every point from left to right and line by line. The signal voltage, applied to the grid, varies the intensity of the spot during the scanning process, to produce the picture.

Problems

(**16-XIV**) The accelerating voltage in a certain cathode-ray tube is 1500. The deflecting plates are 2.5 cm long and 1 cm apart, and the distances from the deflecting plates to the screen are 20 and 25 cm for the X and Y plates, respectively. What voltage must be applied between the X plates to move the spot on the screen a distance of 1 cm? Between the Y terminals?

(**17-XIV**) What voltage between the X deflecting plates of the cathode-ray tube in Problem 16-XIV would cause the electrons to strike the X plate before emerging?

(**18-XIV**) How long is a particular electron under the influence of the X deflecting plates of the cathode-ray tube in Problem 16-XIV? What fraction of a cycle is this if the voltage applied to the deflection plates has a frequency of 1 megacycle?

(**19-XIV**) An alternating voltage having an effective value of 100 and a frequency of 1 megacycle is applied to the X plates of the cathode-ray tube in Problem 16-XIV. What is the displacement current between plates? Assume the width of the plates to be 2 cm.

(20-XIV) An alternating voltage $v_x = 100 \sin 377t$ is applied to the X plates of a cathode-ray tube and an alternating voltage $v_y = 100 \sin (377t + 90°)$ is applied to the Y plates. Assume the sensitivities of the X and Y plates are the same. Calculate the path traced by the spot on the screen.

10. Photoelectric emission. Electrons are ejected under certain conditions when light or radiation impinges upon a metal surface. The essential condition for such emission is that the wave length of the light (or radiation) must be less than a certain critical value for the particular metal used. For tungsten, the critical wave length is 2300 angstrom units (Å); for sodium, 5800; and for caesium, 10,000 Å. (*Note:* One angstrom unit $\equiv 10^{-10}$ m.) The frequency and wave length of light or any radiation are related by the equation

$$f\lambda = 3 \times 10^8, \qquad (14.26)$$

where f is frequency in cycles per second.

λ is wave length in meters.

In place of stating critical wave length, we may, therefore, state critical frequency or, as it is called, **threshold frequency,** below which there is no emission. The threshold frequency for tungsten is thus found to be 1.30×10^{15} cycles per sec.

The number of electrons emitted per second from a unit area depends directly upon the intensity of the light, provided the frequency is above the threshold frequency for the metal tested. In other words, there will be no emission at frequencies lower than the threshold frequency, no matter how intense the light. Above the threshold frequency, the emission varies directly as the intensity of the light, provided the frequency is constant.

The theory of photoelectric emission depends directly on the quantum theory: that radiant energy is not continuous in nature, but is in discrete bundles or **quanta.** The amount of energy in each quantum depends on the frequency according to the equation

$$W = hf, \qquad (14.27)$$

where W is energy per quantum in joules.

h is Planck's constant, which is 6.62×10^{-34} joule-sec.

f is frequency in cycles per sec.

The amount of energy per quantum is, therefore, greater the higher the frequency. Now, as we have seen (Section 3), it requires a definite amount of energy to eject a free electron from a metal. If, then, the frequency of the radiation which falls on a metal surface is high enough so that a quantum of the radiant energy equals or exceeds the required energy for the particular metal, electrons will be emitted.

Below this frequency, a quantum is less than the required amount, and no emission will occur. The energy necessary to eject an electron is ordinarily stated in electron volts, and it is numerically equal to ϕ, the work function. It may be stated in joules as

$$W = \phi(1.60 \times 10^{-19}).$$ (14.28)

Equating (14.27) and (14.28), we obtain

$$(6.62 \times 10^{-34})f = \phi(1.60 \times 10^{-19})$$
$$f = (2.42 \times 10^{14})\phi.$$ (14.29)

This equation says that the threshold frequency should be equal to (2.42×10^{14}) times the work function in volts. Experiments show this relation to be true and proves the validity of our theory.

Problems

(21-XIV) What is the frequency of light having a wave length of 5000 Å?
(22-XIV) What is the threshold frequency for magnesium (work function 2.42 v)? What is the threshold wave length?

11. Photoelectric tubes. If an emitting metal surface is placed in an evacuated bulb, the electrons due to photoelectric emission can be attracted to a suitable anode, and a current subject to control by

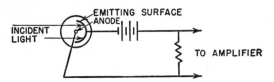

Fig. 14.23. Basic circuit of a photoelectric tube.

light can thus be established in an external circuit. The emitting surface must have a threshold frequency low enough so that it will emit electrons with the desired character of radiation. If it is desired to have the tube respond to light in the visible range (wave length 4000 to 7000 Å) or the infrared region just above the visible range, one of the best materials is caesium oxide on silver. For the ultraviolet region just below the visible range, sodium or tungsten on nickel is satisfactory. Since ordinary glass will filter out ultraviolet radiation, tubes for use in this region must have fused-quartz bulbs.

The current that can be obtained in a photoelectric tube is very small, of the order of a few microamperes, and must ordinarily be amplified (Section 5) before being used to operate any other device. The anode voltage may be adjusted to a high enough value so that the tube is operated at saturation (all the emitted electrons being attracted to the anode), and the tube thus made responsive to the intensity of the illumination on its cathode.

The photoelectric tube, popularly called the *electric eye*, has found an almost endless variety of applications in industry. In simple applications, the tube may be required merely to operate a relay when the illumination is cut off, as in opening and closing doors, turning on drinking fountains, counting cars, and so forth. In other applications, as in sound-on-film projection, it must respond to almost imperceptible variations in the intensity of the light, as the density of the shadow varies on the sound track. In still others, it must respond to differences in the color of the light, operating a mechanism that passes or rejects pieces on production lines depending on their color.

12. The X-ray tube. When electrons accelerated to sufficiently high velocity are allowed to impinge upon a cold metal surface, radiation similar to light, but much shorter in wave length, is produced. This radiation, known as X-rays, has wave lengths of the order of 10^{-10} to 10^{-12} m (the wave lengths of visible light range from 4×10^{-7} to 8×10^{-7} m) and is capable of penetrating substances opaque to visible light. In one sense, this phenomenon is the inverse of the photoelectric effect: instead of radiation causing the emission of electrons, impinging electrons here cause radiation. The necessary condition to the production of X-rays is that the energy carried by an impinging electron must equal a quantum of energy in radiation of the frequency required, according to the equation

$$eV = hf, \tag{14.30}$$

where e is the electronic charge in coulombs.

V is the potential difference in volts through which an electron falls.

h is Planck's constant.

f is frequency in cycles per second.

EXAMPLE: Through what voltage must electrons fall in order to produce X-radiation of wave length 10^{-10} m?

SOLUTION: The frequency of the desired radiation is found from Equation (14.26) to be

$$f = \frac{3 \times 10^8}{10^{-10}} = 3 \times 10^{18} \text{ cycles per sec.}$$

From Equation (14.30),

$$V = \frac{hf}{e} = \frac{(6.62 \times 10^{-34})(3 \times 10^{18})}{1.60 \times 10^{-19}} = 12,400 \text{ volts}$$

The voltage necessary to produce X-rays is thus seen to be very large compared to the work function of the metal.

Practical X-ray tubes are usually diodes with the elements arranged as shown in Fig. 14.24. The anode is a heavy copper rod, in the end of which is a tungsten or molybdenum target from which the X-radiation is emitted. The penetrating power of the radiation varies inversely as its wave length (directly as its frequency) and, consequently, with anode voltage. For X-ray installations used in medical diagnosis and therapy, the anode voltages are commonly from 40 to 100 kv. The installations used in industry for examining castings and welded joints may use anode voltages as high as 2×10^6. Tubes for these high voltages are more elaborate than the one shown in Fig. 14.24, the acceleration of the electrons being accomplished by

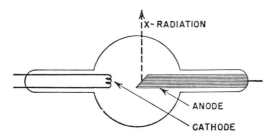

Fig. 14.24.   X-ray tube.

several anodes at successively higher voltages. The efficiency of the production of X-radiation is extremely low; of the energy delivered at the anode by the accelerated electrons less than one per cent appears as X-radiation. The remainder appears as heat and necessitates water-cooling of the anodes of large tubes.

Problems

(**23-XIV**) What is the velocity of the electrons in the foregoing example? If the anode current is 50 ma, how much energy is delivered to the anode per second by the electrons?

(**24-XIV**) What would be the velocity of the electrons in a 1,000,000-v X-ray tube? What percentage of error would be made in the velocity by neglecting the relativity correction for change of mass with velocity? What is the minimum wave length of the X-radiation produced by such a tube?

13. Gaseous ions and conduction in gases. In any volume of gas, there are always present at least a few positive and negative ions. In gases, ionization is not spontaneous, as in solutions, but is produced by the action of one or more of the following agencies: (1) ultraviolet light in the sun's rays, (2) radioactive substances that are present in minute quantities in the earth's crust and in water, and

(3) cosmic radiation which reaches the earth from distant space. The ions share in the thermal agitation of the gas molecules, positive ions having approximately the same average velocity and mean free path as molecules. The negative ions begin their existence as electrons, and being smaller and lighter, their average velocities are greater and their mean free paths longer than those of positive ions. After a short interval of time, an electron may attach itself to a molecule, thus forming a negative ion that behaves more nearly like those of opposite sign. It might be expected that since the ionizing agencies are continually at work, eventually all molecules would be ionized. This would be true if it were not for the fact that positive ions and negative ions are continually recombining to form neutral molecules. The chance of a positive ion and a negative ion coming together in collision obviously depends on how many ions of each sign are present. The number of ions in any volume of gas will, therefore, increase until the rate of recombination equals the rate of ionization. In air, this ordinarily occurs when there are only a few hundred positive ions and an equal number of negative ions per cubic cm.

Suppose, now, a uniform electric field is established between parallel-plate electrodes a short distance apart in air at atmospheric pressure. To begin with, let the electric field intensity be 100 v per m. The positive ions will be urged in the direction of the field and the negative ions in the opposite direction. Instead of experiencing uniform acceleration, however, as do electrons in a vacuum, the positive and negative ions are found to acquire steady average velocities of 1.3 and 1.8 cm per sec, respectively. These drift velocities are governed by the collisions which the ions experience, and are superimposed upon the much higher velocities of thermal agitation. The drift velocities for an electric field intensity of 100 v per m, or 1 v per cm, are the mobilities of the ions. The drift velocities vary directly as the electric field intensity according to the equation

$$v = \mathcal{E}m \text{ cm per sec,} \tag{14.31}$$

where $\mathcal{E}$ is electric field intensity in volts per meter.

m is mobility in centimeters per second in an electric field of 100 v per m.

It is to be observed that the mobilities of gaseous ions, even at atmospheric pressure, are very much greater than those of ions in solution. As the pressure is lowered, the mobilities of gaseous ions increase, as would be expected.

The electrons delivered to the anode by the negative ions move on around the external circuit and constitute a current. In the gas itself, the current consists of the oppositely directed streams of ions. With an electric field intensity of 100 v per m and air at normal pressure, the current would be too small to be measurable, but by the use of artificial ionizing agents, the number of ions present can be increased to where measurements of current are possible, if a very sensitive electrometer is used. If measurements of current are made for various values of potential difference between the plates, it is found that the current increases at first with potential difference, then becomes constant (as shown by the graph in Fig. 14.25) at what is called the **saturation value.** This must mean that the drift velocities of the ions have become high enough at some certain electric field intensity

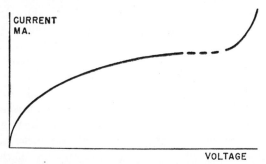

Fig. 14.25. Volt-ampere characteristic of low-voltage discharge, showing saturation effect.

that the ions are carried to the electrodes (and lost by recombination) as fast as they are being formed. Beyond this point no increase in the current occurs until the electric field intensity has been increased to a very high value compared with those considered thus far. Before discussing this matter, however, it will be of interest to consider the effect of reducing the gas pressure.

14. Ionization by collision. Suppose we seal the electrodes into the ends of a glass tube, as in Fig. 14.26, from which we have pumped the air until the pressure is, say $\frac{1}{1000}$ of atmospheric pressure. The saturation value of the current is now found to be less than before. There are fewer molecules and, consequently, fewer ions available to serve as carriers. But now we find that if we raise the electric field intensity to a moderately high value, say a few hundred volts per meter, the current begins again to increase. This must mean that some new source of ions has become available, since the current had previously ceased to increase with increased electric field intensity. The new source referred to is **ionization by collision.**

An ion, under the influence of the electric field between the electrodes, is accelerated and gains kinetic energy until it collides with a molecule and is stopped. At atmospheric pressure, the mean free path is so short that the ions seldom have the opportunity to gain much kinetic energy between collisions.

When the pressure is reduced, however, there are fewer molecules present in the space between the electrodes and, on the average, an ion travels further between collisions and possesses more kinetic energy at the time of collision. If its kinetic energy is sufficient, it may remove an orbital electron from the molecule with which it collides, thus producing a new pair of ions. These ions are then accelerated, gain kinetic energy, and experience collisions, which may result in further ionization. If new ions are produced by this means faster than they are being taken by the electrodes and lost by recombination, the current between the electrodes will increase, its limiting value being determined by the external resistance in the circuit.

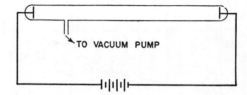

Fig. 14.26. Tube for study of conduction of electricity in gases.

Experiments show that the mobility of the negative ion increases tremendously with decreasing pressure. It is believed that this is due to the fact that at atmospheric pressure, the electron produced by ionizing a molecule attaches itself almost at once to another molecule, whereas at a lower pressure, it retains longer its original status as a free electron. Electrons, having only $1/1837$ of the mass of even the lightest atom, will be accelerated so much more rapidly than the heavier positive ions that they are almost wholly responsible for ionization by collision.

The energy that an electron must possess in order to ionize a molecule of any particular gas is a perfectly definite quantity. Although it might be expressed in ergs or joules, it is common practice to express it in terms of the number of volts potential difference through which the electron would have to move unhindered in order to acquire enough kinetic energy to ionize the given molecule. This potential difference is called the **ionization potential,** and the energy possessed by the electron is expressed in **electron volts.**

The required ionization potential in any instance may be reached by (a) raising the potential difference between the electrodes or moving the electrodes closer together, thus enabling an electron to accelerate more rapidly and attain the required velocity and kinetic energy in a given distance or (b) lowering the gas pressure and allowing the electron to move further before collision, thereby acquiring the necessary velocity and kinetic energy at a given acceleration. It must be made clear that the total amount of ionization by collision may be very small or very large. Even at fairly low potential differences between the electrodes, there must be an occasional electron that escapes collision long enough to acquire the ionization potential. Not every collision produces ionization, even when the electron possesses sufficient energy, and at low electric field intensities, the

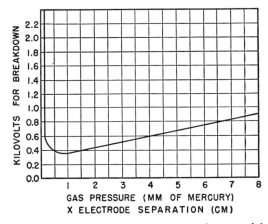

Fig. 14.27. Curve showing breakdown voltage of air as a function of the product of gas pressure and electrode separation.

number of such electrons is itself so small that their total effect is negligible. At some rather well-defined value of electric field intensity, there will be enough electrons having free paths of sufficient length to enable them to attain the ionization potential so that the rate of ionization will exceed the rate of loss of ions, and the current will increase, limited only by the resistance of the external circuit. This is known as **breakdown,** and the potential difference between the electrodes when it occurs is called the **breakdown voltage** of the tube.

Breakdown voltage is related to electrode separation distance and gas pressure by Paschen's law in the following manner: *Breakdown voltage depends on the product of gas pressure and electrode separation, and is constant as long as the product is constant:*

$$V_b = f(PD), \tag{14.32}$$

where V_b is the breakdown voltage.

f means "function of."

P is gas pressure.

D is separation distance.

The function is not a simple one, and is best shown as a curve between V and PD. Such a curve for air is shown in Fig. 14.27. From it, the breakdown voltage for a given pressure and separation distance may be found.

Problems

(**25-XIV**) What velocity would a positive ion acquire in an electric field intensity of 100,000 v per m in air at normal pressure (760 mm of mercury)?

(**26-XIV**) Taking the mass of an electron as 9.1×10^{-28} g, what must be its velocity when it has an energy of 1 ev? What force would have to act on the electron for it to acquire this velocity in a free path 0.05 cm long?

(**27-XIV**) The mean free path of electrons in a gas-filled tube is 0.05 cm and the electric field intensity is 100 v per cm. What energy would be acquired by an electron which had a free path equal to the mean free path?

(**28-XIV**) At what voltage would breakdown occur in a tube containing air at a pressure of 0.1 mm of mercury and having an electrode spacing of 50 cm? At a pressure of 0.05 mm of mercury and electrode spacing of 100 cm?

15. Glow discharge and radiation potential. The gas in a partially evacuated tube such as that discussed in the last section is characterized, when current is flowing, by a luminous glow, and the

FARADAY   POSITIVE COLUMN
DARK
SPACE

Fig. 14.28. Luminous discharge in gas at low pressure.

phenomena within the tube are collectively referred to as a **glow discharge.** Air gives a bluish-white glow; mercury vapor, blue; sodium, yellow; neon, red; and so forth. The glow does not entirely fill the tube: there is a dark space immediately in front of the cathode, then a short luminous region, then another dark space, and then a luminous region which extends to the anode as shown in Fig. 14.28. This luminous region is known as the **positive column.**

An investigation, by means of probes, of the electric field intensity in various parts of the discharge shows that it is highest in the dark space immediately in front of the cathode. In fact, most of the voltage applied to the tube appears across this space, and it is here that the electrons receive most of the energy they expend in the trip toward the anode. The electrons, accelerated to velocities which are large compared to the velocities of the positive ions, move toward the anode through a relatively stationary atmosphere of positive ions.

However, it is obvious that one positive ion must disappear for each electron that reaches the anode; otherwise, the increase in the number of positive ions would be cumulative.   One way that this requirement could be met would be for the cathode to emit one electron for each electron that reaches the anode.   Where the cathode is a hot filament or emittor, as it is in many gas-filled tubes, this presents no difficulty. But in other tubes, the cathode is cold, or at least its temperature is below that necessary for the required electron emission.   In such tubes, the electron supply is evidently obtained from the cathode by virtue of the high electric field intensity existing in the dark space in front of it or by virtue of the positive ions, themselves accelerated by the field, striking the cathode and knocking out electrons with which they then combine.

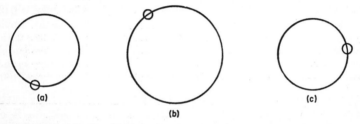

(a)   (c)
(b)

Fig. 14.29.   Steps in the production of radiation from atoms: (a) electron in normal orbit; (b) receives energy from collision, moving to outer orbit; (c) falls back to normal orbit, giving up energy as radiation.

In order to explain the luminosity of the tube, let us again consider the structure of the atom.   All the electrons not contained in the nucleus are pictured as moving in orbits around it.   Each orbit corresponds to a definite **energy level,** the innermost orbit corresponding to the lowest energy level.   Now, a molecule of gas may be struck by a moving electron that has not enough kinetic energy to remove an orbital electron from the molecule entirely, but which does have enough energy to raise an orbital electron from one energy level to the next higher one.   The orbital electron may accept this energy and rotate in the new orbit for a very brief time, but it will always fall back to its old orbit and when it does so, give up as radiation, or light, the energy it had accepted from the flying electron.

The nature of this radiation depends upon the gas and the energy exchange made.   At least part of it lies in the visible range, and is the luminosity which we seek to explain.   The energy required to move an electron from one orbit, or energy level, to the next highest one is a perfectly definite quantity.   If the flying electron does not possess the required amount, the molecule struck cannot accept it, and no transfer of energy at all occurs. The potential difference through which an electron must move unhindered in order to acquire enough energy to move an electron from one orbit to another is known as the **excitation potential** or **radiation potential**. There is always the possibility of an orbital electron being moved to the second higher level, or even further; hence, there may be several radiation potentials for a particular element. The first radiation potentials and the ionization potentials for several elements are given in Table VIII.

TABLE VIII
RADIATION AND IONIZATION POTENTIALS

Gas	Radiation Potential (v)	Ionization Potential (v)
Hydrogen	.....	13.53
Helium	19.7	24.46
Neon	16.6	21.47
Sodium vapor	2.09	5.12
Argon	11.57	15.69
Mercury vapor	4.65	10.38

16. Practical applications to illumination. The radiant energy from the positive column of a glow discharge is an important source of illumination. In sign and display lighting, lengths of glass tubing are bent to form letters, figures, or designs; electrodes are sealed into the ends; and after the tube is evacuated, gas is admitted to a pressure of 1 to 3 mm of mercury. Although all such signs are spoken of as "neon" signs, other gases besides neon are often used to obtain the desired color. Lengths of tubing totaling 50 to 60 ft are used in series, usually excited by an alternating voltage of 10,000 to 15,000 obtained from a small transformer.

Fluorescent lamps contain mercury vapor at a pressure of 1 to 3 mm of mercury. The radiation given off is largely in the ultraviolet range and does not directly serve as a source of light. Its function is to excite radiation within the visible spectrum when it impinges upon the fluorescent coating inside the tube. This material, known as a **phosphor,** is selected to yield secondary radiation of the desired color. Although some fluorescent lamps are designed with cold cathodes for series operation from high-voltage transformers, the most generally used type employs hot-filament electrodes in each end of the tube as shown in Fig. 14.30.

When starting, the switch S is closed, and the filaments and the ballast impedance B are in series across the line. When sufficient time has elapsed for electron emission to begin, the switch S is automatically opened, and ionization by collision and radiation begins in the gas.   The use of the ballast impedance is necessary to limit the current through the tube and render its operation stable.

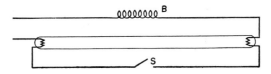

Fig. 14.30.   Connections for starting and operating fluorescent lamp.

Sodium-vapor-filled tubes are used to some extent for street lighting.   Sodium vapor is the most efficient light producer of all, but its low vapor pressure makes it necessary to mix it with neon, and to use a special heat-conserving tube and auxiliary apparatus.

17. Electric arcs.   As explained in Section 13, when ionization by collision, taken together with electron emission from the cathode, is producing ions at a greater rate than that at which they are being lost by recombination in the body of the gas and at the electrodes, the discharge becomes self-sustaining, and the current must be limited by resistance or impedance in the external circuit.   If this resistance is made low enough, the nature of the discharge changes, the current increasing and the voltage drop in front of the cathode decreasing until it is about equal to the ionization potential of the particular gas.   There is increased heating both in the gas and at the electrodes. A discharge having these characteristics is called an **arc.**

The luminous-glow discharge thus merges into the arc when the circuit resistance becomes low enough.   Not all arcs, however, begin in this way, nor is the arc necessarily a low-pressure phenomenon. Likely the most familiar arc of all is that which occurs when a knife switch is used to open a circuit.   As the blade leaves the jaws, the resistance of the switch increases, and a potential difference appears across the gradually widening gap, sufficiently large to start ionization by collision even at atmospheric pressure.   A spot is established on the cathode, which rapidly becomes hot enough to melt the copper and which serves to supply free electrons to maintain the arc.

Such an arc may be drawn out until its increased resistance and the cooling effect of the surrounding air extinguish it.   If an attempt is made to open a circuit with too small a switch, the arc may persist even with the switch wide open, and may continue until the switch is destroyed.   For satisfactorily opening circuits, **circuit breakers** rather than knife switches are used.   The arc is drawn between carbon blocks which are separated at high speed by a spring, actuated in turn by a trip mechanism, which may be operated either manually, or automatically by excessive current in the circuit. Any breaker must be designed to have sufficient interrupting capacity for the duty it is to perform—that is, it must be capable of opening the circuit when the greatest current possible is flowing, without damage to the breaker itself. Such design involves a profound knowledge of gaseous conduction as well as electric circuits and mechanism.

In electric arc welding, one electrode is the work, or object to be welded, the other is a slender metal rod that is touched to the work to start the arc. The rod electrode is then withdrawn to a short distance that is maintained until the arc goes out, and it becomes necessary to start it again. Both electrodes are raised to high temperatures, the material of the rod electrode being melted and dropped into the weld, where it unites with the molten metal of the work. It is possible to perform arc-welding operations in an atmosphere of hydrogen, thus eliminating oxidation of the surfaces being welded, and making possible welding feats that could not otherwise be accomplished. The use of arc welding in the fabrication of all sorts of machines and structures is steadily increasing.

The radiation from arcs between carbon electrodes more nearly approximates sunlight than does the light from any other artificial source. Such lamps are used in therapy to produce artificial erythema, or sunburn, and in the dairy industry to produce vitamin D in irradiated milk. These lamps are also used where intense light sources are needed, as in motion picture projectors and searchlights. For high-intensity outdoor illumination, as along white ways, an arc using as one electrode a copper rod and as the other an iron tube filled with a mixture of magnetite and metallic salts is extensively used.

18. Stabilization of electric arcs and glow discharges. Any electric arc or glow discharge tube which is operated from a constant-potential source, such as the generator shown in Fig. 14.31a, requires a stabilizing resistance or impedance in series with it. That this is so can be seen from the volt-ampere characteristic of an arc as shown in Fig. 14.31b. Suppose the arc were operating at the point p such that the generator supplied exactly the correct voltage for the particular current required by the arc. If no change in conditions occurred, operation at this point might continue indefinitely. But suppose the current momentarily increases. According to its characteristic curve, the arc now requires less voltage than before, but since E remains fixed, there is an excess of voltage over that required, and the current increases still more. Thus, the increase is cumulative, and continues until the current becomes excessive and the arc virtually short-circuits the generator. By putting sufficient resistance in series with the arc, we may obtain an over-all volt-ampere characteristic like curve c in Fig. 14.32. If we are now operating at the point p' on this over-all characteristic, and a momentary increase in current occurs,

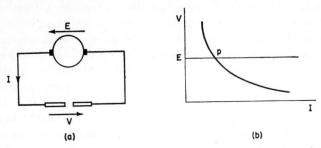

(a)   (b)

Fig. 14.31. (a) Arc connected to constant voltage source; (b) volt-ampere characteristic of arc.

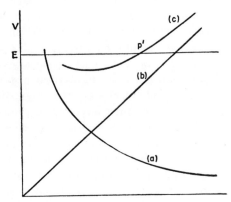

Fig. 14.32. Volt-ampere characteristic of arc, showing effect of stabilizing resistance: (a) arc characteristic; (b) resistance characteristic; (c) combined characteristic.

the emf of the generator is not sufficient to maintain the increased current, and it will have to drop back to its original value.

Problem

(**29-XIV**) The data below are for a carbon arc in air. Plot the volt-ampere characteristic and calculate the minimum series resistance to stabilize the arc at 3 amp. Could the lamp be successfully operated at 3 amp from a 120-v constant-potential circuit? From a 50-v constant-potential circuit?

V	I
50	2.5
43	4.9
41	8.5

19. Gas-filled diodes and triodes. The use of vacuum diodes and triodes for heavy-current applicaticns is limited by the inherently large cathode-anode potential difference. If any considerable plate current is conducted through the tube, the loss in the tube becomes prohibitive. For example, suppose the voltage drop from plate to cathode in a certain diode is 2000 v[1] when the plate current is 1 amp.[1] This means electrical energy is being converted to heat in the tube at the rate of 2000 w (not including energy used to heat the cathode). In such a tube the problem of dissipating this heat becomes formidable. Furthermore, the voltage drop within the tube is of the same order as the voltage drop in the load. Since the current is the same, the loss in the tube may be equal to, or greater than, the power supplied to the load, with consequent low efficiency. If by some means the voltage drop in the tube could be reduced from 2000 to 20 v, it is easy to see that the loss in the tube could be reduced to 1 per cent of what it was, or that the plate current could now be increased to 100 amp with no greater loss than before.

The introduction of gas (usually mercury vapor at a pressure from 0.002 to 0.1 mm) into a tube results in thus radically reducing the cathode-plate voltage drop. This is a consequence of the neutralization of the space charge by the positive ions which result from ionization by collision. Space charge, which limits the current and necessitates large plate voltages in vacuum tubes, thus ceases to be a controlling factor. The conduction in a gas-filled tube is essentially an arc.

The construction of gas-filled tubes differs somewhat from that of vacuum tubes. In general, the cathode must be heavier and capable of producing the required electron emission at fairly low temperature. The anode usually takes the form of graphite or metal disk or cylinder. Instead of the elements being concentric, as in vacuum tubes, they are assembled one above the other within the tube as shown in Fig. 14.33.

Gas-filled diodes (also called **phanotrons**) are primarily rectifiers. Electrons emitted from the hot cathode start ionization by collision. The electrons resulting from these ionizations are carried toward the anode, possibly bringing about further ionizations. The positive ions that result from the collisions drift back to the cathode, neutralizing the space charge and securing increased emission which makes the discharge self-sustaining. Thus, the current will be limited only by the resistance in the external circuit and the possibility of excessive current flowing and damaging the tube is considerably more than for vacuum diodes. There is also an increased possibility of break-

[1] D-c values.

down from anode to cathode, and thus of the tube losing its rectifying properties.   This is called **arc-back,** and imposes a limitation on the inverse peak voltage which may be applied between the anode and cathode during the interval of time that the anode is negative.   Gas-filled diodes are available for currents as large as 75 amp and inverse peak voltages as large as 20,000.

The introduction of gas into the triode makes of it a different sort of device altogether.   If the grid of a gas-filled triode (usually called **thyratron**) is maintained at a sufficiently negative potential with

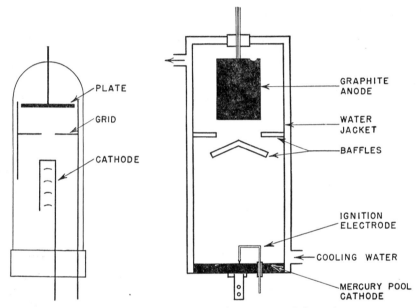

Fig. 14.33.   Arrangement of electrodes in a gas-filled triode.

Fig. 14.34.   Arrangement of electrodes in an ignitron.

respect to the cathode, ionization by collision can be prevented and the current held to a very small or zero value.   The negative potential that must be applied to the grid depends upon the anode voltage. If the grid potential is reduced below a certain critical value, ionization by collision begins at once, and the grid then has no further control over the anode current.   The grid controls the starting of the current, but it has no power to stop the current or to change its magnitude once it has started.   In order to stop the anode current it is necessary to reduce the cathode-anode voltage to zero or to a value too small to support the arc, and to maintain it there long enough for most of the ions to disappear by recombination.   This time is of the order of 0.001 sec. If the source of the cathode-anode voltage is alternating and the frequency is not too high, the arc is automatically extinguished when the voltage passes through zero. The grid then regains control, and is capable of starting the arc again at the desired point on the cycle. The thyratron is thus primarily a relay or switching device. Its usefulness lies in the fact that a very small voltage can control very accurately the starting of a much larger current.

The **ignitron** is not strictly a thermionic tube, but is a gaseous conduction device with a mercury-pool cathode. An additional control electrode in the form of a pointed rod dips into the mercury pool, while the anode is above the mercury pool, in the top of the tube as shown in Fig. 14.34. The tube is started, or "fired," by impressing a voltage between the cathode and the control electrode, whereupon a cathode spot is initiated on the mercury, which serves to supply electrons in immense quantities. As in the thyratron, the control electrode cannot stop the current nor in any way control it after it is started. It is, therefore, a switching device also, and its usefulness lies in its possibilities for carrying large currents, and for accurate timing.

20. Behavior of moving ions and electrons in magnetic fields. It was shown in Chapter X that a particle, carrying a charge of e coulombs and moving at a velocity of V meters per second at right angles to a uniform magnetic field in which the flux density was B webers per square meter, would experience a force

$$f = BeV \text{ newtons} \tag{10.15}$$

at right angles to the field and to the direction in which it was moving. If the moving particle is in a vacuum, and thus free of collisions, this force has the effect of continually changing the direction in which the particle moves without changing its velocity. As a consequence of this, the path described by the particle is circular, as shown in Fig. 14.35. The magnetic force that causes the particle to deviate from a straight line is opposed and counterbalanced by the centrifugal force:

$$f = \frac{mV^2}{r} \text{ newtons,} \tag{14.33}$$

where m is the mass of the particle in kilograms.

V is the velocity of the particle in meters per second.

r is the radius of the path in meters.

Equating (10.15) and (14.33) and solving for r, we obtain

$$r = \frac{mV}{Be}. \tag{14.34}$$

By Equation (14.7), the velocity reached by a charged particle in falling through a difference of potential E is

$$V = \sqrt{\frac{2e}{m}} \sqrt{E}. \qquad (14.7)$$

Substituting (14.7) in (14.34), we obtain

$$r = \frac{1}{B} \sqrt{\frac{2m}{e}} \sqrt{E}. \qquad (14.35)$$

The radius of the path is seen to vary inversely with magnetic flux density and directly as the square root of the accelerating voltage.

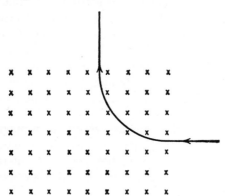

Fig. 14.35. Path of an electron moving in a magnetic field.

For particles having the same charge but different mass, the heavier particle will take a path of greater radius, the radii varying according to the proportion

$$\frac{r_1}{r_2} = \sqrt{\frac{m_1}{m_2}}. \qquad (14.36)$$

21. The mass spectrometer. The fact that charged particles of different masses, moving at right angles to a magnetic field, will be constrained to follow circular paths of different radii is put to practical use in an apparatus for separating ions according to mass.   The essential parts of the apparatus, known as the **mass spectrometer,** are shown in Fig. 14.36.   Ions are formed by collision when the gas to be analyzed is pumped through a stream of electrons emitted by a hot cathode (1) and collected by an anode (3).   The ions thus formed are accelerated by a suitable potential difference between electrodes (4) and (2), and a certain fraction of them pass through a slit into the space between electrodes (2) and (5), where they are further accel-

erated by a potential difference between these electrodes.   The stream
of ions, which may contain ions of various masses, next passes between
the poles of an electromagnet, where the individual ions are directed
into circular paths, the radii of which depend upon the masses of the
ions.   Leaving this section of the tube, the ions impinge upon a plate
containing a slit.   Only ions of a particular mass, directed by the
magnet into a path of certain radius, will pass through the slit: all
others will be stopped.   The ions that pass through are collected
by a suitable electrode, and their number is determined by measuring
the rate at which charge is delivered to this electrode by the ions.

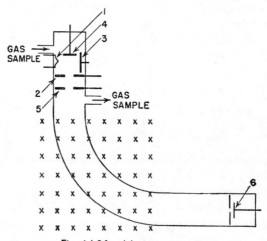

Fig. 14.36.   Mass spectrometer.

From Equation (14.35), it is obvious that by properly adjusting the
ion-accelerating voltage and the magnetic flux density, ions of any
particular mass may be directed into the path of proper radius to
enter the slit.

EXAMPLE: If the critical radius of path for a given spectrometer
tube is 10 cm and the ion-accelerating voltage is 1000, what should be
the magnetic flux density to cause hydrogen ions (mass 1.67×10^{-27}
kg, charge 1.60×10^{-19} coulomb) to pass the slit?

SOLUTION: By Equation (14.35),

$$B = \frac{1}{0.1} \sqrt{\frac{2 \times 1.67 \times 10^{-27}}{1.60 \times 10^{-19}}} \sqrt{1000}$$

$$= 0.046 \text{ weber per sq m.}$$

To admit oxygen ions, which are approximately 16 times as heavy,
the flux density would have to be approximately 4 times as much,
or 0.184 weber per sq m.   With the flux density adjusted to admit

nitrogen, carbon ions (which are lighter) would follow a path of shorter radius and so miss the slit.   On the other hand, oxygen ions, which are heavier, would have too large a radius of path, and would also miss.

The instrument is much more sensitive than the preceding example would imply.   It is not only capable of separating ions of different elements, but of separating ions of isotopes of the same element. In fact, the mass spectrometer made possible the discovery of isotopes, which, since they have the same chemical properties, cannot be separated by chemical methods.   The mass spectrometer is used primarily for rapid analysis of gases in industry, where the ion currents that must be measured are of the order of a few micromicroamperes. It has been adapted to the actual separation of isotopes in quantity, however, and was one of the methods used for separating U235.

Problem

(**30-XIV**) A certain mass spectrometer which has a critical radius of path of 15 cm and operates at a magnetic flux density of 0.1 weber per sq m is to be used to analyze a specimen of air.   What should be the accelerating voltage to cause oxygen ions to pass the slit?   Nitrogen ions?

22. The cyclotron.   The **cyclotron** is an apparatus in which charged particles, usually positive ions, may be accelerated to velocities corresponding to those that would be attained by the particles in falling through a potential difference of several million volts.   The apparatus, shown in Fig. 14.37a, consists essentially of a powerful electromagnet, N, S, between the poles of which are two D-shaped metal boxes, A and B, which will be referred to as **dees**.   The dees are also shown in plan view in Fig. 14.37b, with the path taken by the ions indicated by a spiral.

An alternating-potential difference of the order of 10^5 v (maximum value) is maintained between the dees by a suitable electron-tube oscillator.   The source of ions is at p, between the dees, and ions emerging at this point at an instant when A is positive are accelerated toward B.   The velocity thus acquired carries the ions into the open side of B and beyond the influence of the electric field.   They are not, however, beyond the influence of the magnetic field, which constrains their motion to a circular path of radius determined by Equation 14.34.

$$r = \frac{mv}{Be}.$$

The ions, after describing a semicircle, again emerge into the space between the dees.   But now the alternating electric field has reversed, and B is positive. The ions, which have lost no velocity while describing their semicircle, are again accelerated, and pass inside A with a velocity corresponding to a fall through 2×10^5 v difference of potential, and this time describe a semicircle of $\sqrt{2}$ times the radius of the first one. This cycle of events is repeated over and over until the ions emerge from the field at q with a velocity cor--

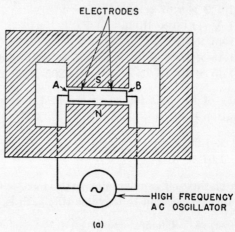

(a)

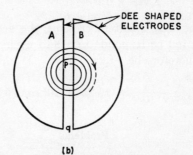

(b)

Fig. 14.37. Cyclotron.

responding to the potential difference between the dees times the number of trips made across the space.

It is obvious that the operation of the cyclotron depends upon the frequency of the alternating field being adjusted so that ions emerging from one of the dees will always find the field intensity at a maximum and properly directed.

EXAMPLE: Hydrogen ions are accelerated in a cyclotron in which the potential between the dees is 10^4 v and the magnetic flux density is 1 weber per sq m. What will be the radius of the first and second semicircles? What should be the frequency of the oscillator?

Solution: For hydrogen ions,

$$e = 1.60 \times 10^{-19} \text{ coulomb.}$$
$$m = 1.67 \times 10^{-27} \text{ kg.}$$

By Equation (14.35), the radius of the paths will be

$$r = \frac{1}{1} \sqrt{\frac{2 \times 1.67 \times 10^{-27}}{1.60 \times 10^{-19}}} \sqrt{E}$$
$$= 1.45 \times 10^{-4} \sqrt{E}.$$
$$r_1 = 1.45 \times 10^{-4} \sqrt{10^4} = 0.0145 \text{ m, or } 1.45 \text{ cm.}$$
$$r_2 = 1.45 \times 10^{-4} \sqrt{2 \times 10^4} = 0.0205 \text{ m, or } 2.05 \text{ cm.}$$

The velocity of the ions following the first accelerating period is found by Equation (14.7):

$$V = \sqrt{\frac{2 \times 1.60 \times 10^{-19}}{1.67 \times 10^{-27}}} \sqrt{10^4} = 1.388 \times 10^6 \text{ m per sec.}$$

The length of the first semicircular path is $\pi r_1 = 0.0455$ m. The time required for the electron to traverse this path is, therefore,

$$t = \frac{0.0455}{1.388 \times 10^6} = 3.28 \times 10^{-8} \text{ sec.}$$

If we neglect the time spent in crossing the accelerating space, the time just calculated corresponds to a half cycle. The oscillator frequency should therefore be

$$f = \frac{1}{2 \times 3.28 \times 10^{-8}} = 15.25 \times 10^6, \text{ or } 15.25 \text{ megacycles.}$$

Problems

(**31-XIV**) If the dees in the foregoing example are 50 cm in diameter, how many revolutions can an ion make before the radius of its path puts it outside the apparatus? What would be its energy at this point? Assume that ions are introduced at the most advantageous point and that the time spent in the accelerating space is negligible.

(**32-XIV**) Show that the time spent in traversing the second semicircle is the same as that spent in traversing the first one or, in general, the time spent in traversing the $(n + 1)$th semicircle is the same as that spent in traversing the nth one.

(**33-XIV**) What energy could be given to deutrons ($e = 1.60 \times 10^{-19}$, $m = 3.34 \times 10^{-27}$) in a cyclotron in which the dees are 1 m in diameter, the potential difference between dees is 50 kv, and the magnetic flux density is 1.5 webers per sq m? What should be the frequency of the oscillator?

Study Questions

1. Consider a 1-liter cubical container filled with air at atmospheric pressure. Could a molecule, starting at one wall, ever reach the opposite wall without collision with other molecules? How are its chances of doing this affected by reducing the pressure in the container?

2. In the best vacuum now obtainable there remain about 3.56×10^8 molecules per cu cm. If means were found to reduce this to 3.56×10^4, could vacuum tubes be radically improved? **Why?**

3. How would the final velocity acquired by a hydrogen ion compare with that of an electron after having fallen through a potential difference of V volts in a vacuum?

4. Would an electron falling through a potential difference of $2V$ in a vacuum acquire a final velocity twice as great as in falling through a potential difference V? Why? Would it acquire twice as much kinetic energy?

5. For the same temperature, and assuming the value of A to be the same for either material, how much emission could be had from an oxide-coated filament as compared with a tungsten filament of the same size?

6. What becomes of the electrons emitted from the filament of an ordinary incandescent lamp?

7. What would be the effect on the operation of a diode of making the cathode positive with respect to the plate?

8. In what way would the characteristics of diodes be changed if there were no space charge?

9. It is difficult to demonstrate the flattening of the characteristic, or saturation effect, using a diode with an oxide-coated filament. Why?

10. Why can a small change in the grid voltage of a triode cause the same change in plate current as does a much larger change in plate voltage?

11. Using the data supplied on the 6C5 triode, calculate the amplification factor for five or ten different points. How nearly constant is the amplification factor?

12. Using the data supplied on the 6C5 triode, determine the grid voltage for cutoff for various values of plate voltage. Can these values be read with much precision? Why?

13. Using the data supplied on the 6C5 triode, calculate the dynamic plate resistance for five or ten different points. How nearly constant is this resistance?

14. Why is the construction of a dynamic transfer characteristic necessary? What is the significance of the point of intersection of the load line with one of the plate-current plate-voltage characteristics of a triode?

15. How do you account for the dip in the tetrode characteristic (Fig. 14.18)? How is this dip avoided in the pentode characteristics?

16. What is the function of the deflection plates in the cathode ray tube of a television receiver? What is the function of the grid?

17. Do the observed facts of photoelectric emission tend to substantiate the quantum theory? In what way?

18. What are the conditions necessary for the production of X-rays?

19. Would it be possible to obtain for experimental purposes a sample of air in which absolutely no ions exist? What precautions would be necessary?

20. What is meant by the statement "the mobility of the negative ion increases tremendously with decreasing pressure." Explain.

21. Is it possible to have ionization by collision taking place in a gas-filled tube without breakdown voltage being applied to the electrodes? Explain.

22. According to the curve shown in Fig. 14.27, it might be possible in certain instances to lower the breakdown voltage of a gas-filled tube by moving the electrodes further apart. This appears to be contradictory. Explain.

23. Distinguish between radiation potential and ionization potential. Which is greater?

24. Why must a ballast resistance be used in series when an arc is to be operated from a constant-potential source?

25. What limits the use of vacuum tubes as power rectifiers? How does the addition of gas remove this limitation?

26. Why cannot a gas-filled triode be used like a vacuum triode?

27. Suppose a cathode-ray tube is fitted with a pair of external coils so that while electrons are in the electric field of the deflection plates they are simultaneously in a magnetic field at right angles to the electric field. Suppose further that the field intensities are so adjusted that the electrons are not deflected, but impinge on the same spot on the screen as they would if neither field were present. Show that the velocity of the electrons is given by

$$V = \frac{\mathcal{E}}{B}.$$

THE CGS SYSTEMS OF ELECTRICAL UNITS

The rationalized MKS system of electric and magnetic units used throughout this book is relatively new. Recommended for adoption by the International Electrotechnical Commission in 1935, to go into use January 1, 1940, it has found favor among writers of electrical engineering textbooks and is rapidly becoming the most favored system. Fortunately, the MKS units of current, potential difference, resistance, power, inductance, and capacitance are identical with the old "practical units," which, though defined only as multiples of the CGS electromagnetic units, have always been the most used units, except in derivations. The adoption of the new system, therefore, made no difference insofar as these quantities were concerned.

There are, however, in existence a great number of textbooks and technical papers which use the CGS systems exclusively, or which use CGS magnetic units and "practical" electric units. It is, therefore, necessary that the student know enough about the CGS systems to read such books and papers.

Basic Units of the CGS Systems

The basic units of any CGS system are the centimeter (unit of length), the gram (unit of mass), and the second (unit of time). The centimeter is defined as $\frac{1}{100}$ of the standard meter and the gram as $\frac{1}{1000}$ of the standard kilogram. From these basic units, a complete set of derived units may be set up for measuring the various quantities of mechanics. Thus, the centimeter per second is the unit of velocity and the centimeter per second per second is the unit of acceleration.

The unit of force (the dyne) is that force which will give an acceleration of one centimeter per second per second to a mass of one gram.

$$(1 \text{ newton} \equiv 10^5 \text{ dynes.})$$

The unit of energy (the erg) is the work done when a body is moved one centimeter against a force of one dyne.

$$(1 \text{ joule} \equiv 10^7 \text{ erg.})$$

The unit of power is the *erg per second.*

$$(1 \text{ watt} \equiv 10^7 \text{ ergs per second.})$$

The CGS Electromagnetic Units

In order to extend the CGS systems to include electric and magnetic units, it is necessary to introduce a fourth fundamental unit. The permeability of free space, arbitrarily given a value of one, serves as this unit. It would hardly be correct to say it was *selected*, because at the time it came into use not many scientists understood that any fourth unit was necessary, or that any selection was being made.

The development of the system rests upon the definition of what is known as a "unit magnetic pole," which is an isolated N (or S) pole of certain strength located at a point in space. Such a pole is not physically realizable for the reason that magnetic poles occur in pairs (N and S). Also, any magnetic pole is distributed through a more or less definite volume instead of being concentrated at a point. The nearest approach to unit poles are the extremities of long, slender bar magnets, and it was with these that the original experiments were performed and the definition framed. Although useful as a theoretical concept, the unit pole is hopelessly inadequate when it comes to actually establishing laboratory standards of high accuracy. The definitions follow:

Unit magnetic pole strength (one unit pole) is that pole strength which, placed at a point in free space at a distance of one centimeter from a point pole of equal strength, will be attracted or repelled by a force of one dyne. Its defining equation is

$$f = \frac{m_1 m_2}{\mu S^2},$$

where f is force in dynes.

m_1 and m_2 are pole strengths in unit poles.

μ is permeability (1 for free space).

S is distance between the poles in centimeters.

There is no counterpart of the unit pole in the MKS system of units.

Unit magnetic field intensity (one oersted) is that field intensity in which a unit pole will be acted upon by a force of one dyne. Its defining equation is

$$f = Hm.$$

(By comparison, 1 oersted $= \dfrac{1}{4\pi} \times 10^3$ ampere-turns per m.)

Unit current (one abampere) is that current which, if it flows in a wire bent into an arc of one centimeter radius, will establish at the center of the arc a magnetic field intensity of one oersted per centimeter length of arc. Its defining equation is

$$H = \frac{lI}{S^2},$$

where l is the length of arc in centimeters.

S is radius of arc in centimeters.

(By comparison, 1 abampere $\equiv$ 10 amp.)

Unit quantity of electricity (one abcoulomb) is that quantity of electricity that passes a reference point on a conductor in one second when the current is one abampere. Its defining equation is

$$Q = IT.$$

(By comparison, 1 abcoulomb $\equiv$ 10 coulombs.)

Unit potential difference (one abvolt) is the potential difference that exists between two points on a conductor when the energy involved in moving one abcoulomb from one point to the other is one erg. Its defining equation is,

$$V = \frac{W}{Q}.$$

(By comparison, 1 abvolt $\equiv 10^{-8}$ v.)

Unit resistance (one abohm) is the resistance of a conductor when a current of one abampere causes a potential difference of one abvolt between the extremities of the conductor. Its defining equation is

$$R = \frac{V}{I}.$$

(By comparison, 1 abohm $\equiv 10^{-9}$ ohm.)

Unit self-inductance (one abhenry) is that self-inductance which will result in an induced emf of one abvolt in a circuit in which the current is changing at the rate of one abampere per second. Its defining equation is

$$E = L\frac{di}{dt}.$$

(By comparison, 1 abhenry $\equiv 10^{-9}$ h.)

Unit magnetic flux density (one gauss) is the flux density in a magnetic field in free space in which the magnetic field intensity is one oersted. Its defining equation is,

$$B = \mu H.$$

(By comparison, 1 gauss $\equiv 10^{-4}$ weber per sq m.)

Unit magnetic flux (one maxwell, or one line) is the total flux passing through a plane area of one square centimeter which is perpendicular to a magnetic field in which the flux density is one gauss. Its defining equation is

$$\phi = BA.$$

(By comparison, 1 maxwell $\equiv 10^{-8}$ weber.)

Unit magnetic potential difference (one gilbert) is the magnetic potential difference that exists between two points separated by a distance of one centimeter (in the direction of the field) in a magnetic field in which the field intensity is one oersted. Its defining equation is

$$F = HL.$$

(By comparison, 1 gilbert $\equiv 1/0.4\pi$ ampere-turn.)

Unit electric field intensity (one abvolt per centimeter) exists when the potential difference between two points one centimeter apart (measured in the direction of the field) is one abvolt. Its defining equation is

$$\varepsilon = \frac{E}{S}.$$

(By comparison, 1 abvolt per cm. $\equiv 10^{-6}$ v per m.)

Unit electric flux (one CGSEM unit) is that flux that passes through the area subtended by unit solid angle on a closed surface that contains a charge of one abcoulomb. In other words, the total electric flux associated with unit charge (one abcoulomb) is 4π CGSEM units. Its defining equation is

$$D = 4\pi Q.$$

(By comparison, 1 CGSEM unit $= 1/0.4\pi$ MKS unit.)

Unit electric flux density (one CGSEM unit per square centimeter) exists in a field when one CGSEM unit of electric flux passes through an area of one square centimeter on a surface perpendicular to the field. Its defining equation is

$$D = \frac{\psi}{A}.$$

(By comparison, 1 CGSEM unit per sq cm $\equiv \dfrac{1}{4\pi} \times 10^{5}$ MKS units per sq m.)

Unit permittivity (one CGSEM unit) exists when an electric field intensity of one abvolt per centimeter causes an electric flux density of one CGSEM unit per square centimeter. The permittivity of any given substance is determined experimentally. The permittivity of free space is thus found to be $\dfrac{1}{9 \times 10^{20}}$ CGSEM units.

Unit capacitance (one abfarad) is that capacitance across which a charge of one abcoulomb will give a potential difference of one abvolt.

Its defining equation is

$$C = \frac{Q}{V}.$$

(By comparison, 1 abfarad $\equiv 10^9$ farads.)

Practical Units

As already mentioned, the CGS electromagnetic units have been much used in theoretical derivations and analysis. With the exception of the units of magnetic flux, flux density, and magnetic field intensity, they have not been used at all for practical measurements and calculations. The sizes of the CGS units were not convenient for such work, and "practical" units were defined as follows:

Unit of potential difference (*one volt*) is 10^8 abvolts.

$$(1 \text{ volt} \equiv 10^8 \text{ abvolts.})$$

Unit of current (*one ampere*) is 10^{-1} abampere.

$$(1 \text{ ampere} \equiv \frac{1}{10} \text{ abampere.})$$

Unit of resistance (*one ohm*) is 10^9 abohms.

$$(1 \text{ ohm} \equiv 10^9 \text{ abohms.})$$

Corresponding practical units of charge, inductance, and capacitance follow logically from these definitions as follows:

$$1 \text{ coulomb} \equiv \frac{1}{10} \text{ abcoulombs.}$$
$$1 \text{ henry} \equiv 10^9 \text{ abhenrys.}$$
$$1 \text{ farad} \equiv 10^{-9} \text{ abfarads.}$$

International Units

The difficulties encountered in obtaining consistent results in absolute measurements of current, voltage, and resistance with the apparatus available in the early days of the electrical industry resulted in the adoption of secondary standards of these quantities. These standards were so chosen that they represented the most reliable values then obtainable by absolute measurement, and were capable of being readily reproduced in any standards laboratory. The definitions were as follows:

Unit current (*one International ampere*) is that current which will cause the deposition of silver at the rate of 0.001118 gram per second under standard conditions.

Unit resistance (*one International ohm*) is the resistance of a column of mercury having a mass of 14.4521 grams, a constant cross section, and a length of 106.3 centimeters at 0° C.

Unit potential difference (one International volt) exists between the extremities of a conductor having a resistance of one international ohm and carrying a current of one international ampere.

By 1935, the techniques of making absolute measurements had advanced to the point where it was known that the International units differed from the corresponding absolute units by several parts in 10,000. It was at this time that the International Electrotechnical Commission voted to recommend the adoption of the MKS system, with the absolute units therein defined to supersede the International units.

The CGS Electrostatic System

If, instead of selecting permeability as the fourth fundamental unit, we select permittivity, and arbitrarily assign a value to the permittivity of free space, we can proceed to build up still another system, known as the CGS Electrostatic System. The value assigned to the permittivity of free space is one. The definitions may then be made in logical order as follows:

Unit quantity of electricity (one statcoulomb) is that charge which, if concentrated at a point in a vacuum at a distance of one centimeter from an equal point charge will be attracted or repelled by a force of 1 dyne. Its defining equation is

$$f = \frac{q_1 q_2}{\epsilon S^2}.$$

$$\left(\text{By comparison, 1 statcoulomb} \equiv \frac{1}{3 \times 10^9} \text{ coulomb.} \right)$$

Unit electric field intensity (one statvolt per centimeter) is that field intensity in which a charge of one statcoulomb is acted upon by a force of one dyne. Its defining equation is

$$f = \mathcal{E}q.$$

(By comparison, 1 statvolt per centimeter $\equiv$ 30,000 volts per meter.)

Unit potential difference (one statvolt) exists between two points when the work required to move a charge of one statcoulomb from one to the other is one erg. Its defining equation is

$$E = \mathcal{E}S.$$

(By comparison, 1 statvolt $\equiv$ 300 volts.)

Unit current (one statampere) is the current when electricity passes a reference point on a conductor at a rate of 1 statcoulomb per second. Its defining equation is

$$I = \frac{Q}{T}.$$

$$\left(\text{By comparison, 1 statampere} \equiv \frac{1}{3 \times 10^9} \text{ ampere.} \right)$$

Unit resistance (*one statohm*) is that resistance which will have a potential difference of one statvolt across its terminals when it carries a current of one statampere. Its defining equation is

$$R = \frac{V}{I}.$$

(By comparison, 1 statohm ≡ 9 × 10¹¹ ohms.)

Unit capacitance (*one statfarad*) is the capacitance across which a charge of one statcoulomb will give a potential difference of one statvolt. Its defining equation is

$$C = \frac{Q}{V}.$$

$$\left(\text{By comparison, 1 statfarad} \equiv \frac{1}{9 \times 10^{11}} \text{ farad.} \right)$$

Unit electric flux density (*one CGSES unit per square centimeter*) is the flux density in an electric field in free space in which the electric field intensity is one statvolt per centimeter. Its defining equation is

$$D = \epsilon\mathcal{E}.$$

$$\left(\text{By comparison, 1 CGSES unit per square centimeter} \equiv \frac{1}{12\pi} \times 10^{-5} \right.$$

$$\left. \text{MKS unit per square meter.} \right)$$

Unit electric flux (*one CGSES unit*) is the total flux passing through a plane area of one square centimeter which is perpendicular to an electric field in which the flux density is one CGSES unit per square centimeter. Its defining equation is

$$\psi = DA.$$

$$\left(\text{By comparison, 1 CGSES unit} \equiv \frac{1}{12\pi} \times 10^{-9} \text{ MKS unit.} \right)$$

CGS electrostatic units of magnetic field intensity, magnetic potential difference, magnetic flux, magnetic flux density, permeability, and self-inductance can be defined, but since the use of the system is limited to theoretical problems in electrostatics, these units will seldom, if ever, be encountered in the literature.

The permeability of free space in the CGS electrostatic system is found by experiment to be $\frac{1}{9 \times 10^{20}}$ CGS electrostatic unit.

INDEX

INDEX